ATLAS OF
OCEANS

EXPLORING THIS HIDDEN WORLD

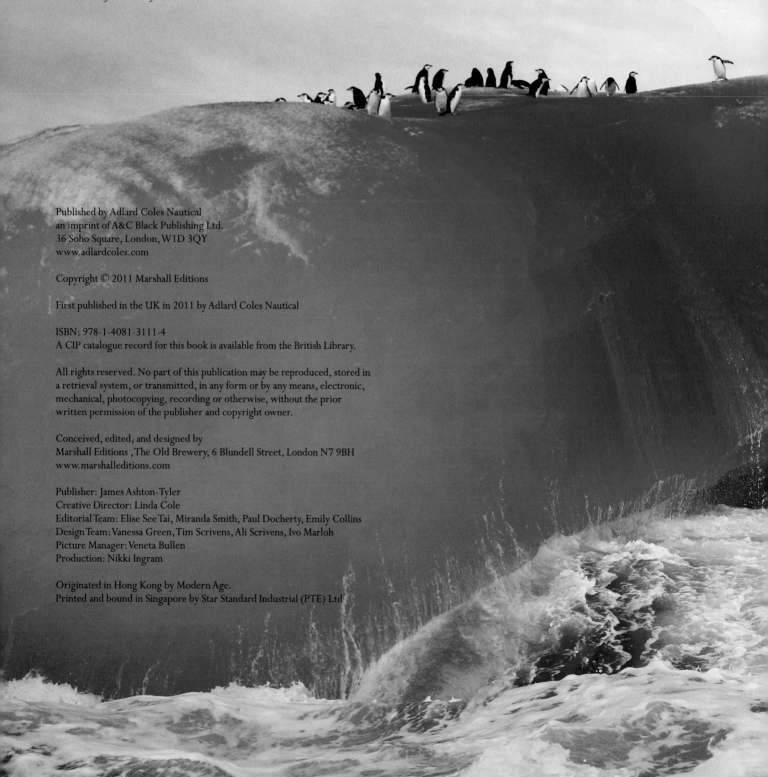

Previous page *Waves break on a rocky shoreline.*

This page *Chinstrap penguins perch on top of an iceberg in the Southern Ocean, where they hunt for the krill and fish that they eat.*

Published by Adlard Coles Nautical
an imprint of A&C Black Publishing Ltd.
36 Soho Square, London, W1D 3QY
www.adlardcoles.com

Copyright © 2011 Marshall Editions

First published in the UK in 2011 by Adlard Coles Nautical

ISBN: 978-1-4081-3111-4
A CIP catalogue record for this book is available from the British Library.

Conceived, edited, and designed by
Marshall Editions , The Old Brewery, 6 Blundell Street, London N7 9BH
www.marshalleditions.com

Publisher: James Ashton-Tyler
Creative Director: Linda Cole
Editorial Team: Elise See Tai, Miranda Smith, Paul Docherty, Emily Collins
Design Team: Vanessa Green, Tim Scrivens, Ali Scrivens, Ivo Marloh
Picture Manager: Veneta Bullen
Production: Nikki Ingram

Originated in Hong Kong by Modern Age.
Printed and bound in Singapore by Star Standard Industrial (PTE) Ltd

ATLAS OF OCEANS

EXPLORING THIS HIDDEN WORLD

John Farndon

Foreword by Carl Safina,
President, Blue Ocean Institute

Consultants: The Cousteau Society

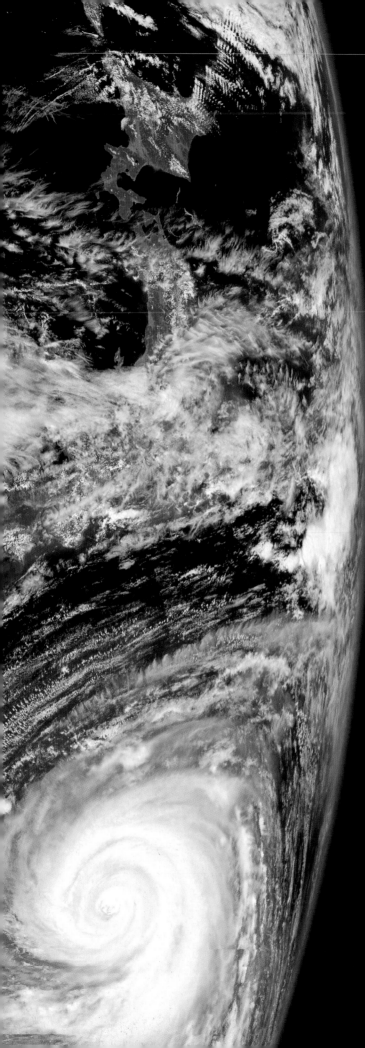

CONTENTS

FOREWORD

Inspiration, Conservation, Fascination – take your pick. Actually, you don't have to. Take them all. They're all here! Oceans cover most of Earth's surface. They are probably where life began. Half the oxygen you breathe – say every other breath you take – was made by drifting plankton in the sea. And all the time, it still is. That's how oceans benefit us. We owe them a hefty note of thanks.

But we seem to have a rather odd way of acknowledging our appreciation. We put too much in and take too much out. Unfortunately, we take out the good stuff – the wildlife such as fish, molluscs and crustaceans that we love to eat as seafood. And in goes the bad: pesticides, fertilizers, plastics, the exhaust gas of all our carbon-fuel burning.

When I was a boy, the sea held every possible fascination. It was the best place to feel the power of the world. The best place to be alone. The best place to share with a special friend. We hunted the shores and scavenged the tidelines. We warmed our shins with driftwood fires. We slept in the dunes. We travelled away from shore. Eventually we travelled beyond sight of shore to the vast places where the whole world was round and blue. We marvelled at tiny plankton, thrilled to fishes, seabirds, and dolphins, and were awed by the vital thunder of whales. The ocean wasn't just a wild place to be in. It was a place to be wild in.

It still is. It is still the ultimate destination, the ultimate beginning. It is still the eternal sea.

It is also a place to look to for our future. As the tide of humanity grows and our resources ebb, the ocean continues to hold out promise. It's been quite generous that way, a pretty forgiving place; maybe it's trying to tell us something, that we have another chance, just a little more time to start getting it right.

We run civilization mainly on the energy of long-ago sunlight, locked away in oil and coal. The easy oil is gone, and for our liquid-fuel future we have looked to the sea. And again, as the sea provides, we add to it insult and injury. But fossil fuels cannot be our future. And here again, the sea whispers its answers.

In addition to showing us the great bounty of life by which the ocean distinguishes us from anything in the known universe, this book also shows us the eternal energy that truly runs the planet: the surge of tides, the force of wind, the heat of the Earth that circulates the ocean around the planet, the living legions of energy-packed algae with which we may power our travel on land and in the air in the not-distant future.

The ocean provides room to roam and space to dream. It is vast – but not infinite. We are bumping up against its limits, its tendency to be so generous and accommodating. As you will read in these pages, the sea has been too forgiving for its own good. And we have been too short-sighted for ours. The ocean may be downstream of all of us, but it has a way of making its presence felt. It is, after all, the planet's landlord. We mess up our place at our own peril. But if we are to reform our thinking and solve our problems, we must start with both the inspiration that will motivate us and the understanding to begin charting a new path. And as I said, it's all right here.

This book is not just a thing to read. It is a realm to explore. A place for sparking interest and ideas. You'll find yourself being drawn back into it, as to the ocean itself, again and again and again…

Carl Safina
President, Blue Ocean Institute
www.carlsafina.org

◁ *Waves of water meet waves of sand in this aerial view of the Pacific Coast of Southern Peru. The beach sand has formed crescent-shaped barchan dunes, which are caused by strong winds always oriented in the same direction.*

INTRODUCTION
OCEANS IN PERIL

Out beyond the coasts of the lands where we live, beneath the apparently inscrutable surface of the vast oceans, there is a crisis going on.

The vast oceans are still a place of mystery, and the life within them remains a source of wonder and often of beauty. But as the world pays attention to environmental problems on land and laments the loss of rain forests, of wilderness, and of endangered animals, there is an even greater tragedy being played out silently beneath the waves.

It was thought that the oceans are so vast and the life in them so teeming that nothing we do could affect them. Now it is becoming clear that the creatures of the sea are if anything more vulnerable than their land counterparts. The problem is the increasing scale and pressure of human activity. It is not simply that the human population has increased five-fold in the last century and a half. The impact of each person has escalated, too, and especially that of people in richer countries. And in recent years, technology has given us the means to attack and devour the ocean's riches as never before.

The impacts are many and complex. Wherever rivers flow into the sea from intensively farmed land, for instance, the runoff of fertilizers from farms far inland can create 'dead zones' where virtually all life has been suffocated out of existence by an uncontrollable growth of plankton. Where trawlers drag heavy nets over the seabed, bottom-dwelling communities of sponges, corals, bryozoans, and shellfish and invertebrates may be invisibly uprooted and destroyed. Vast quantities of plastic are littering the oceans to create giant patches of rubbish, which choke and poison marine life. And the rapacious maw of industrial-scale fishing fleets has swept some populations of fish away already – it seems likely that unless something is done soon to curb their appetite, they will virtually clean out the ocean of edible wild fish in a shockingly short time.

There is still much to marvel at in the oceans – a wealth and variety of life and lifestyles that is almost impossible to imagine. There may be even more that remains yet to be discovered. It is the purpose of this book to remind us of the diversity of life in the oceans, and celebrate its richness. But it is also its purpose to throw a spotlight on the growing crisis in the oceans in the hope that awareness of the problems may help us take better care in future.

◁ *Large brown globules of oil washing ashore on the Gulf Coast of the USA are an all-too-visible consequence of the disastrous blowout of the Deepwater Horizon offshore drilling rig on 20 April, 2010. Many of the dangers to the life of the oceans are much less visible, and therefore receive much less attention in the media.*

OCEAN WATCH

Dismayed by the impact of a corporation dam on migrating shad, the young American author and philosopher Henry David Thoreau wrote in 1839, 'Who hears the fishes when they cry?' Today, this seems a remarkably prophetic observation.

It is indeed difficult to be sure what is going on in the oceans. Both their huge scale and their inaccessibility means that scientists can sometimes only guess at the problems, and their findings are constantly disputed, especially by those with vested interests. It has only been in the last few decades that the ocean bed has been fully mapped, and just a tiny percentage has been fully explored. So we only know a small portion of what goes on in a healthy ocean. It is that much harder to be sure how it is being damaged. Sometimes it is only practical to take small samples – a study of a single species, or even a small population, or a small location – to find out what is happening.

Yet gradually the picture is beginning to snap into focus. It is becoming more and more clear that the human impact on the oceans is escalating. What is more it is happening rapidly. Indeed, it is happening at such a speed that it has caught everyone by surprise. As recently as 1951, Rachel Carson, the pioneering environmental campaigner, wrote, 'man … cannot control or change the ocean as, in his brief tenancy of Earth, he has subdued and plundered the continents.' However, it is now becoming clear just how mistaken that view was.

NO CORNER LEFT CLEAN

In February 2008, an international team of scientists led by Dr. Benjamin Halpern of the National Center for Ecological Analysis and Synthesis in Santa Barbara, USA, developed the first detailed global map of human impacts on the seas, using a sophisticated model to handle huge amounts of data. The team divided the world's oceans into square kilometre sections and combined data for each on 17 different human impacts to oceans, including fishing, coastal development, fertilizer runoff, and pollution from shipping traffic.

Their map showed that just 4 percent of the world's oceans are now entirely undamaged by human activity. Climate change, fishing, pollution, and other human factors have taken their toll in some way on all the other 96 percent of the world's oceans. Forty-one percent of the oceans are seriously damaged. Even the scientists working on the map were shocked to find that virtually nowhere seems to have escaped – and they believe that soon even the small area of pristine waters near the poles will be affected as climate change melts the polar ice caps.

The result was shocking because previously the true scale of the problems had been masked by focusing only on single problems and small areas. As Dr. Halpern said, 'In the past, many studies have shown the impact of individual activities. But here for the first time we have produced a global map of all of these different activities layered on top of each other so that we can get this big picture of the overall impact that humans are having rather than just single impacts.' The big picture

△ *Only recently have scientists begun to reveal the astonishing variety of creatures in the deep ocean, including the ferocious viperfish, but now the once inaccessible deeps are the target of industrial fishing.*

Human Impact on the Oceans

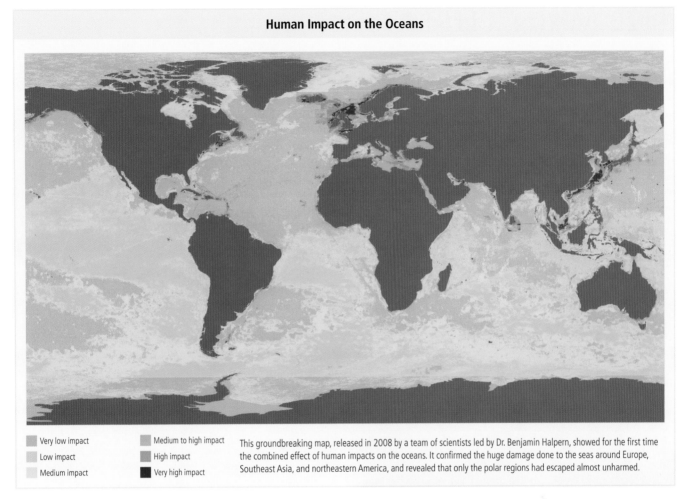

■ Very low impact	■ Medium to high impact
■ Low impact	■ High impact
■ Medium impact	■ Very high impact

This groundbreaking map, released in 2008 by a team of scientists led by Dr. Benjamin Halpern, showed for the first time the combined effect of human impacts on the oceans. It confirmed the huge damage done to the seas around Europe, Southeast Asia, and northeastern America, and revealed that only the polar regions had escaped almost unharmed.

is so alarming that the authors of the map described it as a real 'wake-up call' for policy-makers.

SURVEY OF LIFE

One of the ironies is that marine life is coming under threat just as we are beginning to learn how astonishingly rich it is. In 2010, the results of the extraordinary ten-year Census of Marine Life (see pages 62–63) were announced. The aim of the Census was to produce the first ever comprehensive survey of life in the ocean. The oceans are so vast that the Census can give only an impression of what is out there. Yet it has shown that the variety of life in the oceans is much, much, much greater than scientists ever imagined. Thousands of previously unknown species have been discovered, and it is absolutely certain there are many more yet to be discovered.

As the famous oceanographer Sylvia Earle writes in her foreword to *World Ocean Census*, a book illustrating the work of the Census of Marine Life, 'The importance of the Census is made urgent because at the same time that more is being learned about the diversity of life in the sea than during all preceding history, more is being lost.' It is a crucial observation.

▷ *Amazing shots of deep-sea species like this medusa jellyfish are captured on cameras triggered by the creature's bioluminescence. It looks red because the light from the camera is red, out of the medusa's vision range.*

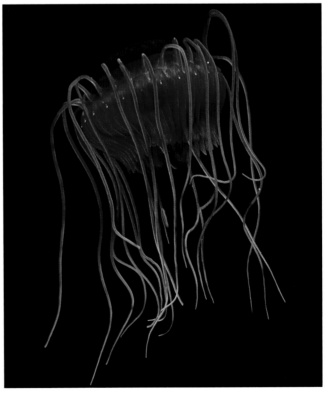

THE MAIN THREATS

MANY OF THE HUMAN THREATS to the oceans centre on what we take out and what we put in. Over the last half century, hundreds of millions of tons of fish and other creatures have been taken from the oceans. Meanwhile, hundreds of millions of tons of waste have been dumped into them.

The introduction of fishing quotas and much publicized campaigns to avoid eating endangered cod or bluefin tuna have failed to halt the pace at which every fish that is vaguely edible is scooped from the ocean by industrial trawlers. Well over

90 million tonnes (99 million tons) of fish are taken from the sea every year, and that rate of catch is simply too much. The world's fish population is large, but not limitless, and more and more populations are being fished to exhaustion. Since the 1950s, the numbers of bluefin tuna, Atlantic cod, American eels, and some sharks have been reduced by 95 percent. As one population is exhausted, the fishing industry simply moves on to another. But they cannot move on continuously, or wild fish of any kind will be off the menu forever, and the biodiversity of the ocean will be restricted with unpredictable consequences.

Moreover, an incredibly wasteful quarter of the tonnage of marine creatures taken from the sea never reaches the dining table – or even the fish meal factory. This is 'useless' by-catch caught up in the nets then discarded. Every year, hundreds of millions of fish, marine mammals such as dolphins and seals, and sea turtles and seabirds perish in this way.

Meanwhile whaling, which has already brought many species, such as the blue whale, to the point of extinction, could be legal once more if a recent proposal to lift the ban is not rejected. And if seal hunting is now, thankfully, less common than it was, tens of thousands of seals are still being deliberately killed each year.

WHAT WE PUT IN

In the past, the oceans were seen as a dump with almost limitless capacity for anything from sewage to nuclear waste. Scientists are now aware just how mistaken this view was, but that does not stop vast amounts of fertilizers, pesticides, sewage, plastics, and industrial waste being poured into coastal waters all the time.

Untreated sewage and fertilizers from farms carried downriver to the sea have created more than 400 'dead zones', where there is virtually no marine life, from the Gulf of Mexico to the Yellow Sea. Toxic chemicals from pesticides and industrial waste leaking into the oceans work their way up the food chain, becoming increasingly concentrated until animals at the top, such as polar bears and killer whales, are carrying around bodies full of poison. Nearly 635 million tonnes (700 million tons) of oil ends up in the sea, too, mostly from discarded oil poured down the drain, but also from ship operation and from tanker spillages. And vast amounts of waste plastic now floats through the ocean where it slowly disintegrates into tiny pellets deadly to sea creatures that swallow them inadvertently, or drifts intact in giant patches of rubbish that can entangle anything from sea turtles to dolphins.

Locally, human activity interferes with marine life in countless ways. These include the noise and disturbance of boats, of coastal developments, of port and harbour works, and of housing and leisure developments. Even swimmers playing with dolphins and divers exploring coral reefs can do significant damage.

◁ *Industrial fishing boats scoop fish from the ocean at a truly frightening rate. A single trawler is able to haul 200 tonnes (220 tons) of fish aboard in only one hour. In the last few decades, such fishing methods have decimated fish stocks.*

△ It was once thought that the oceans were so vast that they could wash away any rubbish we dumped in them, but the huge quantities of industrial and urban waste poured into them every day are building up a toxic brew.

▽ Our obsession with cars is the major threat to the oceans, because the carbon they belch into the atmosphere not only promotes global warming but increases the acidity levels of the oceans as well.

GLOBAL WARMING AND CHEMICAL CHANGES

A potentially even bigger threat to the oceans is global warming and its related effects. It is enormously difficult to measure temperature right across the world, and even harder to be certain if trends are general. Nonetheless, studies by the National Oceanic and Atmospheric Administration (NOAA) suggest that global sea temperatures rose by more than half a degree in the surface layers between 1960 and 2000 – significant, since the oceans take a very long time to heat up. The National Climatic Data Center recorded that, in July 2009, the world's oceans were hotter than ever before – well over one degree warmer than the 20th century average and beating the previous record of 1998. Once warmed up like this, the oceans take a long time to cool.

Ocean warming could affect marine life. Besides melting sea ice and altering polar ecosystems, it could upset plankton growth by keeping down the cold waters that bring nutrients to the surface. If so, the effects could spread right through the food chain. Ocean warming already seems to be damaging coral reefs by triggering bleaching events as the corals expel their symbiotic algae in response to the warmth. It seems to be raising sea levels, too, with potentially devastating effects on coastal wetlands and other ecosystems.

Scientists reported to the American Association for the Advancement of Science (AAAS) in 2005 that ocean warming is almost certainly being caused by the extra carbon added to the atmosphere by human activities. Raised levels of atmospheric carbon might have another devastating effect – turning the oceans more acid as they soak up some of the excess carbon.

That extra acidity could wreak havoc on the availability in the ocean of the dissolved carbonates that are vital for the shells and skeletons of all kinds of living things from phytoplankton and corals to much larger creatures. It may be that healthy marine life could adapt to these changes, but far too many species have been so reduced and weakened by overfishing that this combination could be the final straw.

13

MOST ENDANGERED PLACES

THERE ARE DANGERS TO MARINE LIFE all around the world, on both a global and local scale, but four kinds of marine zone stand out as being particularly vulnerable: coral reefs, coasts, continental shelves, and the great open ocean.

Corals are particularly sensitive to changes. Disease, coral bleaching, acidification, and ocean warming have all begun to take their toll. Well over half of the world's live coral has been lost since the 1950s. In the Caribbean and the Indo-Pacific, there are places where more than 80 percent has gone. There are now scores of corals on the International Union for Conservation of Nature's (IUCN) list of critically endangered species. Reef fish stocks are down, too, with large predators rare, and a sharp decline in sponges and sea turtles.

COASTS

Coastal shallows, wetlands, and estuaries are all vulnerable, too. They are marginal zones, not just because they are around the sea's margins but because any small shift in conditions can have a dramatic effect. A slight rise in sea levels or a small change in the quality of the water can have a huge impact on marine life in these delicately balanced ecosystems. Yet because they are closer to human activity than any other ocean zones, they are exposed to a wide variety of threats from urban development to tourism. These habitats are among the first to be completely lost. Two-thirds of wetlands and 90 percent of mangroves have been removed in the last half century. Meanwhile, coastal fish and shellfish are subject to severe overfishing, eutrophication caused by pollution (see page 18), and destruction of their habitat.

CONTINENTAL SHELVES

Close to the shore and fairly shallow, the continental shelves are exposed to a wide range of human activity. They are also the most biologically productive areas of the ocean, because nutrients are brought readily to the surface in their shallow waters. It is not surprising to discover that, when the NOAA decided to designate 64 regions around the world as Large Marine Ecosystems (LME) for conservation purposes, all of them are on continental shelves or on the outer margins of ocean current systems.

The 64 LMEs yield 80 percent of the world's annual fishery catch. But they are focuses of coastal ocean pollution and nutrient over-enrichment, habitat degradation (such as the loss of seagrass beds, corals, and mangrove swamps), overfishing, biodiversity loss, and climate change effects. Many large fish populations have been severely overfished, and in the absence of predators,

other smaller prey species, such as rays and sea urchins, have multiplied with often devastating effects on shellfish and seaweed communities. Dead zones caused by eutrophication are spreading, and invasive species, such as jellyfish discharged from ships' ballast water, are wreaking havoc in some places.

OPEN OCEAN

The open ocean is so vast and so remote that it is hard to imagine human activities having much effect. Yet fishing has taken a huge toll on populations of large hunting species such as tuna, sharks, and billfish. Global warming is also beginning to interfere with the slow rise of nutrients that is so vital to the vast mass of plankton that fills the ocean's upper layers and provides the basis for all other life in the open ocean. Now fisheries, driven from the shallows by overfishing, are beginning to chase prey deep in the open ocean, and the slow-growing, much scarcer deep-water fish, such as orange roughies, are now becoming as endangered as their cousins in the shallows.

▷ *Seagrass meadows are the nurseries of the temperate ocean waters, yet out of sight beneath the water they are being destroyed by human activity even faster than is the Amazon rain forest.*

▽ *Coastal marine ecosystems are exposed to the full brunt of human activity in many places, particularly those with numerous industrial units and power plants situated close by. Here, a nuclear plant in Xiamen, China, sits on the shore of the South China Sea.*

△ *Despite its profusion, life in coral reefs is very finely balanced, and reefs are sensitive to a range of threats, including ocean warming. More than half the world's reefs have been destroyed since the 1950s.*

DEAD ZONES

ONE OF THE MOST DISTURBING FEATURES of the last few decades has been the rapid growth of 'dead zones'. Dead zones are regions of sea that are so hypoxic (lacking in oxygen) that most creatures literally suffocate. Every creature that depends on oxygen dies or leaves the area.

The combined area of all these dead zones is now bigger than New Zealand, and they are growing in number. In the 1950s, there were less than 20 of them; now there are well over 400. And they are growing in extent. The biggest is in the Baltic Sea, but there is an almost equally large one in the Gulf of Mexico, covering an area the size of New Jersey, that has been growing steadily for the last few decades. Most of them are found in shallow temperate waters, around the coast of Europe and eastern North America in places such as Chesapeake Bay, but now an increasing number are appearing in tropical waters such as in the Gulf of Thailand.

ALGAL BLOOM

Dead zones occur where an excess of nutrients in the water precipitates an algal bloom – a massive growth of phytoplankton. An algal bloom can create a carpet of algae so dense that the sea beneath is thrown into deep shadow, making life very difficult for creatures that need to see to find their food. Red-brown algae can grow so thick that the sea turns red, creating the infamous red tides. But the worst effect of these blooms occurs as the algae dies off and drifts down to the seafloor. There, bacteria that feed on the decaying matter multiply and consume massive amounts of oxygen from the surrounding water. The availability of oxygen for bottom-dwelling creatures and the fish that feed on them is drastically reduced, and life suffocates. This process is called 'eutrophication'.

Many places suffer these oxygen depletion bouts only in spring. The Mexican Gulf dead zone lasts from late spring through the summer. If nutrient levels stay high, they can persist all year round, as in the Baltic.

THE CULPRITS

The main culprits for these algal blooms are nitrogen and phosphorus from farms, sewage, and burning fossil fuels. In the North Sea, dead zones are usually triggered by nitrogen put into the atmosphere by burning fuels. In the Gulf of Mexico, they are mainly down to nitrogen and phosphorus from farm runoff. When farmers put fertilizer on their crops, rain washes huge quantities of nitrates and phosphates into the ground, where it

▽ *This 2009 satellite photograph from NASA's SeaWiFS (Sea-viewing Wide Field-of-view Sensor) clearly reveals the pale swirls of plankton growth that signify the development of a dead zone in the Gulf of Mexico.*

Dead Zones Around the World

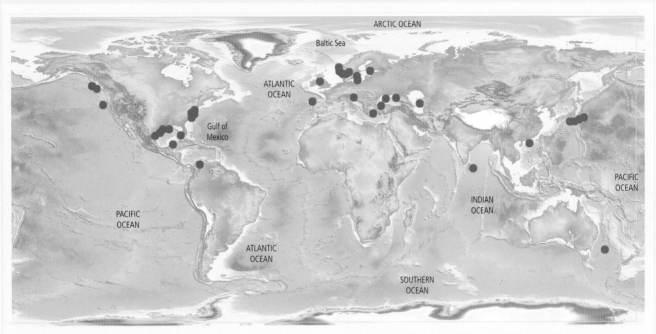

ARCTIC OCEAN

Baltic Sea

ATLANTIC OCEAN

Gulf of Mexico

PACIFIC OCEAN

PACIFIC OCEAN

ATLANTIC OCEAN

INDIAN OCEAN

PACIFIC OCEAN

SOUTHERN OCEAN

More than 400 dead zones have been identified in the world's seas. This map plots areas of highest dead-zone concentration (red dots) that occur mainly around the shores of North America and Europe, where the world's largest zones exist in the Baltic and the Gulf of Mexico. Dead zones are, however, now developing all around the world.

seeps into rivers. So the increase in dead zones can be directly linked to the increasing use of fertilizers.

Worldwide, annual fertilizer use has risen tenfold over the last half century, from barely 15 million tonnes (16.5 million tons) in the 1950s to more than 145 million tonnes (160 million tons) today. In that same time, the amount of nutrients washed down the Mississippi to trigger the Gulf of Mexico dead zone has risen by 300 percent. It rose by a third between 2002 and 2007 alone, a rise largely attributable to the increase in the acreage of corn grown for biofuel, since the crop is very demanding of fertilizer.

As fertilizer use continues to rise, so will the number and persistence of dead zones. As if this was not problem enough, scientists at the Monterey Bay Aquarium Research Institute (MBARI) have found that when carbon dioxide gas from the atmosphere dissolves in the sea, besides causing acidification of the oceans (see pages 46–47), it can also make it harder for fish to extract oxygen. As the burning of fossil fuels puts more carbon dioxide into the air, so ocean life becomes ever more susceptible to oxygen depletion. Heavier rain precipitated by climate change could also wash more farm fertilizers into rivers and so into the sea.

RISING FROM THE DEAD

However, the news is not all depressing. In the early 1990s, the Black Sea had the world's largest dead zones, triggered by huge amounts of nutrients flooding in down the Danube River, in particular from Soviet farms in places as far away as Slovenia. But the collapse of the Soviet regime dramatically reduced farmers' access to fertilizers, sharply lowering the level of nutrients in rivers flowing into the Black Sea. The Black Sea's dead zones are now showing real signs of recovery.

Similarly, after algal blooms all but destroyed the lobster industry in the Kattegat Strait between Denmark and Sweden, the Danish government embarked on an action plan in the late 1980s and cut emissions from sewage plants and industry dramatically. When combined with efforts to restore coastal wetlands that take up some of the nutrients, and reduction in the use of fertilizers on farms, the Danish plan succeeded in reducing plankton growth and increasing oxygen levels. Interestingly, reductions in fertilizer use have not reduced crop yields, so it is clear that farmers may have been using too much fertilizer. This is not only good news for farmers, who save money by not having to pay for the fertilizers, but also good news for fish.

◁ A disturbing effect of plankton blooms has recently been discovered by monitoring California sea lions (left). When a pregnant sea lion feeds on fish such as sardines and herrings that have fed on blooms, she ingests toxic domoic acid. The damage done by the acid to her foetus' brain only emerges later when the baby seal grows to adulthood.

MOST ENDANGERED SPECIES

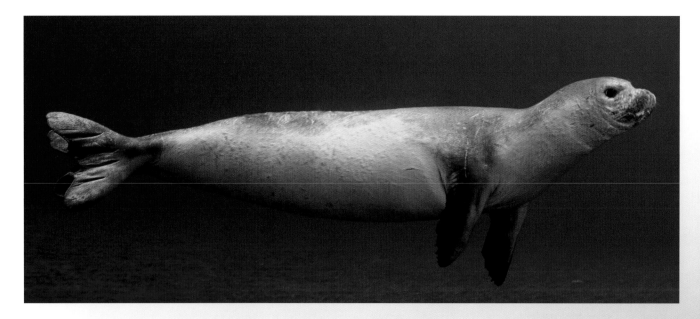

EVERY DAY, AROUND THE WORLD, a species becomes extinct. We are now going through one of the biggest extinction events since the death of the dinosaurs 65 million years ago. While some of these losses undoubtedly have natural causes, the blame for many can be directed at humankind.

In time, evolution will, no doubt, allow new species to thrive in place of those lost, but that could take a very long time, and in the meantime there is a dramatic loss of diversity – and also the potential loss of some highly cherished species.

WHALES
The highest-profile victims are undoubtedly marine mammals. They are not only larger and more visible than most fish and invertebrates; they are usually fewer in number because they are at the top of the food chain and so are highly vulnerable to environmental changes, as well as easy and attractive targets for human hunters. Whaling brought most of the large whale populations to a severe low before a moratorium on whaling brought some back from the brink. Blue whales, humpbacks, right whales, and bowhead whales remain seriously endangered. Only the grey has made a genuine recovery.

SEALS AND SEA COWS
Seals, sea cows, manatees, and dugongs, too, suffered dreadfully from hunting. The Steller sea cow and the Caribbean monk seal are extinct, and Guadalupe fur seals, Mediterranean monk seals, manatees, and dugongs are on the verge of extinction. Like whales, most are now largely protected, and northern elephant seals like grey whales have come back from the brink. But problems such as accidental by-catch in fishing operations and

△ The Mediterranean monk seal is the world's rarest seal, with fewer than 500 individuals left in two widely separated groups.

competition for food from commercial fisheries are taking their toll on northern fur seals, harbour seals, and Steller sea lions. And slow-moving manatees are losing their habitat as well as being killed when they are hit by boats.

SEA TURTLES
Like mammals, sea turtles have been decimated by hunting. However, now they are protected they are threatened by a range of other environmental pressures, such as the effects of coastal development on their nesting beaches and the possibility of entanglement in fishing nets. Six out of the seven species of sea turtles are now either threatened or endangered.

▷ The Critically Endangered beluga sturgeon has been fished almost to extinction for its prized roe.

BIG FISH IN DANGER

The plight of all these larger creatures has been known for some time. But now they are being joined on the danger list by scores of species that few people would have imagined being in trouble just a few decades ago. First of all, there are big fish that have been severely overfished, such as northern cod, bluefin tuna, Atlantic swordfish, the Chilean sea bass, the orange roughy, and the beluga sturgeon. Many shark species are now joining them on the list, either because they have been targeted deliberately for their fins, or because they are caught up as by-catch. Reef fish, such as the Banggai cardinalfish, are also in danger as they are taken for food and live fish restaurants, or for the aquarium trade.

CORALS AND ALGAE

Then in 2007, the IUCN put coral species on its Red List of Threatened Species for the first time, revealing how global changes can affect marine life. Two of the corals – floreana coral (*Tubastraea floreana*) and Wellington's solitary coral (*Rhizopsammia wellingtoni*) – were listed as Critically Endangered, while a third – Galapagos coral (*Polycyathus isabela*) – is listed as Vulnerable. Many other corals are now on the list as endangered to some degree. They are joined by scores of algae species – a recognition that these smaller species are in danger, too. The loss of even such apparently minor species matters because it is organisms like these that form the basis of the food chain on which larger creatures depend. Loss of the diversity of species like these makes the whole ocean food chain far more vulnerable to disease and changing conditions.

△ *In spite of a recent recovery, humpback whales are still thought to be endangered in places such as the Arabian Sea.*

▽ *The hawksbill turtle is Critically Endangered. 'Critically Endangered' means that numbers of a species have decreased, or will decrease by 80 percent, within three generations – so there is a high risk of it becoming extinct in the next decade.*

OCEAN FLOOR MAPS

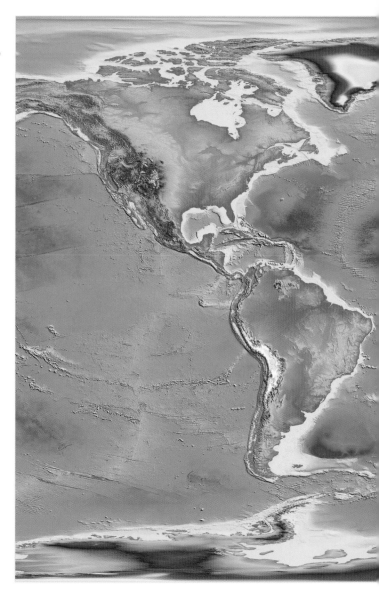

Less than half a century ago, even the most detailed navigational charts covered only a tiny fraction of the ocean floor in the coastal shallows. Now the demands of science, oil prospecting, and the fishing industry have driven a revolution in survey technology that has enabled the entire ocean floor to be mapped in some detail to produce the amazing 3D maps used throughout this book. These maps effectively strip away the waters to reveal all the mountains and valleys of the ocean bed as if they were dry land – even though the deepest valleys may be 10,000 m (33,000 ft) below the surface in the perpetual darkness. These vast global maps depend on techniques that enable scientists to effectively 'see through' the water to the seabed. The process of mapping the seafloor like this is called bathymetry.

The first maps of the ocean floor were produced by sonar, a technology developed in World War II for detecting submarines by picking up the reflections of sound waves from underwater objects. Sonar is still the main method used, but modern systems enable vast areas to be surveyed quickly. Two key sonar systems are 'swath-mapping' and 'side-scan' sonar. In swath-mapping, the survey ship beams pulses of acoustic energy onto the seafloor to enable a wide strip or swath to be mapped in a single survey run. In side-scan sonar, pulses of sound fan out perpendicularly from a scanner mounted under a survey ship's hull, or on a unit towed underwater behind a ship. The soundings are located with reference to the Global Positioning Systems of satellites.

Satellites also provide a second key source of data by a method called altimetry. This involves measuring the height of sea surface with millimetre accuracy by beaming microwaves at the sea surface from radar systems mounted on linked satellites. Slight variations in the height of the sea surface reveal underwater features through their gravitational effect on the water above.

The maps in this book were created by combining a bathymetric computer model of the ocean floor built up mainly from sonar data by Dr. Walter Smith from NOAA Geosciences Laboratory and Professor David Sandwell from Scripps Institution of Oceanography, USA, with altimetric data compiled by Professor Philippa Berry of De Montfort University, UK.

The World's Oceans

Area: 361 million sq. km (139 million sq. miles)
Average depth: 3,790 m (12,430 ft)

The world's ocean waters are divided into five major interconnected oceans. The three largest – the Pacific, Atlantic, and Indian – are all linked in the south through the Southern Ocean that encircles Antarctica. The Pacific and Atlantic have a narrow connection at the north, too, via the Arctic Ocean. The world's ocean area also includes seas that are connected to the oceans, such as the Mediterranean, Black Sea, and Baltic, but does not include seas that are not connected, notably the Caspian.

Atlantic Ocean
Area: 82,400,000 sq. km
(31,800,000 sq. miles)
Deepest part: Puerto Rico Trench
8,605 m (28,232 ft)

Pacific Ocean
Area: 169.2 million sq. km
(63.8 million sq. miles)
Deepest part: Mariana Trench
10,911 m (35,797 ft)

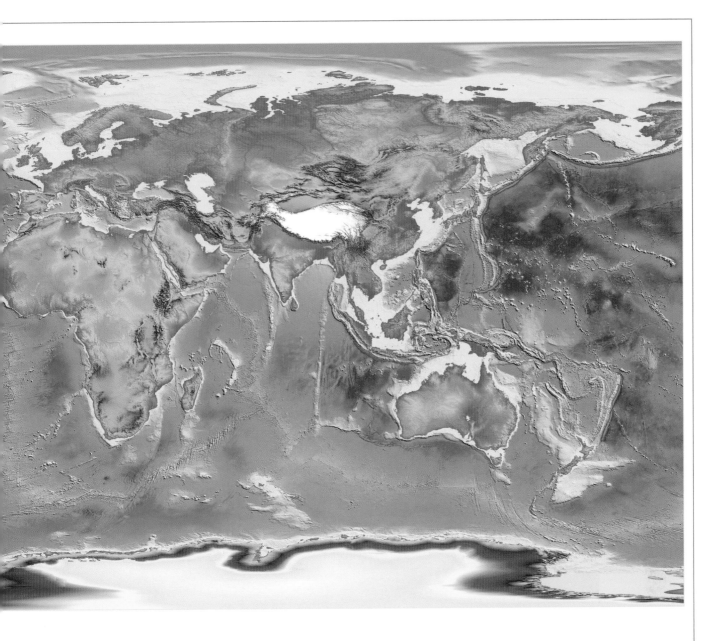

Indian Ocean

Area: 28,400,000 sq. miles
(73,556,000 sq. km))
Deepest part: Java Trench
23,812 ft (7,258 m)

Southern Ocean

Area: 20,327,000 sq. km
(7,848,298 sq. miles)
Deepest part: In dispute

Arctic Ocean

Area: 14,056,000 sq. km
(5,427,000 sq. miles)
Deepest part: Arctic Basin
5,625 m (18,456 ft)

OCEAN WORLD: ROCKS AND WATER
OCEAN GEOLOGY

The world's oceans are ancient – almost as old as the planet itself. They formed some four billion years ago mainly from water vapour delivered as ice by meteorites and comets that crashed in their thousands into the hot, early Earth.

As the Earth cooled, the vapour condensed into clouds, then fell as endless torrents of rain to pour down in myriad streams over the surface and gather in the Earth's deepest hollows. Gradually, over the aeons, these hollows filled deeper and deeper, and the oceans swelled until nearly three-quarters of the planet was drowned.

Remarkably, the clouds then cleared, the rains largely ceased, and the oceans have remained washing over much the same proportion of the planet, at much the same average depth, ever since, rising and falling only minimally. Even more remarkably, the ocean basins are not just places where the Earth's surface is covered by water. They are actually geologically distinct from the land. While continental cores are ancient and stable, the seafloor is locked in a perpetual battle of renewal and decay. And while the oceans themselves are ancient, the ocean floor is nowhere older than a few hundred million years old – very young in geological terms – and is constantly on the move, forever shifting the continents and reshaping the oceans, with profound consequences for marine life.

On the grand geological scale, a human life is but the tiniest blink of an eye. But as the ocean floor moves through the ages they form new marine habitats again and again, reshape the seabed, throw up undersea mountains, shift rocks and mud in coastal waters, and change countless other factors that affect the balance of life in the sea.

◁ *The world's shorelines are the scene of an epic battle between the oceans and the land that has continued for more than four billion years, and has seen the rocks of the shore shaped and reshaped countless times.*

EARTH'S BROKEN SHELL

THE DIVISION OF THE WORLD into land and sea seems so natural and timeless that it is hard to imagine it any other way. Yet the very existence of continents and oceans is unique to planet Earth, and their behaviour is even more remarkable.

Early in the 20th century, a German meteorologist named Alfred Wegener noted the extraordinary way coastlines of continents seemed to match across the oceans, like the separated pieces of a vast jigsaw. He suggested that this was because the continents were once joined together and the oceans between them opened up as they split apart and drifted around the world over many millions of years. For a long time, the idea was considered too weird for serious geologists to contemplate, but in the years after World War II, a rising tide of evidence, including matching fossils found on continents an ocean apart, broke down their resistance.

GOING CONTINENTAL

By the 1960s, geologists were convinced of the reality of 'continental drift' – the idea that the continents have moved right around the Earth, breaking apart and coming together. Today, incredibly accurate satellite laser ranging measures this movement in real time. On average, it is no more than 1 cm (0.4 in) a year – no faster than a fingernail growing. But on the geological timescale that is fast enough to redraw the world map completely over and over again – fast enough to open up the entire Atlantic Ocean in just 40 million years. The process is ongoing. As you read, New York is moving farther from London.

A turning point in the case for continental drift was the discovery of a mechanism that could make it happen, a discovery that was even more astounding in its implications than continental drift. It is not just the continents that are on the move, but the entire surface of the Earth, and the continents are simply swept along on them like so many goods on a conveyor belt.

In fact, the Earth's surface, far from being a complete shell, is cracked into huge slabs or 'tectonic plates'. Each of these slabs is a thick chunk of 'lithosphere', the cool, rigid outer layer of the Earth topped by the crust. The scale of some of these plates is vast. They are typically just 100 km (60 miles) thick but some of them encompass entire oceans or continents. There are dozens of moderate-sized plates and seven gigantic ones. The biggest of all, the Pacific plate, underlies most of the Pacific Ocean.

◁ *The sea floor grows ever wider either side of the great cracks in the Earth's crust, continuing here beneath Thingvallavatn Lake in Iceland.*

▽ *The arms of the Red Sea mark the widening divisions between tectonic plates that will in time grow to form ocean floors.*

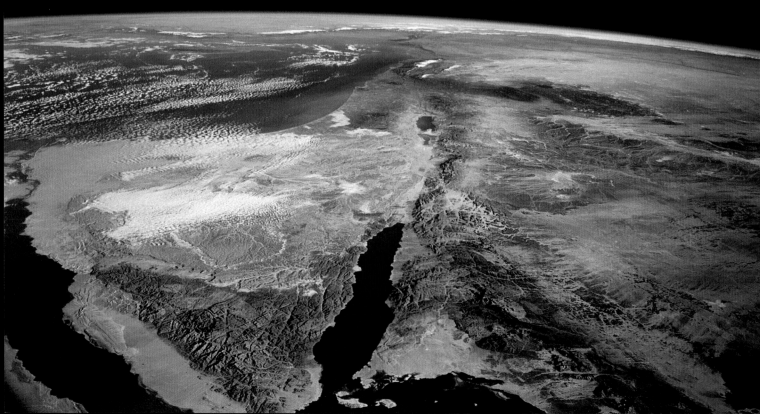

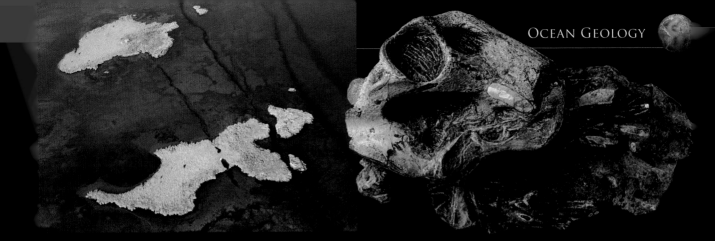

△ *Here on the bed of Iceland's Lake Thingvallavatn, the splitting of the Earth's crust along the ridge is clearly visible. On the left of the cracks is the North American tectonic plate; on the right the Eurasian.*

△ *This is a fossilized skull of a Lystrosaurus, a pig-sized reptile that lived around 250 million years ago. Discoveries of Lystrosaurus fossils in Antarctica, South Africa, and India are strong evidence that these continents were once joined together.*

t is the only plate that is entirely oceanic. The others – Eurasian, African, Indian, Australian, North American, South American, and Antarctic – carry continents as well as forming the ocean bed.

THE EARTH DOES MOVE

t seems hard to imagine how such vast slabs of rock could ever move, yet they are moving all the time. What is more, they are not even permanent features of the Earth's surface. The cores of continents are stable and very ancient, often containing rocks that are billions of years old, and they preserve intact the plates on which they ride over aeons of time. But they are islands in a turbulent world. All around, under the oceans, the plates are continually breaking apart and fusing together, growing at the edges as new molten rock welling up from the interior is welded onto them, or destroyed when driven against the continental plates and thrust underneath into the Earth's hot interior.

THE OLD CONTINENT

What is especially interesting is just how different the continents are geologically from the ocean floor. The continents are essentially chunks of ancient granite-like rock – pale in colour

and light in weight – and the oldest pieces are almost four billion years old (the Earth is about 4.6 billion years old). The ocean floor, however, is mostly young basalt rock, dark and dense, and mainly just a few tens of millions of years old.

The basalt that forms the bulk of the Earth's crust forms when magma (molten rock) wells up from the Earth's warm mantle to cool and turn solid at the surface. The granite in continents cannot form directly from mantle melts like this. Instead, it forms when basalt remelts, changing its chemistry and mixing with other substances met at the surface. Long ago, when the Earth was young, all the Earth's surface was as changeable and impermanent as the ocean floor. But gradually parts of it remelted and coagulated to form these chunks of granite. You could say that the continents are the scum of the Earth. Unlike the ocean floors, which go through a continual cycle of renewal and decay, the continents survive through the ages because they float on top of the denser basalt and so, unlike basalt, are never dragged down to destruction in the mantle again Most of the geological action goes on beneath the sea, while the continents rise above it all. That is of course what makes the oceans such an extraordinary place for life.

Movement of the Tectonic Plates

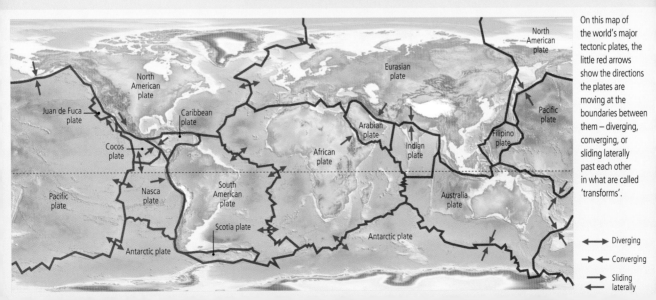

On this map of the world's major tectonic plates, the little red arrows show the directions the plates are moving at the boundaries between them – diverging, converging, or sliding laterally past each other in what are called 'transforms'.

North American plate

Juan de Fuca plate

North American plate

Caribbean plate

Eurasian plate

Arabian plate

Pacific plate

Filipino plate

Cocos plate

African plate

Indian plate

Nasca plate

South American plate

Australia plate

Pacific plate

Scotia plate

Antarctic plate

Antarctic plate

Antarctic plate

⟷ Diverging

→← Converging

→
← Sliding laterally

Ancient Oceans

IN THE TRADITIONAL SCIENTIFIC VIEW, the young Earth was indeed a vision of hell – a furnace of fiery volcanoes smothered in the gases that were belched out, and a boiling, ever-changing surface where transient fragments of crust formed briefly before sinking into the hot abyss of the mantle.

Gradually, however, the Earth cooled enough for some fragments of crust to remain intact for longer as they sank deep into the interior, where their chemistry was so altered as they melted that it produced an entirely new, lighter granitic material. This new material drifted up to the surface through fissures in the crust. Too light to be drawn down into the mantle again, it survived in narrow strips of rock along the fissures to form the first infant continents, tiny islands of stable rock amid the shifting surface. It was not long after that things cooled down enough for the clouds to turn to rain and waters to gather in the deepest hollows of the crust to form the first oceans, though the waters in these first oceans may have been a scalding 300°C (572°F).

IN ANCIENT DAYS

This process all started some 3.8–4 billion years ago, and marks the beginning of that ancient period in Earth's history that geologists dub the Archean. It is so long ago, and the Earth has changed so much since, that much of our understanding of the period is largely educated speculation based on isolated clues. In recent years, scientists have begun to question the traditional view, and suggest that the early Earth was not quite so hellish, that atmospheric gases came not from volcanoes as originally believed but from the impact of meteors and comets, and that continents formed very early on.

Nonetheless, it is clear that at some distant time, a recognizable Earth began to emerge, with the narrow strips of rock beginning to grow into landmasses, the spaces in between filling with oceans, the thick atmosphere beginning to clear, and, most remarkably of all, the first microbial signs of life.

About 2.5 billion years ago, the Archean gave way to what geologists named the Proterozoic, which means 'early life', even though ancient rocks have now revealed traces of life dating back a billion years earlier. The Proterozoic marks a crucial time in Earth's history. The few small islands in the vast world ocean grew into fully fledged continents covering a quarter of the world's surface. The atmosphere filled with oxygen effused by the countless tiny organisms that were already teeming in the vast oceans. And all the signs are that many of these organisms combined and evolved to form the first complex, multi-celled forms of marine life – the first of the astonishingly rich variety that live in the oceans today.

AT THE HEART OF CONTINENTS

No one can be sure how many continents there were in these distant times, nor what shape they were. But studying the rocks and dating them by the state of decay of radioactive isotopes within them, geologists have discovered that there is ancient core, or 'craton', at the heart of every modern continent. Today's continents have formed as rock has been added to or broken off these old cratons.

Although each modern continent has its old craton, that does not mean the continents have always existed in the form they have today. A key discovery in the last century was that many rocks contain grains of magnetite, a magnetic mineral. These grains behaved like tiny compasses, lining up with the North Pole and then staying fixed in that direction as the rock formed. Surprisingly, the grains in ancient rocks point in varying directions and only rarely to the North Pole. Geologists thought this was because the North Pole had shifted through history. Then

△ *The Nuvvuagittuq belt region along the coast of Hudson's Bay in Northern Quebec, Canada, is the home of ancient rocks that may be as old as 4.28 billion years.*

they realized that it was not the poles that had moved at all; it was the continents in which the rocks were embedded! In fact, these 'paleomagnets' provided a remarkable record, enabling geologists to map precisely the twists and turns of the continents, tracking the changing shapes and positions of the continents and oceans through at least the last half billion years of the Earth's history.

SUPERCONTINENTS AND SUPEROCEANS

It turns out that the cratons at the heart of modern continents have drifted far and wide across the globe, sometimes merging together to form a single huge supercontinent surrounded by a universal ocean, and sometimes breaking asunder to create new continents and new oceans.

About 1,100 million years ago, all the continents may have been joined as one at the South Pole in what geologists dub Rodinia after the Russian word *rodina* for 'motherland'. When Rodinia began to split up about 700 million years ago, the changing conditions may have had a profound effect on life. The Earth became extremely cool, and the altered ocean habitat is thought to have triggered the sudden and rapid evolution of new and complex species of marine life that marks the Ediacaran and early Cambrian periods, 500–635 million years ago.

The fragments of Rodinia formed new continents – some gigantic such as Gondwanaland (consisting of what is now South America and Africa combined), some much smaller such as Baltica (Scandinavia and a bit of northern Germany and European Russia). These fragments in turn coalesced between 360 and 206 million years ago into another supercontinent, known as Pangaea, surrounded by a world ocean known as Panthalassa. Pangaea was not an entirely stable single continent, though, and was often just a loose assemblage. It eventually broke up as an arm of the world ocean known as the Tethys Sea (now the Mediterranean) cracked deeper and deeper across Pangaea until it split. Today's continents and oceans are the result of 200 million years of shifting and rearrangement since that time.

◁ *Great cliffs formed from the sediments that gathered on seabeds long ago, such as these in Gros Morne National Park, Newfoundland, Canada, bear dramatic witness to the mighty upheavals of land and sea through time.*

The Making of the Oceans and Continents

Around 200 million years ago, when dinosaurs dominated the land, all the continents were joined in one supercontinent in the southern hemisphere, known as Pangaea. There was just a single vast ocean dubbed Panthalassa, surrounding it like an island. Today's continents are the drifting fragments left when the relentless shifting of the world's tectonic plates finally rent Pangaea asunder.

420 million years ago Fragments of an earlier supercontinent, Rodinia, begin to drift together.

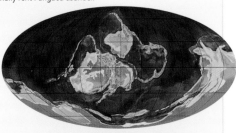

220 million years ago The fragments of Rodinia finally coalesce to form the supercontinent Pangaea.

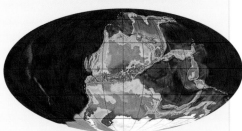

170 million years ago Pangaea is beginning to split on the east as the arm of the ocean known as Tethys Sea widens.

110 million years ago The widening Tethys splits Pangaea in two, between Gondwanaland in the south and Laurasia in the north.

70 million years ago India splits from Africa and Australia from Antarctica, and the Atlantic starts to open up.

Present day India is now joined to Asia, Australia and Antarctica are now completely isolated, and the Atlantic is now a great ocean.

Early Ocean Life

Life is the Earth's, and maybe the Universe's, greatest miracle. As far as we can tell, all life on Earth is descended from an astonishing chance coupling of complex chemicals early in our planet's history – a coupling that created a remarkable organic structure that could not only grow but could also reproduce itself.

Organic chemicals – the carbon chemicals that are the basis of life – are far from unique to Earth. Many organic chemicals are found in meteorites that land on Earth, including amino acids, the chemicals that join to make proteins, the building blocks of life. Analyzing light from interstellar clouds shows that they contain organic chemicals, too. Some estimates suggest comets passing the early Earth may have dusted it with 10 million tonnes (11 million tons) of organic chemicals every year.

SURVIVE AND PROSPER

However, it is a huge leap from proteins to a chemical that can reproduce itself, and a huge leap again to the first 'living cell', the bag that wraps these chemicals up in a self-contained unit.

It now seems these huge leaps were taken in conditions where most living things today could not survive, let alone prosper. The first living cells were tiny bacteria, which may have appeared nearly four billion years ago. They survive today, but only in boiling volcanic springs – and in ocean deeps in the scalding plumes of volcanic vents. In boiling water and without the oxygen now vital to most life, these bacteria multiplied, feeding on sulphur and other volcanic chemicals. Before long, new kinds of bacteria and other single-celled organisms spread through the Earth's new oceans.

GREEN FOR GO

The pioneers left few traces as those early oceans vanished, and only on the ancient margins of continents are any faint signs left. Scientists infer their presence by looking for subtle differences in the carbon content of ancient rock that indicate that carbon-processing life was going on. But the signs are difficult to interpret, and even dating is hard. In 2008, telltale raised levels of 'light' carbon, linked with life processes, were found in zircon crystals in 4.2 billion-year-old diamonds discovered in Australia's Jack Hills. If they do indicate life, then life on Earth began remarkably early in its history.

The oldest fossilized remnants of life may be microscopic matlike wrinkles in rocks that date back 3.46 billion years, and were probably created by colonies of the blue-green algae cyanobacteria. The conventional theory is that these proliferated through the oceans wherever there was light in the oceans, using the light's effect on a green pigment called chlorophyll to break up carbon dioxide into carbon and oxygen. The carbon they used for their own nourishment; the oxygen was wasted into the atmosphere. Over a billion years, all these tiny puffs of oxygen

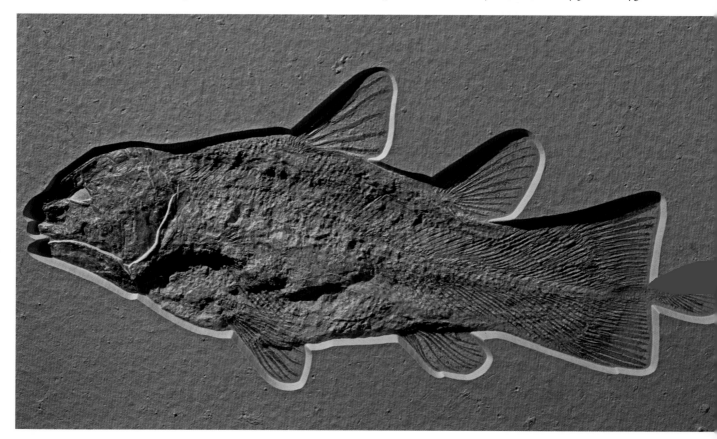

gradually changed the Earth's atmosphere, preparing the way for the rich variety of life that has filled the Earth since.

LIFE GETS COMPLEX

For billions of years, simple, single-celled organisms and their communities were the only life. Today's bacteria and their primitive ancestors have no central nucleus and are known as prokaryotes. But, maybe about two billion years ago, life forms called protists, which included amoebas, appeared. They, too, are made from a single cell, but they are eukaryotic, which means they had developed a nucleus like the cells in all modern plants and animals.

Then, in rocks dating back 700 million years, faint imprints of the most ancient of all multi-celled creatures appear – sponges and jellyfish. These creatures are entirely soft, but were made from many kinds of cell, each suited to a certain task.

THE CAMBRIAN EXPLOSION

Soon after, the variety of life in the ocean increased dramatically – so dramatically that it is sometimes called the 'Cambrian explosion'. No one is quite sure why this happened. Maybe it was a response to changing conditions, or maybe life simply found ways to exploit new places to live. In fact, there was an earlier explosion of life forms about 580 million years ago – some 40 million years before the Cambrian – as remarkable finds of fossils at Ediacara in Australia testify. The Ediacaran fossils belong to the first genuinely complex forms of life, and seem to have appeared as the Earth thawed from the bitterest of its many ice ages.

Strangely, the Ediacaran fauna vanished from the record, maybe unable to survive the dramatic upheaval of habitats that followed the break-up of the supercontinent Rodinia. Whatever the reason, the Cambrian saw the arrival of a wave of ever more complex sea creatures – creatures that are the ancestors of all plants and animals alive on Earth today. Over the next 100 million years, a bewildering array of creatures with hard parts (shells and bones) appeared – and then half a billion years ago, even before the end of the Cambrian, fish, the first creatures with backbones, appeared. These first fish were tiny, jawless fish related to modern lampreys, but by 420 millions years ago, the first predatory sharks were hunting the oceans.

The Cambrian explosion, which established all the major animal groups, was followed by the Great Ordovician Biodiversification Event, discovered by scientists only recently. In this event, marine genera multiplied fourfold in just 25 million years from 488 million years ago, establishing much of the variety of life we see in the oceans today.

▷ *These strange mounds in Shark Bay, Australia, are stromatolites made by mats of blue-green algae that lived in the ocean shallows 2,000–3,000 years ago. The world's oldest fossils, dating back 3.45 billion years, may be stromatolites like these.*

◁ *One of the very earliest kinds of fish, coelacanths, have survived for almost 400 million years. This fossil dates from the Jurassic period, 145–199 million years ago. But coelacanths are now threatened by deep-sea trawling.*

SPREADING OCEANS

THE WORLD'S LONGEST MOUNTAIN CHAIN is not the Andes of South America, or the Cordillera of North America. Instead it lies under the ocean and is know as the Mid-Ocean Ridge. This extraordinary feature winds around the world on the ocean floor like the seam of a baseball. It winds down through the Atlantic from north to south, through the Southern and Indian oceans into the Pacific and up north to Canada, in a single unbroken chain more than 65,000 km (40,400 miles) long. But it is not just a mountain range. It is a long, jagged fissure in the Earth's surface, riven with the world's most continually active volcanoes.

MOVING AWAY

The Mid-Ocean Ridge (and similar ridges under the Pacific) are the crust's renewal lines. It marks the boundary between ocean floor plates that are actually moving apart. All the time, new molten material wells up from the mantle along the line of the ridge to join onto the plates either side as they diverge. In the middle of the ridge is an extraordinary canyon, deeper than the Grand Canyon, and far beneath this trough, deep in the mantle, magma melts in response to reduced pressure as the plates move apart. As the magma melts it rises up through the fissure. Some freezes on the underside of the crust without ever emerging. Some oozes up into vertical cracks opened up by the pressure of the magma to form sheets of rock called dikes as it freezes. Some bursts right through to spill out onto the seafloor, where it freezes instantly in the cold water in blobs called pillow lavas.

Scientists debate whether the material welling up from the mantle along the mid-ocean ridges is actively pushing the plates either side apart, or whether the material is simply oozing into the gap left as the plates diverge by other means. One likely notion seems to be that the plates are sliding 'downhill' over the mantle away from the ridge, since the ridges are a good 2–3 km (1–2 miles) higher than the far edges of the plates around the ocean rims. Another theory is that the plates are like a cloth sliding off a table, pulled by their increasing density and weight as they cool away from the heat of the mid-ocean ridges.

THE GROWING OCEAN FLOOR

Whatever the cause, the remarkable truth is that the floors of nearly every ocean are spreading wider and wider, by 1 m (3 ft) or more every decade. The evidence is there in the age of the rocks that get older and older in both directions either side of the ridge, as seafloor drill samples make clear. It is there even more startlingly in the magnetic striping either side of the ridge. Magnetic equipment originally designed to detect submarines in World War II reveal that the polarity of magnetic material in rocks reverses in neatly matching stripes either side of the ridge – revealing the way the rock has moved away from the fissure either side, capturing the Earth's changing magnetic polarity as it formed.

The spreading of the seafloors has profound effects on habitats for marine life. The effects are particularly pronounced along the ridge itself. Here, cool seawater is drawn continually through the hot rocks, dissolving metals and depositing them on the seafloor. Fractures around the volcanoes fill with water that gets tremendously hot as well as dense with dissolved minerals. Remarkably, these hot, chemically challenging environments act as incubators to microbes that can not only survive but thrive even in some of the harshest conditions life has ever been found to endure. Indeed, it may have been in places like these and with microbes like these that life on Earth began.

▷ *A volcano erupted suddenly, along the Mid-Atlantic Ridge, under the sea off Iceland in the 1960s, forming the new island of Surtsey.*

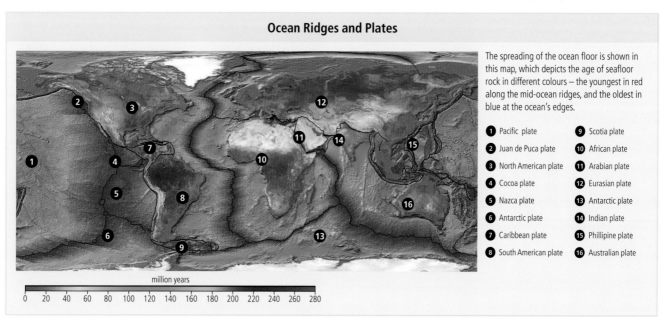

Ocean Ridges and Plates

The spreading of the ocean floor is shown in this map, which depicts the age of seafloor rock in different colours – the youngest in red along the mid-ocean ridges, and the oldest in blue at the ocean's edges.

1 Pacific plate
2 Juan de Puca plate
3 North American plate
4 Cocoa plate
5 Nazca plate
6 Antarctic plate
7 Caribbean plate
8 South American plate
9 Scotia plate
10 African plate
11 Arabian plate
12 Eurasian plate
13 Antarctic plate
14 Indian plate
15 Phillipine plate
16 Australian plate

million years

0 20 40 60 80 100 120 140 160 180 200 220 240 260 280

SEAFLOOR OASES

THE SUMMITS OF ANCIENT UNDERSEA VOLCANOES KNOWN AS SEAMOUNTS ARE RECENTLY
DISCOVERED HOT SPOTS OF MARINE LIFE IN THE OPEN OCEAN. BUT THEIR VERY WEALTH OF LIFE
PUTS THEM UNDER THREAT FROM THE FISHING INDUSTRY AS IT TURNS AWAY FROM EXHAUSTED
COASTAL WATERS TO PLUNDER THESE SUBMARINE OASES.

MOST OF THE DEEP SEAFLOOR IS FLAT and featureless, with few locations for a variety of marine life to develop. But here and there are seamounts, defined as mountains of more than 1,000 m (3,300 ft) high. A few protrude above the surface to create islands in the ocean. But most remain hidden beneath the waves, and it is only recently, with the advance of satellite sea surface altimetry, that they have been mapped to any extent. This technique reveals slight bulges in the sea surface that reflect the extra gravitational pull of the mountain's mass.

▷ *Satellite altimetry and sonar soundings from ships have been combined to make this computer model of the western Pacific ocean floor, which reveals the presence of thousands of submerged seamounts.*

SEAMOUNTS

There may be anything between 10,000 and 100,000 seamounts under the world's oceans, at least half of them in the Pacific, and most of the rest in the Atlantic and Indian oceans. They are typically cone-shaped, which gives a clue to their volcanic origin. They formed as volcanoes erupting near the mid-ocean ridges, or above an especially hot spot in the mantle called a mantle plume. But most have been carried far away from their point of origin by the relentless movement of the seafloor, and they now

△ *This computer model shows the Brothers seamount chain off the coast of New Zealand. The wildlife on these seamounts has already been damaged by bottom trawling. Now it may be threatened by the world's first deep-sea mines.*

stand isolated and inactive in the middle of the vast abyssal plain. It is their very isolation, though, that makes them such special places for marine life. Species on seamounts are very different from those on the surrounding seafloor. All the different levels of the mount and all its nooks and crannies provide special niches for a unique and varied range of life forms, as scientists are just beginning to appreciate. These undersea oases also act as stepping stones or service stations for creatures making their way across the undersea void of the open ocean.

THE MOUNTAIN FEAST

The Census of Marine Life (see pages 62–63) is making a special effort to sample these distinctive habitats and they have already discovered an astonishing diversity. Thousands of entirely new species have already been recognized, 600 of them occurring on just five seamounts alone. In sharp contrast to the deep seabed populated by sediment feeders, the hard, rocky slopes of seamounts offer little direct nourishment so the dominant creatures here are suspension feeders – creatures such as corals, sponges, and sea fans that rely on snatching and filtering food as it wafts by.

Cold currents deflected up the slopes ensure a rich mass of plankton and other floating food around the summits of seamounts, which draws in a bewildering array of creatures that feed on it. Fish flock here in large numbers, and in turn attract many other creatures to make the most of the rich pickings – marine mammals, sharks, tuna, and squid.

SEAMOUNT PERIL

Yet it is this very richness that has put seamount life in danger. As continental shelf fisheries have been depleted or declared out of bounds, so fishing fleets have hunted farther afield for their catches – and the seamounts seemed a perfect target. The problem is that seamount species such as the orange roughy, pelagic armorhead, and blue ling are not especially abundant or fast growing. They simply concentrate here for certain times of their life, such as for feeding. The result is that seamount fisheries go through a real boom where they briefly provide a bumper catch, then a sudden bust as stocks are depleted. With no near neighbours to take over, and a long life cycle, it may take decades for numbers to recover, if ever. The devastating impact of deep-sea trawl nets dragged across cold-water coral colonies like a tank through a cottage garden only exacerbates the peril to these undersea oases.

In Australia and New Zealand, people have begun to recognize the threat and give some level of protection, but in the Atlantic all that has so far happened is for the threat to be noted by appearing on the OSPAR Commission's list of sites that might require conservation action. The European Commission, meanwhile, is conducting a study called the OASIS project. For the seamount dwellers, though, it could all be too little, too late.

▽ *Nudibranch sea slugs, such as* Phyllidia varicosa, *sometimes called the scrambled egg nudibranch, are among the most colourful inhabitants of the seamounts of the western Pacific.*

▷ *Hammerhead sharks often gather around seamounts, leading to speculation that they use the mounts as stepping stones as they migrate across the ocean floor.*

THE ETERNAL ABYSS

THE VAST DEEP OCEAN FLOORS, unseen and until recently, virtually unknown, cover well over half the entire surface of the Earth. Known as the abyssal plains, they are the flattest, most featureless places imaginable.

If there was enough light to see, the plains would appear to stretch, level as a playing field, beyond the horizon in every direction. But of course no sunlight ever penetrates this deep down – over 1,000 m (3,250 ft).

The darkness here is total. Even the most powerful lights from the rare submersible that explores the depths shine only a little way through the murk. And it is icy cold, rarely climbing much above 0°C (32°F). Despite the cold, though, there is no danger of it freezing, because the pressure here is so immense – more than enough to completely crush all but the most robust submersible.

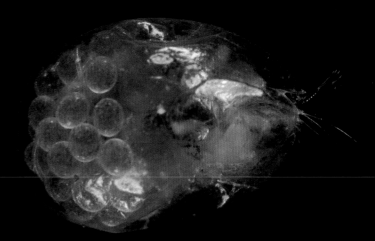

△ *The unreal-looking ostracod shrimp,* Gigantocypris dracontovalis, *is one of the most ubiquitous creatures of the deep abyss, and plays a key role in the food chain there. Unusually, its eyes use mirrors, not lenses, to focus light.*

SEAFLOOR BLANKET

The rock under the abyssal plain is every bit as jagged and twisted as the newly formed rocks of the mid-ocean ridges. Indeed, they are the same rocks, just a little older after moving away on the ocean floor conveyor belt. What makes the plains so smooth and level is the sediment that covers them, in a vast blanket that has lain virtually undisturbed for tens of millions of years. Less than 2.5 cm (1 inch) of sediment is added every century, and geologists once believed they were entirely unchanging. But of course over geological time, the accumulation is significant, and now deep ocean currents have been discovered that scour the plain in places, creating small but significant valleys and hills, and pockets of different sedimentation that provide a much more varied habitat for marine life than was ever imagined.

Much of the sediment is swept down here from the continental shelf in whirling 'turbidity' currents launched sporadically and violently down the canyons that notch the edge of the shelf, driven by the weight of solid material they contain. A lot is

wind-blown dust, carried off the continents – volcanic ash, silt, and so on – and settling down through the ocean waters until it reaches the seabed. Only a tiny fraction of the billions of tonnes of silt washed into the sea by rivers ever reaches the abyssal plain, though. Even less of the sediment comes from the gentle snow of organic material – dead plants and animals, bits of shells – that falls from above, though this provides vital nutrition for the organisms that do live here, far from sunlight.

METAL POTATOES

Vast areas of the seafloor are littered with knobbly metallic lumps known as manganese nodules, mostly about the size of potatoes. They vary in their makeup but the most interesting ones are manganese, with a little nickel, cobalt, and copper. Sliced in half they reveal onion layers that build up gradually as metallic ions are deposited from the water, perhaps starting with a shell fragment as a 'seed'. So low is the concentration of metals in sea water that the process takes many millions of years. But there are now thought to be about a billion tonnes of these metal balls scattered across the abyssal plain.

The nodules were first discovered in the 1870s by the HMS *Challenger* voyage, but their true prevalence was realized only in the years after World War II. During the 1960s and 1970s, mining companies began to get excited about all this mineral wealth lying there, apparently free for the taking, and invested millions of dollars in developing possibilities for recovering them, especially in the Clarion-Clipperton Fracture Zone of the North Pacific. Interest fell away, though, when it became apparent that the current demand for manganese and nickel could be met from more cheaply accessible land sources. The recent discovery in nodules of the rare metals selenium and molybdenum, both valuable raw materials for the electronics industry, has sparked renewed interest, however.

△ *Mining companies are investigating ways of scooping up the trillions of manganese nodules littering the ocean floor, but mining them could devastate seabed communities.*

The initial flurry of interest in nodules provoked a furore about ownership, and in the 1980s, the United Nations (UN) set up the International Seabed Authority under the Law of the Sea Convention to control exploitation of the ocean beyond national limits. The intention was that no one should own the open ocean. Mining companies operate under licence and give a portion of the profits to be divided among rich and poor nations alike. But it has been a source of bitter contention and the United States, for instance, has not joined in fully. Moreover, nations have pushed farther and farther out into the open ocean. The United States now claims an Exclusive Economic Zone (EEZ) – the area to which it has sole mining and fishing rights – as large as its entire land area, including an area off Hawaii that is bigger than Mexico.

But it is not just ownership of resources that is at stake. The deep seafloor is a vital part of the global ecosystem, harbouring hundreds of thousands of unique species, many yet to be discovered, let alone studied. The deep seafloor has long been exploited as a dumping ground for nuclear and other wastes, but mining could be much more devastating. Seafloor silt has remained undisturbed for millions of years, and the fragile, deep-sea organisms survive simply sitting on the surface to catch the drifting snow of biological detritus from above. Even a slight disturbance of the seabed silt could destroy their fragile wafer-thin habitat entirely.

▷ *Tripodfish use their extraordinarily long, stiff pectoral fins to rest on the ocean floor. When standing in this position, they look like a camera tripod. The fish simply stands waiting for small crustaceans to swim into the fins in the dark, then uses one fin like a spoon to scoop the meal towards its mouth.*

Features of the Seafloor

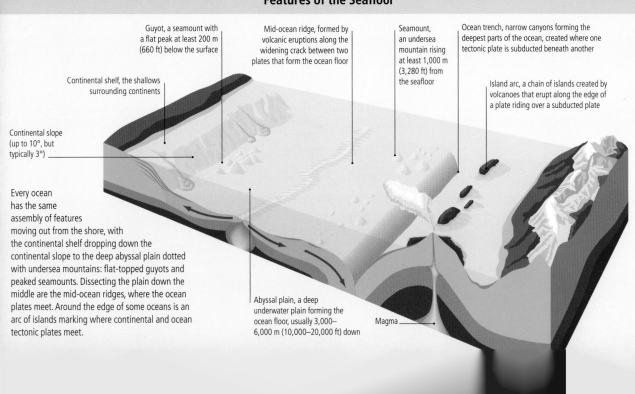

Guyot, a seamount with a flat peak at least 200 m (660 ft) below the surface

Mid-ocean ridge, formed by volcanic eruptions along the widening crack between two plates that form the ocean floor

Seamount, an undersea mountain rising at least 1,000 m (3,280 ft) from the seafloor

Ocean trench, narrow canyons forming the deepest parts of the ocean, created where one tectonic plate is subducted beneath another

Continental shelf, the shallows surrounding continents

Island arc, a chain of islands created by volcanoes that erupt along the edge of a plate riding over a subducted plate

Continental slope (up to 10°, but typically 3°)

Every ocean has the same assembly of features moving out from the shore, with the continental shelf dropping down the continental slope to the deep abyssal plain dotted with undersea mountains: flat-topped guyots and peaked seamounts. Dissecting the plain down the middle are the mid-ocean ridges, where the ocean plates meet. Around the edge of some oceans is an arc of islands marking where continental and ocean tectonic plates meet.

Abyssal plain, a deep underwater plain forming the ocean floor, usually 3,000–6,000 m (10,000–20,000 ft) down

Magma

THE DEEPEST OCEAN

If NEW MATERIAL IS FOREVER BEING ADDED to the Earth's crust along the mid-ocean ridges, and the seafloor is continually spreading, why does the Earth not simply grow larger? That was the puzzle some geologists pondered for a while when the phenomenon of seafloor spreading was discovered.

It eventually turned out that what is being gained in the middle of the oceans is being lost at the edge. Here, the upstart new ocean plate is thrust down again under an old continental plate to be consumed in the heat of the mantle in a process called subduction.

Subduction zones occur typically, but not always, around the edges of oceans. There is a particularly marked string of them along the western edge of the Pacific, where the westward moving Pacific plate runs up against the almost immobile East Asian plate, and the slower moving Philippines plate. Subduction is the result of a collision or divergence between two plates. When an inexorably moving ocean plate runs up against an unmoving continental plate, or another slower-moving ocean plate,

something has to give – and it is usually the faster-moving ocean plate. Scientists are as yet unsure how subduction begins, but it seems that the continental plate rides up over the edge of the ocean plate because it is less dense. As soon as it begins to ride up over the top, its weight begins to thrust the ocean plate down into the mantle. Once the plate begins to descend, it bends at the edge and starts sliding into the mantle.

RING OF FIRE

As it goes down, the plate starts to melt, releasing hot, volatile materials, water, and even molten rock, creating magma. Plumes of magma begin to rise up through the edge of the continental plate above, where it has been shattered and faulted by the collision. Some of the magma erupts in an arc of volcanoes, or an arc of volcanic islands, right along the plate margin, a little way in, like stitches along a giant hem. The volcanoes created in this way are typically very violent, because contamination by materials from the overlying plate makes the magma very sticky and rich in gases so that it erupts in explosive fits and starts.

The Pacific is surrounded by a ring of violent volcanoes like this, aptly named the Ring of Fire. It is not only volcanoes that make subduction zones particularly violent places. As the subducted plate shudders down into the mantle, the vibration can set off earthquakes, creating a Wadati-Benioff zone – a zone where deep-focus earthquakes originate, up to 700 km (435 miles) down.

THE OCEAN TRENCHES

For oceanographers and marine biologists, however, the fascinating thing about subduction is that it creates the deepest places in the ocean, the ocean trenches. The trenches are deep, V-shaped notches in the crust between the two plates, with a steep slope on the continental side and a shallower slope on the oceanic side. Of the world's 20-odd major trench systems, 17 are in the Pacific, with only the Puerto Rico trench and the Sandwich Island trench in the Atlantic and just the Java trench in the Indian Ocean. The Pacific trenches are the deepest, too, with five of them plunging more than 10,000 m (32,800 ft) – easily enough to entirely swallow Mount Everest.

The deepest of all is the Mariana Trench off the Mariana Islands in the Pacific, which, in the small slot known as the Challenger Deep, descends nearly 11,000 m (36,000 ft), the deepest known point in the oceans. Only three descents have ever been made into the Challenger Deep – named after HMS *Challenger*, which made the first sounding there in 1875. The first was the extraordinary trip in 1960 of the bathyscaphe *Trieste* with Jacques Piccard and Don Walsh on board, the only men to have ever been down there. The other two, the *Kaiko* in 1995 and the *Nereus* in 2009, were both unmanned robot submersibles.

◁ *Well-known as features of mid-ocean ridges, hydrothermal vents have recently been found near ocean trenches such as this one that is 1.5 km (1 mile) beneath the surface on the northwestern Eifuku seamount near the Mariana Trench.*

△ *The 1960s saw the first real explorations of the deep sea with special submersibles, such as the* Deepstar 4000 *– designed by renowned marine scientist Jacques Cousteau – seen here in Mexico.*

It was once thought the very bottom of the ocean was a lifeless 'azoic' zone. What the Challenger Deep descents proved was that life extends right through the ocean to the very deepest places. As they reached the very bottom and the *Trieste* began to show signs of cracking under the pressure, Piccard and Walsh were astonished to see a solelike fish calmly swimming past their porthole. And *Nereus*, with its robotic arms, collected samples that revealed more than 400 different species of the plankton foraminifera alone living in these depths at unimaginable pressures, far beyond the reach of sunlight.

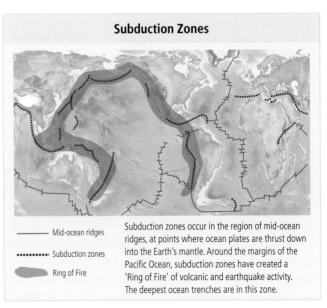

Subduction Zones

— Mid-ocean ridges

∙∙∙∙∙∙∙∙∙ Subduction zones

⬭ Ring of Fire

Subduction zones occur in the region of mid-ocean ridges, at points where ocean plates are thrust down into the Earth's mantle. Around the margins of the Pacific Ocean, subduction zones have created a 'Ring of Fire' of volcanic and earthquake activity. The deepest ocean trenches are in this zone.

THE CONTINENTAL SHELF

THE OCEAN DEEPS DO NOT BEGIN at the edge of the land. Instead, a band of shallow water surrounds each continent, sloping away gently from the shore before dropping off suddenly to the ocean deeps at about 130–200 m (425–655 ft). Beyond this, it descends steeply (about 1 in 14) down what is known as the continental slope to the abyssal plain.

The width of the continental shelf varies considerably, from just a few kilometres wide off Chile to 1,500 km (932 miles) in the Russian Arctic. It is narrowest along 'active' plate margins, where the collision of tectonic plates throws up mountain chains such as the Andes and Rockies. It is widest on passive lowland coasts far from plate margins, such as eastern North America, where it extends nearly 500 km (310 miles) out into the Atlantic.

THE ICE AGE COAST

The outer edge of the continental shelf may actually be where the coast once was. During the last ice age, when a great deal of the world's water was frozen in giant ice sheets, the sea was about 130 m (427 ft) below its present level. What is now the continental shelf could well have been, in the last ice age, a bleak windswept plain, carved smooth at the edges by ocean waves, but gradually extended seaward by sediment washed down by rivers, which carved their own river valleys here. When the ice melted and the sea rose again, the shelf was drowned, along with the lower portions of the river valleys, creating distinctive flooded valleys or rias along some coasts, such as the coasts of southern Cornwall and Devon in the UK, and deep fjords in once glaciated valleys. The traces of old river courses, ancient valleys, and drowned hills can all be found under the water on the continental shelf, along with thick layers of sediment, which help make this geologically very distinct from the rest of the ocean. Occasionally, fishermen dredge up the bones and teeth of land animals that lived here in the ice age.

The edge of the shelf is notched by deep submarine canyons that run all the way down to the abyssal plain. Some look like deep river valleys and seem to correspond to the mouths of rivers on land, such as the Congo and the Hudson, which is why some geologists think they may be the remnants of old river valleys carved out in the ice age when the sea was lower. But others seem far away from river mouths. What seems likely is that they have been much deepened, if not originally formed, by turbidity currents – massive, periodic slumps of mud and water off the continental shelf into deeper water.

△ *Known as the monkfish in Europe, the goosefish is one of the stranger inhabitants of the continental shelf seabed, preying on just about anything from herring to seabirds. Its delicate flesh has made it a target for bottom trawling, which destroys its seabed habitat.*

▽ *This computer model built from sonar data reveals the shallow flatness of the continental shelf off California – it is so clearly part of the continent even though it is underwater, and then the seafloor suddenly plunges sharply down the almost clifflike continental slope to the deep ocean.*

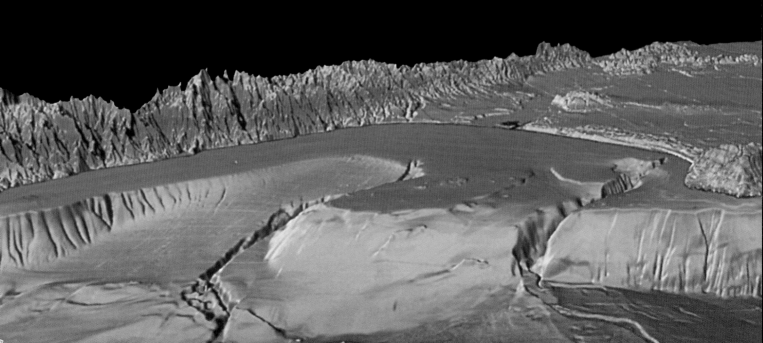

THE DISPUTED SHELF

Altogether, the continental shelves occupy barely 8 percent of the world's oceans, but they contain some of the richest and most varied of all marine habitats. They are also the most accessible parts of the ocean to humans, and that is what makes them so vulnerable. They are exploited for their once abundant fish and shellfish, and also for oil and gas and minerals, such as aggregate, sand, and heavy minerals rich in rare elements, such as titanium and chromium. Shallow waters are also 'reclaimed' for land and seabed sand is engineered to produce new coastal forms. The continental seabed is a dumping place for various wastes, and the overlying water is often polluted with industrial effluents and untreated sewage.

Even the very definition of the shelf is in serious dispute as nations vie for rights to exploit its resources. Oceanographers regard it as the flat seabed extending to where it drops away steeply down the continental slope. But international lawyers have found different definitions in order to clarify the extent

△ *Filled with sunlight by day, the shallow waters of the continental shelf are rich in marine life – but are immensely vulnerable to the effects of human activity because they are so close to the shore.*

of a nation's legal claim and responsibilities. The legal concept of an 'extended continental shelf' encompasses the whole area underlain by continental crust, and includes not only the shelf and the slope, but also some distance across the deep ocean floor. The formula for determining the outer limit is incredibly complex, and depends on the thickness of sedimentary rocks, which underlines the idea that the shelf is the natural extension of a state's land territory. If a nation wishes to extend its claim to the continental shelf beyond 370 nautical km (200 miles) – up to a limit of 650 nautical km (350 miles) – it must submit scientific, technical, and legal details about the limits of its continental shelf to the UN Commission on the Limits of the Continental Shelf. But while nations are willing to claim exploitation rights, few are so willing to shoulder the burden of protecting it.

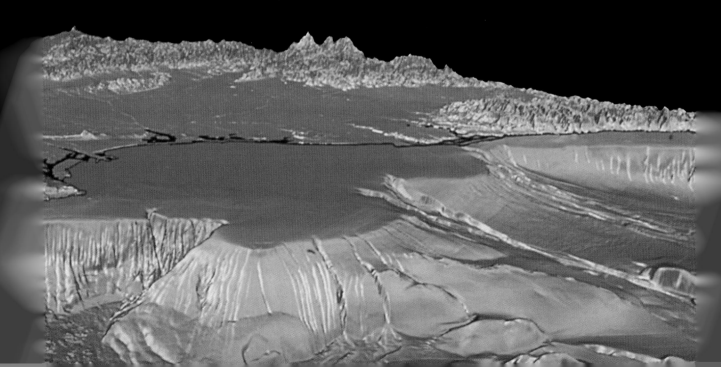

CHANGING SEA LEVELS

THE HEIGHTS OF MOUNTAINS and the altitude of aircraft are often given as 'above sea level', as if the level of the sea was permanently fixed. Yet even in the present day, it is very difficult to pinpoint the level of the sea accurately. The sea moves continuously, not only with the tides, but with wind, waves, and currents, and even daily changes in temperature and chemistry. In the UK, heights are measured relative to the Ordnance Datum, an average achieved by year upon year of measurements of the mean sea level shown by tide gauges at particular sites.

Elsewhere, the markers are different. Satellite measurements from the Topex/Poseidon mission in the 1990s and more recently by the Ocean Surface Topography Mission on the *Jason-2* satellite can measure the height of the sea surface globally with extraordinary accuracy. But this, if anything, only serves to complicate the picture, revealing, for instance, that the sea surface is actually higher above undersea mountains and lower above submarine canyons because of gravitational differences.

SEABED SEDIMENTS

In fact, the level of the sea has varied enormously throughout geological history. The widespread occurrence of sedimentary rocks formed from seabed sediments, for instance, is testament to the fact that huge areas that are now dry land were once underwater. The famous white chalk rocks of southern England, the US state of Kansas, and many other places were formed when the seas rose so much in the warm Cretaceous period 80 million years ago that only a few higher parts of what is now Europe and North America were left above the waves as islands. The oceans then were fully 200 m (656 ft) above their level today, and the thickness of the chalk rocks, formed largely from the remains of tiny sea creatures, shows just how deep the sea was then.

Plotting the changes in sea level over geological time is an incredibly complicated business, because the relationship between sea and land is continually altered, both locally and globally, by the constant movement of the tectonic plates, the break-up and convergence of landmasses, the continual creation of new mountains, as well as the destruction of old mountains, and a host of other factors.

Nevertheless, geologists have been able to plot changing global sea levels over the last 550 million years. Half a billion years ago, at the end of the Cambrian, the sea was up to 400 m (1,300 ft) above its current level. Then, about 300 million years ago, it dropped for a while below its current level, before gradually rising throughout the age of the dinosaurs to reach the Cretaceous maximum

about 80 million years ago before starting to fall again. The sea is now pretty much at its lowest ebb in geological history, which is why in the long-term future, it can only really go up.

RISING AND FALLING

Typically, sea levels were higher in periods when the ocean floor was much younger and made of many smaller, less dense plates. When this was so, the ocean floor rode higher on the mantle and sea levels rose. When the floor was older and plates were larger and denser, the ocean floor sank and so did the sea level. Typically, too, sea levels fluctuated more when the continents were near the poles rather than the equator, because then, huge amounts of water could be locked up on land in polar ice caps.

THE ICE AGE CHANGES

On the whole, changes in global sea levels depend on two factors – the height at which the continents float on the mantle (isostatic change), and the amount of water in the oceans (eustatic change). At the beginning of the last ice age, the formation of huge ice sheets locked up huge amounts of water on land and the oceans shrank and fell by up to 130 m (427 ft) below their present level about 16,000 years ago, exposing the present-day continental shelf. But the mass of ice on the land weighed down the land, like an overladen ship, so that towards the end of the ice age, ocean levels actually began to rise again. And with warmer temperatures at the end of the ice age, sea levels rose higher still as the ice on land melted and swelled the oceans.

◁ *Port Hacking in New South Wales, Australia, is a ria, a river valley drowned by the rising of global sea levels at the end of the last ice age.*

△ *Raised platforms, such as these near Wellington, New Zealand, were cut by the waves when the sea level was much higher. They are clear evidence that the sea can rise and fall dramatically.*

All around the world, low-lying coastal plains and river valleys were drowned, creating estuaries, rias, and fjords.

At the same time, however, the melting of the ice was like jettisoning the ship's load, and the depressed land began to slowly rise again in places. In Scotland, ancient beaches raised tens of feet above the current shoreline bear clear witness to the scale of this 'isostatic rebound'. Interestingly, while the northwest of the UK, which had born the greatest weight of ice, bobbed up higher, the southeast was tilted lower – allowing the flooding of the English Channel, which was once dry land, about 4,000 years ago.

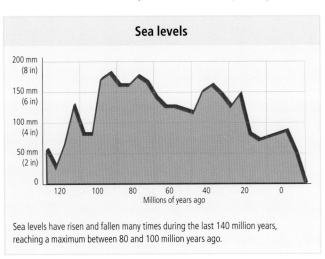

Sea levels

Sea levels have risen and fallen many times during the last 140 million years, reaching a maximum between 80 and 100 million years ago.

FLOODING THE WORLD

ACCORDING TO MANY REPORTS, THE RISE IN SEA LEVELS TRIGGERED BY GLOBAL WARMING COULD DEVASTATE LOW-LYING COUNTRIES AND DROWN MANY OF THE WORLD'S MAJOR SEABOARD CITIES. BUT JUST HOW BAD IS IT LIKELY TO BE?

THE STEADY RISE IN SEA LEVELS over the last 6,000 years since their almost record lows during the last ice age can be seen in the estuaries, fjords, and wetlands around the world. But during the last century the rise in sea levels seems to have suddenly accelerated.

On average, the sea has risen about 0.5 mm (0.02 in) a year over the last 6,000 years. However, since 1900 it has risen at 1–2.5 mm (0.04–0.1 in) a year. Satellite measurements of the sea surface suggest that since 1992, the rate of sea level rise has been more than 3 mm (0.12 in) a year (see graph).

In a report in 2007, the Intergovernmental Panel on Climate Change (IPCC) suggested that the global average sea level would rise between 280 and 430 mm (11 and 17 in) by 2100. But data gathered since then has suggested that this prediction was way too low, because it did not factor in the effect of ice sheets melting under the influence of global warming. A report based on melting of the West Antarctic ice sheet in December 2009 suggested that the sea could rise at least 1.4 m (4.5 ft) over the next century.

GLOBAL FLOOD

That may not sound that much, but some densely inhabited parts of the world are very low lying. Bangladesh and Calcutta already suffer from frequent, devastating floods. Even a small rise could wreak havoc. The densely populated Nile delta would become uninhabitable, driving tens of millions of people from their homes. There are currently 46 million people around the world living in places vulnerable to storm surges. A rise of just 0.5 m (20 in) would double that number. A rise as much as 1 m (3 ft) would drown almost a fifth of Bangladesh, and 6 percent of the Netherlands entirely – and it would swamp the eastern seaboard of the USA, flooding cities from Boston to Miami and spell the end for New Orleans. The effect on marine life in fragile coastal habitats could be just as catastrophic.

Most of the rise in sea levels so far has been due to thermal expansion; as the oceans get gradually warmer with the world's climate, so the water in them expands. The concern is that as global warming accelerates, so more and more water will pour into the sea as ice sheets and glaciers melt. The effect of floating

△ *Low-lying areas, such as Gujarat in east India, already prone to floods like this one in August 2004, could be devastated by even a small rise in global sea levels.*

◁ *Melting sea ice is clear evidence of warming in the atmosphere, but it is the melting of land-based ice sheets and glaciers, such as this, the Neumayer glacier on South Georgia, that will raise sea levels.*

ice melting is fairly negligible, because the amount of water added when the ice melts is pretty much equivalent to the space it takes as it floats. What matters is ice on land. When that melts, water that was locked up on land is suddenly added to the sea.

MELTING ICE

Until recently, it was thought that only low-level glaciers and floating ice such as the Arctic ice cap and sea ice in Antarctica might melt. Although the effects of such melts are already clearly visible and may have dramatic effects on wildlife, their impact on sea levels is probably negligible. Now, however, it seems there are signs that high-mountain glaciers and the land-based ice sheets of Greenland and Antarctica could begin to melt, too. There are enough signs that this process has started for scientists to begin to suggest that sea level rise could accelerate dramatically in the near future.

The Greenland ice sheet contains enough water to raise the global sea level 7 m (23 ft) if it ever melted, while the melting of the largest of the ice sheets, the East Antarctic, would add a gigantic 64 m (210 ft) to the sea. That is unlikely to happen. Nor are any of the other ice sheets likely to melt entirely for a very long time, even if the world gets much hotter. But a report in February 2010 suggested that huge chunks of ice are already being lost from the Greenland ice sheet. As the ocean warms, it is melting the ice from underneath, allowing ice to slide off the land and into the sea. Satellite surveys in 2009 showed that more than 1,500 cu. km (360 cu. miles) of water has been lost from the Greenland ice sheet since 2000.

Climate change sceptics contest these figures vigorously, but no one disputes that sea levels are rising. It is only the scale that is in doubt. Most people believe it makes sense to take precautionary measures. It is not easy to decide what these measures should be, since hard barriers such as sea walls can create as many problems as they solve. That is why it is worth thinking about the problem now, rather than when it is too late.

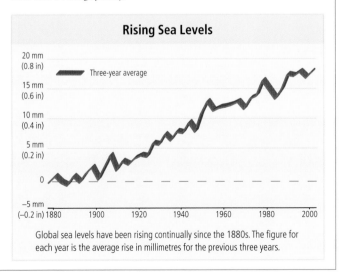

△ *Low-lying coral shores in the Indo-Pacific Ocean, such as these on the island of aux Cerfs in Mauritius, could well disappear if global sea levels were to rise significantly.*

Rising Sea Levels

Three-year average

20 mm (0.8 in)	
15 mm (0.6 in)	
10 mm (0.4 in)	
5 mm (0.2 in)	
0	
−5 mm (−0.2 in)	1880 1900 1920 1940 1960 1980 2000

Global sea levels have been rising continually since the 1880s. The figure for each year is the average rise in millimetres for the previous three years.

THE CHEMICAL OCEAN

Swallowing a mouthful of sea water can tell you instantly that the water in the sea is by no means pure. In fact, it is only 96.5 percent water, and sea water is actually a solution that contains a huge range of chemicals.

So far, 72 separate elements have been found in the sea, and the chances are that nearly every naturally occurring element is in there somewhere. In every cubic kilometre of sea water there is a staggering 82 million tonnes (90 million tons) of chlorine, 45 million tonnes (50 million tons) of sodium, 5.4 million tonnes (6 million tons) of magnesium, 3.6 million tonnes (4 million tons) of sulphur, and not far short of 1.8 million tonnes (2 million tons) of calcium and potassium. There is even a fair amount of lead and even gold!

THE OLD BRINY

All these elements, but principally sodium and chlorine, combine to make sea water salty or 'briny'. On average, the salinity of sea water is about 3.5 percent, which means 35 parts salt to 1,000 of water, the equivalent of a teaspoon of salt in a glass of water. There are about

45 million billion tonnes (50 million billion tons) of salt in the oceans – enough to cover the Earth to a depth of 152 m (500 ft)!

The salt concentration varies from place to place, as we know mostly from a series of worldwide chemical tests conducted in the 1880s by William Dittmar on HMS *Challenger*. The concentration is highest in the Red Sea and Persian Gulf, and lowest in the Baltic and Arctic oceans. Levels are high in warm seas where evaporation of pure water concentrates the salt in the water left behind; they are low in cool seas, where pure water is continually added to by melting ice and rivers.

WHERE DOES THE SALT COME FROM?

The original ocean waters were essentially fresh water, since they fell, distilled, from clouds. Salt was continually added by rivers flowing into the sea, hydrothermal vents, and undersea volcanoes. Rain water is fairly pure, though it is turned slightly acidic by dissolved, atmospheric gases. That is why rivers are fresh water. Yet even the purest river water contains some dissolved salts and other salts. And the combined effect of all the world's rivers

△ The sea trout is 'anadromous', migrating from rivers to the sea. It is a migratory form of the brown trout, which lives only in freshwater.

△ Polychaetes worms react to subtle changes in ocean chemistry by changing colour, so they are often used as pollution monitors.

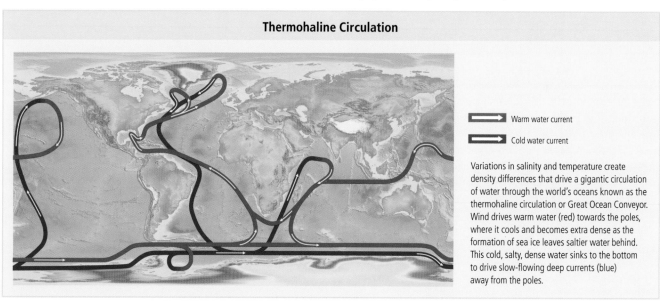

Thermohaline Circulation

⬜➤ Warm water current

⬜➤ Cold water current

Variations in salinity and temperature create density differences that drive a gigantic circulation of water through the world's oceans known as the thermohaline circulation or Great Ocean Conveyor. Wind drives warm water (red) towards the poles, where it cools and becomes extra dense as the formation of sea ice leaves saltier water behind. This cold, salty, dense water sinks to the bottom to drive slow-flowing deep currents (blue) away from the poles.

pouring into the sea adds a huge amount of salt. It is estimated that every year 3.6 billion tonnes (4 billion tons) of salt are washed into the oceans. The rivers do not dilute the sea much because fresh water evaporates continually from the surface. That is why salinity is highest in the open oceans and lowest near the coasts where rivers flood in fresh water. Remarkably, the amount of salt washed in by rivers seems to balance exactly the amount of water that evaporates into the atmosphere, so that despite local variations, the overall salt content of the sea stays constant.

THE CHEMICALS OF LIFE

Interestingly, freshwater rivers tend to carry much more calcium, bicarbonate, and silica into the sea. Yet sea water contains more sodium and chloride. One reason for this is that marine life plays a significant role in the chemical balance of the oceans. A lot of calcium is extracted from the oceans by molluscs, crustaceans, foraminifera, and corals that use calcium to build skeletons and shells. Diatoms extract silica. Other creatures influence the chemical content in subtler ways, such as snails that extract lead.

▽ *The Dead Sea, which lies between Israel and Jordan, gains its salt from rivers, as do other seas, but its salt content has become 8.6 times more concentrated than that of other seas due to its high evaporation rates.*

Ancient Chemistry

Until recently, scientists believed it was the slow oxygenation of the air by cyanobacteria that paved the way for complex life to emerge 700 million years ago. The turning point, apparently, was the 'Great Oxygenation Event' (GOE) 2.4 billion years ago, when cyanobacteria at last began to produce more oxygen than other organisms consumed. But is this true?

First, some scientists have cast doubt on the authenticity of 3.5-billion-year-old cyanobacteria fossils from Australia and suggest that cyanobacteria really emerged barely 2 billion years ago – too recently to have created the GOE. Second, banded iron formations – layers formed under the sea by iron released by the effect of oxygen on iron in rocks (rusting) – suggest that oxygen levels were actually dwindling 1.9 billion years ago, not rising.

Indeed, geological and chemical processes may have contributed as much as cyanobacteria to the GOE, if not more, and may also have boosted oxygen levels in the sea more than in the air. If so, it could actually have triggered a collapse of the greenhouse effect that plunged the world, according to the 'snowball earth' hypothesis, into a half-billion-year-long mega ice age that took its toll on the cyanobacteria. When the planet finally warmed up, and oxygen-producing cyanobacteria recovered, they were joined by hydrogen sulphide-producing bacteria that made the oceans as stagnant and smelly as sewers for a billion years.

The crucial event may actually have been the greening of the land by algae and the first lichen 800 million years ago. This not only oxygenated the air, but added nutrients to the sea as the algae and lichen broke down rocks, enabling the sudden blooming of complex life in the oceans.

Ocean Acidification

With all the attention given to global warming, a second potentially devastating effect of the human addition of carbon dioxide to the air has rather slipped under the radar – the increasing acidity of the oceans.

The oceans have probably saved us from the worst effects of global warming already, by soaking up huge amounts of the carbon dioxide pumped into the air by human activity. Estimates vary, but anything between a third and a half of all the carbon dioxide added has been absorbed by the oceans. This ocean buffer comes at a cost. Carbon dioxide does not simply disappear when it goes into the oceans; it alters the chemistry of the oceans, turning them slightly acidic.

Acidity is measured on the pH scale that shows on a scale of 0 to 14 how acid or alkaline a liquid is by the concentration of hydrogen ions: 0 is the most extreme acid; 14 is the most extreme alkali; 7 is neutral. Sea water is slightly alkaline, with a pH ranging from 7.5 to 8.4. This alkalinity is important, because numerous creatures from corals to pteropod shellfish rely on the availability of carbonates in the water to build their shells and skeletons, which are rich in calcium carbonates.

DIPPED IN ACID

Acidity would have to rise dramatically before shells and skeletons were actually dissolved in a nightmarish acid bath

▽ *If acidification reduces levels of aragonite – a form of calcium carbonate – below a critical level in the oceans, corals could start to dissolve. Even the relatively healthy Great Barrier Reef, part of which is seen here in Cairns, Australia, would then be at risk of rapid reduction. Recent studies suggest that this critical level may be reached as early as 2050.*

scenario, but even a slight decrease in alkalinity could reduce the availability of carbonates and seriously disrupt growth. Experiments have shown that pH has to change by just 0.2 to hamper the growth of sensitive creatures such as corals and plankton. The ocean's pH has already dropped by 0.1 since pre-industrial times. Scientists at the Carnegie Institution believe it could fall by 0.35 over the next 50 years. The acidification could be even more extreme in surface waters, where the vast majority of marine life lives, because carbon dioxide is absorbed at the surface. The focus so far has been on corals, which some marine biologists suggest could be destroyed entirely around the world by acidification in just a few decades – even if they survive other environmental hazards. But the effects of acidification could reverberate through the whole marine ecosystem. For a start, it can affect calcification (the formation of bone and shell) for a huge range of sea creatures. Young and developing organisms are very vulnerable, since they need ample carbonates for growth. If many species spend much longer in the larval stage, they might become much more vulnerable to predation.

ACID TRIP

Acidification could also have a dramatic impact through the damage it causes to key species, such as phytoplankton. Phytoplankton build themselves calcium carbonate shells to protect them from microscopic predators such as ciliate

protozoa. If robbed of their carbonate armour, plankton could be gorged on by protozoa, with the effects of their decline rippling right the way through the food chain – and having even more significant consequences as their huge addition of oxygen to the environment is curtailed. Similarly, if pteropods decline because they are unable to make their shells, their natural predators may be forced to look elsewhere for food, which could cause major disruption to fish populations.

Some believe that acidification may also be playing a part in the decline of fish stock in coastal waters, where there are other environmental problems. But with all the focus on the terrestrial

△ *Already threatened by the warmer seas caused by global warming, corals may face an even bigger enemy in the acidification of the oceans by carbon dioxide from the atmosphere, which impairs their ability to build their skeletons.*

effects of greenhouse gases and climate change, the research into the effects of ocean acidification are only just getting under way. Yet there is genuine cause for concern. The acidification in the oceans is far harder to turn around than atmospheric greenhouse gases. To prevent the pH dropping to 0.2, the level at which corals and many other creatures would be seriously threatened, carbon dioxide emissions would have to be cut right now.

Global Acidity Levels

Most alkaline   Least alkaline

Sea water is mildly alkaline, with an average pH of about 8.1, but this varies across the world. It is generally most alkaline in polar waters (8.2) and least so in tropical waters (8.0), and where cold upwellings bring carbon dioxide up from the deeps the pH may drop below 8.

Ocean World: Rocks and Water
The Moving Ocean

The world's oceans are never, ever still, not even for a moment. There is always movement, everywhere, from the ceaseless undulation of waves on the surface of the water to the daily ebb and flow of the tide.

Some movements are as miniscule as the slight disturbance of a coral taking food from the water. Some are rapid, such as a riptide surging through a break in the rocks. Some are slow and gigantic, such as the vast, deep water currents that circulate water through all the world's oceans over the course of a millennium.

The great motor for much of the oceans' restless motion is the heat of the Sun. It disturbs the surface layers of the water by creating the variations in air temperature that set winds in motion. Winds not only whip up waves but also set in motion powerful surface currents that circulate in vast loops through every ocean. The Sun also helps drive the deep water currents by creating variations in the density of ocean water on a global scale. The second great engine of ocean movement is the combination of gravity and the Earth's rotation, which creates the tides that slosh the ocean waters to and fro twice daily, as the Earth passes beneath the Moon.

The pattern of ocean movements is complex, and its pattern is the result of a huge and subtle range of influences. But what has become increasingly clear in recent years is that even a slight change to the pattern can have profound consequences for human and animal life around the world. The press often focuses on the effects of the occasional switches of the ocean circulation in the South Pacific known as El Niño and La Niña – creating anything from calamitous storms in Chile to drought in Africa. But could global warming have an even more dramatic effect?

◁ *Huge breakers, so famous in the Pacific, are the result of the interplay between the wind and the ocean surface over vast distances. Even bigger ocean movements are created by variations in temperature and salinity.*

CIRCULATING WATER

S AILORS HAVE LONG BEEN AWARE of currents on the ocean surface that could carry them huge distances off course if they did not take precautions. But it is only in the last half-century that oceanographers have become aware that these currents are simply part of a gigantic circulation that extends through the depths of the ocean on a global scale.

Ocean circulation is driven by persistent winds at the surface and density differences lower down. The pattern of wind-surface currents is dominated by five great loops or 'gyres': two in the Atlantic, two in the Pacific, and a fifth in the Indian Ocean. Pulled by the prevailing winds, they are curled into loops firstly by running up against land barriers and secondly by the effect of the Earth's rotation.

SPIN DOCTORED

The Earth's rotation is crucial because, as it spins, wind and water moving across its surface are deflected from their courses – a phenomenon known as the Coriolis effect. As they are blown by the wind, currents are deflected to the right in the northern hemisphere and to the left in the south. The deflection increases as you go deeper, creating a spiral of deflection known as the Ekman spiral, after the Swedish oceanographer Vagn Ekman (1874–1954). On average, the current flows at right angles to the prevailing wind.

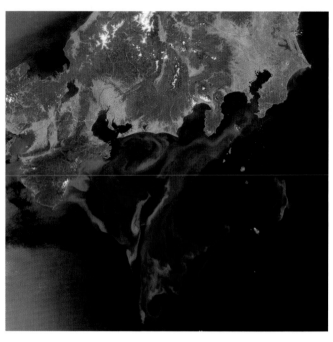

△ Where cold and warm currents meet, there may be rich blooms of phytoplankton, triggered by the stirring up of nutrients that have fallen into the deeps. This bloom is on the coast of Honshu, Japan.

Oceanic Currents

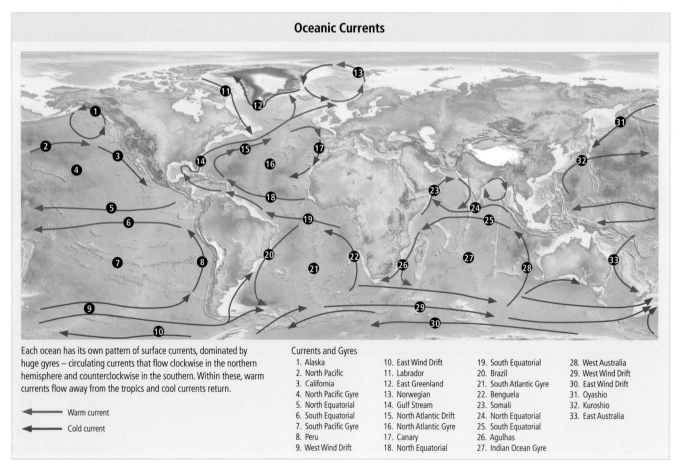

Each ocean has its own pattern of surface currents, dominated by huge gyres – circulating currents that flow clockwise in the northern hemisphere and counterclockwise in the southern. Within these, warm currents flow away from the tropics and cool currents return.

⟵ Warm current

⟵ Cold current

Currents and Gyres

1. Alaska	10. East Wind Drift	19. South Equatorial	28. West Australia
2. North Pacific	11. Labrador	20. Brazil	29. West Wind Drift
3. California	12. East Greenland	21. South Atlantic Gyre	30. East Wind Drift
4. North Pacific Gyre	13. Norwegian	22. Benguela	31. Oyashio
5. North Equatorial	14. Gulf Stream	23. Somali	32. Kuroshio
6. South Equatorial	15. North Atlantic Drift	24. North Equatorial	33. East Australia
7. South Pacific Gyre	16. North Atlantic Gyre	25. South Equatorial	
8. Peru	17. Canary	26. Agulhas	
9. West Wind Drift	18. North Equatorial	27. Indian Ocean Gyre	

The effect creates clockwise-circulating gyres in the northern hemisphere and counterclockwise gyres in the south. Driven westward in the tropics by easterly trade winds, currents turn to flow away from the tropics up the western edges of the oceans as warm 'western boundary currents'. Then, driven back east across the ocean by westerly winds in the mid-latitudes, they turn again to flow back to the tropics down the eastern edge of continents as cool 'eastern boundary currents'.

BOUNDARY CURRENTS

Western boundary currents are narrow, fast-flowing rivers in the sea. The Gulf Stream is 100 km (60 miles) wide and about 1,000 m (3,280 ft) deep, and reaches speeds of 2.5 m (8 ft) a second. As it passes Newfoundland, it carries 150 million cu. m (196 million cubic yards) of water every second – about 250 times as much as all the rivers emptying into the Atlantic combined. Such vast currents carry huge quantities of heat from the tropics to the mid-latitudes, and play a big part in making these regions habitable for wildlife, and for humans, too. The British Isles, for instance, owes its mild climate, which would otherwise be Siberian, to the Gulf Stream.

Eastern boundary currents, such as the Canary Current and the California Current, by contrast, are much broader and weaker. However, they generate upwellings of nutrient-rich water from the deeps in eddies around capes and promontories. The feast these upwellings provide attracts huge numbers of fish, making eastern boundary currents some of the world's richest fisheries.

DEEP WATER CIRCULATION

In the ocean deeps, water is moved by variations in water density. Because these density variations depend on heat and salt, it is known as the thermohaline circulation. As water cools or gets saltier, it becomes denser and sinks. But this simple process generates movement on a massive scale, and it moves water right around the world in what is sometimes known as the Great Ocean Conveyor.

In polar regions, dense water tends to sink into the deep ocean basins. Polar water is not just denser because it is cool but because when it freezes into ice sheets, it leaves the salt behind in the unfrozen water. Even the warmer water brought in by western boundary currents is dense, because evaporation leaves it saltier.

In the North Atlantic, this dense water, sometimes known as North Atlantic Deep Water (NADW) slowly sinks and starts to push dense water southwards ahead of it. It flows deep down through the Atlantic right across the equator to meet the even denser Antarctic Bottom Water (AABW). The circulation moves slowly eastwards deep in the Southern Ocean, past South Africa and Australia, to run through the Pacific before finally rising to the surface and warming up to flow westwards through the Pacific and Indian oceans into the Atlantic in the top layers of the ocean. Finally, it heads north through the Atlantic to Greenland to start the cycle again. It takes a millennium or more for water to go right around – so water coming back to Greenland now began its journey in the time of the Vikings.

▽ The sunset cup coral, which is small, yellow, and star-shaped, is a largely tropical species, but it relies on warm water swept in by the Gulf Stream to allow it to survive as far north as the British Isles.

OCEANS AND CLIMATE

THE VASTNESS OF THE OCEANS means they have a profound influence on the world's climate. But it is not simply their size; they interact with the atmosphere in a way that land does not – firstly by storing heat energy and moving it around in ocean currents, and secondly by adding and absorbing gases, notably water vapour and carbon dioxide.

Soil and rock have a much lower heat capacity than water, so continents lose and gain heat readily, heating up quickly going into summer and cooling down quickly going into winter. By contrast, sea water is very slow to heat up but slow to cool down. The ocean acts as a vast heat reservoir, taking a while to warm up, but acting like a night storage heater in cooler times. This is important in keeping the world's climate equable rather than extreme. It is also why continental interiors, such as central Siberia and the North American Midwest, tend to have much more extreme climates with hot summers and icy winters, whereas 'maritime' regions near the coast have much more moderated climates with cooler summers and mild winters. The difference is accentuated by the dryness of the air far from the sea in continental interiors and its wetness in coastal regions.

The weather pattern in each region, though, may be complicated by air masses – large bodies of air with similar characteristics – that form in particular areas. Sometimes dry, continental air masses flood out over regions that are normally maritime. When a cold, dry continental air mass extends over the British Isles in winter, it can pick up moisture as it crosses the North Sea and so bring snow.

HEAT AND STORMS

Huge amounts of water evaporate from the sea each year, and provide most of the moisture that eventually falls as rain. But evaporation does not simply add moisture to the air, it adds heat energy, too. This is why global warming may make the world a much stormier place. As the ocean warms, evaporation accelerates, adding more moisture and more energy to the atmosphere. Some scientists suggest that global warming has already triggered an increase in the number and severity of hurricanes each year – and predict that things could soon get really rough. If so, fragile coastal habitats could be put at severe risk, as well as human habitation. But it is too early to tell yet.

The world's weather patterns, too, depend on the way currents move the ocean's reservoir of heat energy around. Western boundary currents, for instance, bring tropical warmth and milder weather – sometimes, as in the Gulf Stream, carrying mild weather right across the oceans to western Europe. Cooler eastern boundary currents tend to bring cooler summers and fogs.

▽ *Normally dry areas of Bolivia were suddenly inundated by the floods that followed the heavy rains brought by the El Niño event of 1997. Around 23,000 cattle were drowned and 350,000 people, their homes, and livelihoods were badly affected.*

EL NIÑO AND LA NIÑA

Sometimes, however, the pattern of currents varies – with dramatic consequences. In the South Pacific summer, trade winds are normally drawn across the ocean towards a warm, low pressure zone in the west, and these winds drive the westward-flowing South Equatorial Current. But the pattern is continually disrupted by what is called the El Niño Southern Oscillation (ENSO), with effects on climate felt around the world.

Every two to ten years, the warm zone spreads eastwards right across to South America. The trade winds weaken and with them the South Equatorial Current. The slackening of the current locks warm water in the eastern ocean, and the south-flowing cold Peru Current dives beneath it, disrupting the cold upwelling of nutrient-rich water that normally brings such rich fishing to the South American coast. At the same time, storms burst all the way down the South American coast, while far across the Pacific, drought hits Australia and East Africa as the trade winds are

△ *The powerful waves generated by a hurricane reach much farther below the surface of the water than normal waves – and can wreck fragile coral reefs as this picture shows. Reefs may be increasingly at risk of serious damage as global warming boosts the frequency and power of hurricanes.*

robbed of moisture. These events are known as El Niño (Spanish for 'the Christ child' or 'boy child').

Often an El Niño event is followed closely by La Niña ('girl child') in which the opposite happens and the warm zone shifts even farther to the west than normal, strengthening the South Equatorial Current. Australia and Southeast Asia are lashed by rains during this time, while the cooling of the waters off South America brings drought this time to South America.

▽ *This sequence shows how the warmest water (in red and white) moved gradually eastwards across the South Pacific in 1997 to create an El Niño event with its dramatic impact on weather across the southern hemisphere.*

May 1997 June 1997 September 1997 November 1997 December 1997

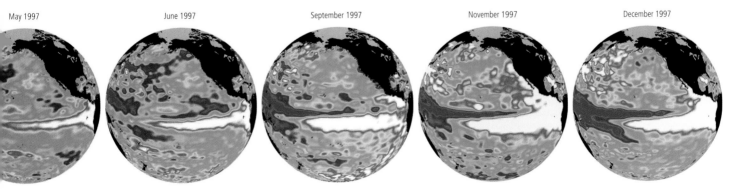

WAVES

W AVES KEEP THE OCEAN SURFACE in constant motion. They vary from gentle ripples to mountainous seas that can swamp the largest boat. But they all start with the wind, which tugs at the water as it blows across the sea.

The friction between wind and the ocean surface, known as wind stress, is enough for the wind to drag the water along, particle by particle. If the wind blows for a long enough time in the same direction, a mass of moving particles may build into ripples. If the wind blows harder and farther over the water, the ripples may build into waves.

It might seem as if waves keep water moving forward, but the water in them actually stays in much the same place. A sea wave is a travelling peak of energy, not water. If you flick one end of

a rope fixed tightly at the other end, the energy of the flick snakes down the rope but the two ends of the rope do not move at all. In a way, the water in a wave moves like the rollers in a conveyor belt because the water in them just turns over on the spot in an 'orbital path'. As a wave passes, individual water particles are lifted up and swept forward a little way before sinking back again and being rolled over as the wave moves onto the next particle.

A SWELL PARTY

The power of a wave depends not only on the strength of the wind, and how long it blows, but also on the fetch – how far it blows over the water. A wind that continually veers and blows only for a short fetch, churns up the sea into a chaotic pattern of waves travelling in all directions, called a 'sea'. A wind that blows for a long time in the same direction, and over a long fetch begins to build up large, regular waves that sweep along in the same direction, known as a 'swell'. Such swells develop frequently in the large oceans, such as the Atlantic and Pacific, where strong winds blow over huge expanses of water.

The waves in swells sweep for thousands of kilometres across the ocean until they strike a coast. As they travel, they gradually lose energy, and the shorter, slower moving waves are gradually left behind, until all that are left are faster, longer waves. These waves are very smooth and even, and free from the choppiness of other sea waves. They create the waves that surfers love.

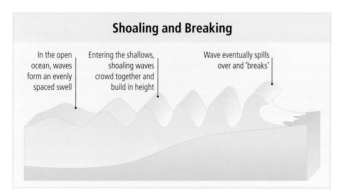

Shoaling and Breaking

In the open ocean, waves form an evenly spaced swell

Entering the shallows, shoaling waves crowd together and build in height

Wave eventually spills over and 'breaks'

△ *Lines of seaweed mark the limits reached by the highest waves as they spill and run up the beach until their momentum is spent.*

BREAKING WAVES

When waves move into shallow water, the circular rolling motion runs into the seabed and the waves begin to pile into an ellipse, getting closer and closer together and growing steeper. Eventually, each wave gets so tall that it topples over. The top spills forwards, breaking the wave and dispelling its energy as it surges against the coast.

Where it breaks on a beach, the spilling water runs up the beach as 'swash' until its momentum is spent. It then drops back down the beach again as 'backwash'. Both swash and backwash can move sand on the beach. If the swash is stronger, the wave piles sand onto the beach and is said to be constructive. If the backwash is stronger, the wave drags sand away from the beach and is said to be destructive. On gently sloping shores, breakers are tall and tumbling and are called spilling breakers. On steeper shores, they are lower and smoother and are called surging breakers. In between are plunging and collapsing breakers. The biggest breakers of all are the huge rollers beloved by surfers that are created by a swell that has travelled far across the ocean and consists entirely of fast-moving, long waves. Breakers like these are familiar in Hawaii and along other Pacific coasts, where they have developed in the world's biggest ocean.

Giant Waves

Storms can generate gigantic waves, and tales of mountainous seas abound. It is difficult to verify the height of such large waves, but the largest that was officially recorded was 34 m (112 ft), measured from the USS *Ramapo* in a hurricane in the Pacific in 1933. On the whole, giant waves seem to be random occurrences. There is little basis to the myth that every seventh wave is higher than the rest, but it has been calculated that one wave in 300,000 is four times the average height. Sometimes, however, ocean currents help to focus wave energy and produce freak waves. This seems to happen off the coast of South Africa, where the southward-flowing Agulhas Current is whipped up by winds roaring uninterrupted across the southern oceans. Here, several huge ships have been completely overwhelmed by monster waves as they headed south using the current to speed their progress.

△ *A freak wave that was generated during a huge storm in the Atlantic threatens a ship in the Bay of Biscay off the coast of France in 1953.*

THE TIDAL OCEAN

TWICE A DAY, THE SEA RISES UP THE SHORE then falls back again in tides. However, the effect is only local. While the tide is rising in one place, it is falling in another, as huge forces are exerted on the vast mass of water in the oceans.

Tides fall in one place and rise in another because the water in the oceans is moving around, flowing this way and that across the face of the planet, so that it piles up in one place, making the tide flow in, and drops away in another, making the tide ebb. It is this continual ebb and flow of ocean water that makes many simple explanations of why tides occur misleading or wrong.

THE MOON AND THE SUN

Tides do not occur simply because the oceans are lifted up by the Moon's gravity as they pass beneath it. The mutual gravitational attraction between the Moon and the Earth is indeed at the heart of it, but the Moon does not just pull the waters up. As the Moon and the Earth circle around their mutual gravitational centre, the attraction between all parts of them distorts both, stretching them out into slight ovals. Of course, the solid Earth and the Moon are too rigid to be distorted by more than a couple of inches. But because water can flow freely, the effect on the Earth's oceans is more dramatic. As the solid Earth is pulled towards the Moon through its oceans, like a ship tugged through the sea, the ocean waters flow around its surface to create a bulge of water several feet high on either side of the world.

But while the Earth spins, the oceans flow so that the bulges stay in line with the Moon, which stays in pretty much the same place. Of course, on Earth it seems as if it is the bulges that move, not the Earth, and the effect is that the bulges run around the world, making the tide rise and fall twice a day as they pass. Actually, the

Moon moves slightly farther around the Earth every day, so tides occur not every 12 hours, but every 12 hours 25 minutes. And because the Earth is also tilted, the Moon is alternately overhead north and south of the equator, so one tide each day is slightly higher than the other as well.

An additional factor is the Sun. The Sun may be far away but it is so massive that it also affects the tides. When the Moon and Sun line up every fortnight at the Full Moon and New Moon, their pulling power combines to create extreme high and low tides that are called Spring Tides. When they are at right angles to each other, at the Half Moon, they counteract each other, creating shallow Neap Tides.

TIDAL SLOSHING

If the Earth was completely smooth and turned only slowly, everywhere would experience this neat twice-daily, twice-monthly rhythm of tides. But the world is neither smooth, nor does it turn slowly. Tidal forces are far too weak to overcome friction with the ocean bed sufficiently to prevent the tidal wave getting very slightly 'left behind' the Moon. Moreover, they do not sweep unhindered around the Earth. Their path is continually blocked by continents, and they are given a particular twist by the spinning of the Earth beneath.

The effect is that the tidal waves slosh counterclockwise around and around the ocean basins, rising and falling with a rhythm that does not quite tie in with the passage of the Moon. As a result, high tides do not necessarily occur when the Moon is overhead, but when a combination of these sloshing oscillations and tidal forces piles water to its greatest height.

Each ocean basin is a very different shape and so has its own tidal flow. In the South Atlantic, for instance, tides slosh from south to north, taking 12 hours or so to sweep from the tip of Africa to the equator. In the North Atlantic, they sweep around counterclockwise. In the Gulf of Mexico, there is just one tide a day, not two.

STANDING WAVES

The picture is further complicated by the effect of coastlines and shallows. In the open ocean, tides tend to raise the water only 1 m (3 ft) or so. But shallows and inlets funnel the waters, setting all kinds of other rhythms in motion. Enclosed seas such as the Mediterranean have their own unique tidal cycle, often created as standing waves called 'seiches' sweep back and forth like a ripple in a bathtub. These waves can cancel out tides altogether if the sea's natural period of oscillation is very different from that of the open ocean tides. But if they match, a resonance may be set up – like wind through an organ pipe – that piles up very high tides, like those of the Bay of Fundy in Nova Scotia, which can rise and fall more than 15 m (50 ft).

This extraordinary complexity has meant that, in the past, the only way to predict tides was to collect data over enough years

△ *Blue mussels, found on the rocky North Atlantic coasts of North America and Europe, use small threads to grip tightly to rocks in the intertidal zone.*

to extrapolate forwards into the future. Nowadays, however, oceanographers use computer models that take into account detailed shapes of the ocean floor and coastline. These are being combined with increasingly accurate measurements of the height of the ocean surface – called ocean altimetry – and of the ocean bed made possible by satellite technology.

◁ *On gently sloping shores, such as this beach in Ankify, Madagascar, the sea may recede a long way as the tide ebbs, exposing for a short while a vast area of sand that looks like a wet desert, but is actually home to many small sea creatures that burrow into the sand as the sea goes out.*

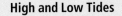

High and Low Tides

Ocean tides are created by the interplay between the gravitational attraction of the Moon and the Earth and the inertial force that would otherwise fling them apart as they rotate together. Directly beneath the Moon, gravity's pull wins out, raising the oceans there. On the far side of the Earth, the pull is weaker and inertial force wins out, flinging the oceans up in another bulge there. As the Earth rotates, these two bulges seem to run around the planet, making tides ebb and flow.

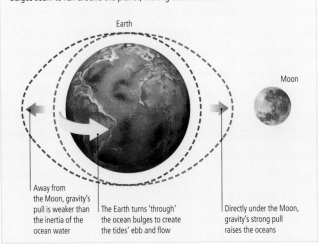

Earth

Moon

Away from the Moon, gravity's pull is weaker than the inertia of the ocean water

The Earth turns 'through' the ocean bulges to create the tides' ebb and flow

Directly under the Moon, gravity's strong pull raises the oceans

OCEAN LIFE ZONES
CATALOGUING LIFE

There is life everywhere in the ocean. There is life in the coastal shallows. There is life in the open oceans. There is even life, much to the surprise of scientists, in the very deepest parts of the ocean.

Scientists currently know of around 230,000 marine species, but there may be many, many more yet to be discovered. Back in 2000, when the UN Environment Program's Global Biodiversity Assessment programme asked the experts how many species there were in the sea altogether, they were given estimates that varied widely between one million and ten million, but recent research is beginning to show that even these hugely varying estimates could be completely wrong.

At a time when scientists and environmentalists are campaigning vigorously against the loss of biodiversity, it seems important to know just how diverse the ocean is. That is why the vague answers to the UNEP's programme triggered the great Census of Marine Life, which began in 2000. It is not yet certain how many creatures the Census will log, and it is almost certain that they will only log a fraction. But it has more than confirmed that there are a vast number of species in the oceans. As US oceanographer Sylvia Earle puts it so eloquently, 'In a single swirl of sea water, a plankton-feeding whale shark may swallow the larval or adult stages of 15 or more phyla (or divisions) of animals – as many as all terrestrial phyla of animals combined.' It is also equally clear, though, that the diversity is not limitless, and that there is a limit to how far humankind can prune the species without doing grave harm to the whole ocean ecosystem.

Ocean creatures are not so neatly restricted to particular habitats as land animals tend to be. Salmon, for instance, spend some of their lives at the head of freshwater rivers, and some thousands of kilometres away in the deep ocean – two dramatically contrasting places. Nevertheless, the ocean can be divided into biomes or life zones, depending essentially on their distance from the shore and their depth from the surface, which controls how much light they receive among other things.

◁ *The remarkable marine lakes of Palau Island in the Pacific, linked to the sea by fissures in the reef rock, are teeming with their own unique species of jellyfish, the golden jellyfish (seen here), and the moon jellyfish.*

EXPLORING THE DEEP

IT IS SOMETHING OF A CLICHÉ that we know less about the bottom of the oceans than we do about Mars. But there is truth in this – the oceans are mapped in less detail than the surface of the planet Mars. Fewer explorers have been to the very bottom of the ocean than astronauts have travelled to the Moon. However, this very lack of knowledge means that there are tremendous discoveries still to be made.

OCEAN REVELATIONS

In the last half century alone, oceanographers have made discoveries under the sea such as: the world's biggest mountain range, the Mid-Ocean Ridge, which stretches more than 65,000 km (40,400 miles) through the oceans; undersea volcanoes taller than Mount Everest; hot volcanic jets on the seabed, which support their own unique communities of life that survive incredible heat, entirely without creatures that need sunlight; corals that live in cold water thousands of feet below the sea; the body of a colossal squid, the world's largest invertebrate; fish living more than 7,000 m (23,000 ft) down in the ocean; mats of microbes as big as France on the seafloor. The latter two discoveries have been made in the last ten years. So there is clearly much to learn; in fact, barely 3 percent of the ocean has been explored in detail.

MAPPING TECHNOLOGY

The big problem with undersea exploration is seeing through the water. In the 1870s, when HMS *Challenger* made its pioneering voyage to explore the world's oceans, all it could use to help it were weights and scoops lowered into the water. That is why the development of sonar has been so crucial. Sonar, which works by beaming sound and using its echo to find objects, was originally developed in World War II to hunt for submarines, but it was soon realized that, with different frequencies, it could be used to map the ocean floor, and even the rocks beneath the seabed. It was with sonar that the first proper maps of the seafloor were made during the 1950s. Multi-beam sonar arrays now provide a much more detailed view.

Even the latest sonar, though, takes a long time to map just a tiny portion of the seabed. That is why the addition of satellite technology has been so crucial. In 1995, the US declassified data from the Navy's Geosat satellite, which by mapping minute variations in the sea surface height revealed the relief of the seafloor. It works through gravitational differences. The sea surface, for instance, is fractionally raised by the extra gravitational attraction of an undersea mountain's bulk. This technique, known as satellite altimetry, only works for large objects, but it covers vast areas and has revealed the presence of tens of thousands of previously unsuspected undersea mountains. Meanwhile, other satellites, with their global overview, can show surface currents, sea surface temperatures, salinity, and even biological productivity. Global positioning systems, too, have made it much easier to establish locations accurately.

SUBMERSIBLES

At the same time, just as the last 50 years have seen the development of spacecraft for exploring the hitherto unreachable realm of space, so submersibles have been developed that have allowed humans to travel to the very deepest parts of the ocean. In 1960, Jacques Piccard and Don Walsh dived 10,915 m (35,810 ft) down in the bathyscaphe *Trieste* to the very bottom of Challenger Deep in the Mariana Trench, the world's deepest place (see page 37). Since then, submersibles, such as the Woods

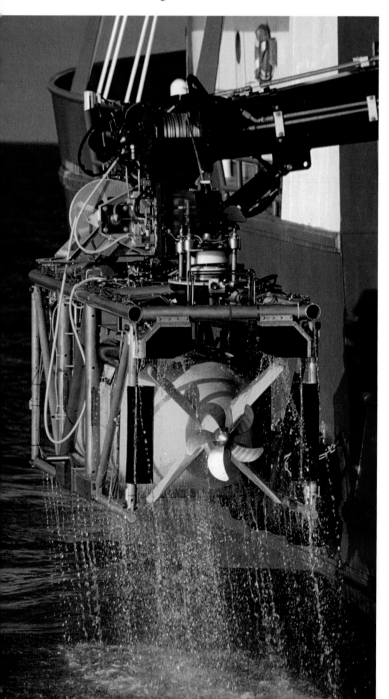

◁ *Robot submersibles enable long explorations to extreme depths that would be impossible, or very costly, for manned craft. This is an Automonous Underwater Vehicle (AUV) programmed to operate underwater without any remote control.*

Hole Oceanographic Institution's *Alvin*, have allowed explorers to make many voyages into the deep ocean.

But manned submersibles are very expensive to construct and are often limited in the places they can reach. Tremendous advances in computer and communications technology have led to the development of numerous Remote Operated Vehicles (ROVs) and there are now hundreds of these in operation, gliding through the deep ocean, operated from the surface by researchers sitting comfortably at a screen rather than peering through a murky porthole. It was the ROVs named Argo and Jason that explored the wreck of the *Titanic* in the 1980s, relaying back live video images. Simple ROVs called gliders can remain on a mission for up to a year, programmed to follow particular routes and track deep-sea currents, beaming back information all the time. This is how oceanographers have discovered the massive global circulation of ocean water deep down, which is known as the thermohaline circulation. They are also discovering major new currents continually, such as the Kerguelen current, a deep-sea current off the coast of Antarctica with a flow 40 times as big as the Amazon River, discovered in April 2010.

The advances have been massive, and it is clear that we are learning more and more about the oceans all the time. At the Monterey Bay Aquarium Research Institute in California, visitors can watch live videos beamed from the deep seafloor. Online, you can see live webcam footage from the NOAA's permanent underwater laboratory Aquarius located 20 m (66 ft) down in the Florida Keys. Ships, such as the *Okeanos Explorer*, are roaming the world mapping the oceans in hitherto unachieved detail.

▷ *A combination of satellite data and a variety of sophisticated sonar systems have enabled oceanographers to finally map the ocean floor and create 3D computer images like this.*

A network of hundreds of Integrated Ocean Observing Systems (IOOS) is helping to build a comprehensive and continually updated picture. And the combined efforts of the researchers who are working on the Marine Census (see pages 62–63) are building up a remarkably detailed picture of life in the oceans.

▽ *Small sonar devices like this can map the seafloor in detail. This device is being used to scan the seabed for traces of ancient settlements in the Mediterranean off the coast of France.*

THE WORLD CENSUS

IN THE YEAR 2000, SCIENTISTS FROM AROUND THE WORLD EMBARKED ON A MASSIVE
TEN-YEAR PROJECT CALLED THE CENSUS OF MARINE LIFE. ITS GRAND AIM WAS,
QUITE SIMPLY, TO IDENTIFY AND CATALOGUE ALL THE SPECIES IN THE OCEANS.

WHEN THE CENSUS OF MARINE LIFE project was initiated, it brought together 2,000 scientists from 82 nations. Their brief was to answer three key questions: What once lived in the global ocean? What is living there now? What will live there in the future? It was a massive brief, and involved scientists and researchers delving into the farthest extremes of the ocean.

CENSUS TECHNIQUES

It would be impossible to survey the whole ocean. Instead, the Census selected 14 representative samples or field projects to study in depth. Eleven of these focus on particular habitats, such as the seamounts of the Arctic or mid-ocean ridges. Three are global in scale and home in on particular worldwide groups – plankton, microbes, and predators such as tuna. Each project has benefited from recent advances in underwater research technology. These involve tracking organisms using acoustics and sound, special optics and cameras, tagging individuals, genetic and DNA studies, and the occasional live capture.

Researchers working on the continental shelf off the western coast of the USA surgically implanted fish with almond-sized

tags so that electronic devices on the ocean floor over a 1,550-km (965-mile) span, scan each fish as it passes by. Satellites track other electronically tagged creatures, such as sharks, turtles, and seals. Meanwhile, Census scientists are developing genetic mapping systems developed from the Human Genome Project to give DNA barcodes for each species, which enable them to be rapidly and accurately identified.

NEW SPECIES

As the Census progressed, scientists found themselves discovering many thousands of new species. Indeed, Census scientists discovered, on average, four or five new species every day. They expect to discover 7,000 new species of zooplankton alone – double the figure known as recently as 2004. New discoveries are particularly abundant among microbes and in the deeps.

A single study in the English Channel in 2007 revealed the existence of 7,000 new genera of micro-organisms. Off the west coast of South America, explorers discovered microbe mats the size of Greece. Indeed, Census scientists now estimate that marine microbes make up 50–90 percent of the ocean's biomass, comically summed up as the weight of 240 billion elephants. Some Census scientists now believe there may be a billion or more species of marine microbes! There may even be hundreds of millions of different microbes living on and in whales alone.

DISCOVERIES IN THE DEEP

Previously little explored, the ocean deeps are proving to be far richer in life than ever imagined. By the end of 2009, the Census had recorded 17,650 species living in the twilight and dark zones below 200 m (656 ft), including 5,722 species that are only seen below a depth of 1,000 m (3,280 ft), and whale-bone eating worms and crawling sea cucumbers, such as Enypniastes sp., that look like creatures from another world. Down between 1,000 and 3,000 m (3,280 and 9,843 ft), they discovered strange kinds of octopus with fins, which they called 'Dumbos' because the fins look like the flapping ears of the Disney cartoon elephant – including one specimen that was more than 2 m (6.5 ft) long, which came to be called the Jumbo Dumbo. They even found cold water corals living at more than 1,000 m (3,280 ft) down on seamounts off the coast of New Zealand.

◁ *Researcher Neil Bruce of the University of Tropical Queensland studies specimens in a lighted aquarium on Lizard Island Reef, Queensland, as part of a research project that revealed hundreds of new species on Australian reefs.*

In 2008, scientists filmed a fish swimming 7,700 m (25,262 ft) down in the Japan Trench. Pale pink in colour, with a bulbous body and a long tail, *Pseudoliparis amblystomopsis* was the deepest living fish ever filmed. The following year, scientists photographed a similar fish, *Notoliparis kermadecensis*, living almost as far down in the Kermadec Trench off New Zealand. Neither of these is as deep, though, as *Abyssobrotula galatheae*, which was dredged from the bottom of the Puerto Rico Trench at a depth of more than 8,370 m (27,460 ft) in 1970 but was dead by the time it reached the surface.

A FISH BY ANY OTHER NAME

Interestingly, though, it has not all been a matter of adding to the list of species. By the end of 2008, the Census had logged 122,500 of the estimated 230,000 marine species known. However, they actually eliminated more than 56,000 species from their list because they turned out to be aliases for other species. The four species of sperm whale, for instance, turned out to be just one. Some species were found to be known not by just one or two other Latin names but by dozens. The record belongs to the breadcrumb sponge, *Halichondria panicea*, which had no less than 56 different aliases!

△ *Enypniastes sp. is one of many interesting deep-sea creatures discovered by the Marine Census. It looks like a jellyfish, but it is actually a sea cucumber, an echinoderm related to starfish, and feeds on seabed sediment.*

▽ *When Census scientists discovered this octopod, its large fins led to it being dubbed the 'Dumbo' after the cartoon character. The biggest species of dumbo octopod is quite naturally named the Jumbo Dumbo.*

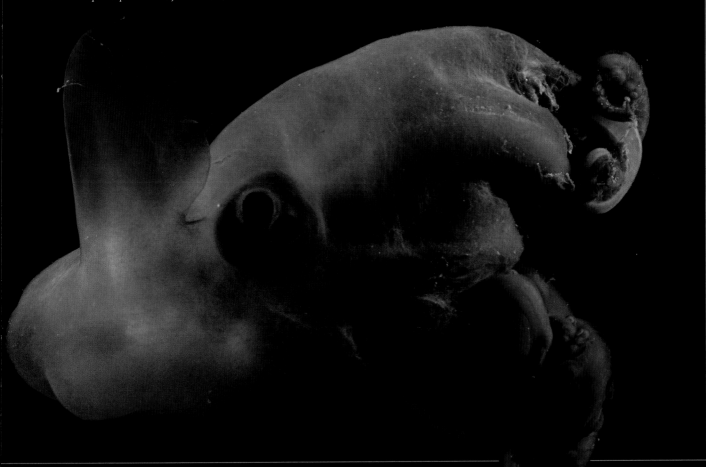

OCEAN LIFE ZONES
COASTAL WATERS

The world's 1.6 million km (1 million miles) of coastline, where the land meets the sea, is a narrow zone rarely more than a few hundred feet wide. Yet it presents an extraordinary range of habitats for life, from shining white coral sand beaches lapped only by the gentlest waves to rugged cliffs pounded all through the year.

All of these coastal habitats, though, are marginal environments in all senses of the word. Not only are they on the margins of the sea and land; they are also on the margins of conditions where life can survive. Many coastal places are incredibly demanding – while they are often pleasant places for humans to visit while on holiday, they provide a hard life for permanent residents.

Coasts are exposed to some of the world's stormiest weather. They are exposed to a spray of salt and other chemicals. They are desiccated by bright sunshine. They are pounded by waves that hurl huge weights of water at them. What makes it all the more extreme is that conditions are changing all the time. As the waves roll in and out, and as the tide ebbs and flows, the coastal habitat can change from the driest, desertlike terrestrial environment to one that is entirely aquatic and marine in just a few hours – again and again, day after day. So any organisms that live there have to cope with some of the widest range of conditions of any on Earth.

They must also cope with the proximity of humans. Maybe half the world's population live within 100 km (60 miles) of the sea, with many living right next to it, and coastal waters have become the part of the marine ecosystem most under pressure from human activity.

◁ *With their crashing waves and tidal pools, rocky coasts such as this one on the Mornington Peninsular near Melbourne, Australia, create a unique and challenging habitat for marine life.*

EVER-CHANGING SHORELINES

IF THERE IS ONE THING THAT DOMINATES the lives of organisms that dwell on the coast, it is the ups and downs of the sea in waves and tides. On some coasts, the sea recedes dramatically at low tide to reveal vast desertlike flat sands and mud, where there is little visible life but a few wading birds probing for food. Within a few hours, though, the tide can flood back in to completely cover the mudflats and create a rich shallow water environment lapping up against the shore.

TIDAL STRESSES

The tidal range and pattern varies tremendously from place to place, but even where it is minimal, animals and plants that live in the intertidal zone must cope with the sudden change that the tide brings. After being immersed entirely in salt water for several hours, organisms are suddenly exposed to the air by the falling tide. Out in the wind and sun, they could quickly dry out if they had no mechanism to retain moisture. Sensitive organisms used only to the mild temperatures of the sea might also scorch in the blaze of the sun or freeze in the chill of the night. The evaporation of water from zones lapped at high tide can leave a huge amount of salt behind, too. And of course, organisms protected by water at high tide are suddenly revealed in all their vulnerability to the predators that prowl the shore – and as the tide flows in, it can also carry with it waterborne predators. Even the water itself can be a hazard, throwing a huge weight

of water in waves at the shore as it ebbs and flows.

The severity of the changes though varies up and down the shore. The changes are most extreme at the top of the tidal range, which the sea leaves exposed entirely for hours on end as it recedes. The changes are least severe at the lowest end of the tidal range, where the sea is gone for only a short while. And so life on the shore is zoned, with the hardiest organisms in the high tide zone and the more vulnerable in the low tide zone.

DINING TIMES

Despite the hazards, many organisms find ways to cope and the shore attracts a rich variety of life. One interesting effect is feeding time. When the tide goes out, many organisms, such as shore-dwelling shellfish and seaweed, effectively go dormant, putting life on hold until the tide rolls in and the good times begin again. While the tide is out, their sole strategy is simply aimed at surviving. Some shellfish lock themselves on to rocks inside their shells. Other organisms burrow into the sand or hide in crevices in the rocks. For predators such as birds, the falling of the tide is a signal for the feasting to begin, as a whole new source of food is revealed. When the tide floods in again, it is all change. Now the organisms that went to sleep or into hiding at low tide come back to life again and start feeding furiously in the water, and fish swim in to feast in the place of birds.

▽ *When the tide goes out, the shore, like the one here near Mowbray River in Queensland, Australia, may look like a desert, devoid of life, but the life is there, burrowed into the sand until the tide washes back in and it can safely emerge again.*

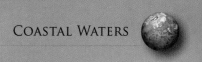

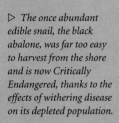

▷ *The once abundant edible snail, the black abalone, was far too easy to harvest from the shore and is now Critically Endangered, thanks to the effects of withering disease on its depleted population.*

For many species, the tide offers many species a degree of safety from predators. Mussels, for instance, can tolerate longer periods out of water than the starfish that prey on them. So mussels can evade starfish by attaching themselves higher up the tide zone to rocks exposed to the air too long for starfish to survive. It is this refuge aspect that sets the lower limits for many species. Conversely, their upper limits are set, like those of starfish, by the extremity of conditions they can tolerate.

The tide can even create safe nurseries for offspring. Californian grunions, for instance, actually emerge from the water to spawn at the very highest spring tides. They surf the highest waves and wriggle as far up the beach as possible, with each female accompanied by several males. As she quickly lays her egg and buries it in the sand, the males try to fertilize it. Spawning done, they all catch the next wave back out to sea, leaving the eggs safe in the sand above the following tides, and well out of reach of marine predators, until they are ready to hatch ten days later. Then the infant grunions can catch the next spring tide out.

Coastal Threats

The proximity of coastal ecosystems to human activity has put them under severe pressure. A recent Nature Conservancy report found that 60 percent of the coast of South America, a comparatively empty continent, is being impacted by very high use. In some parts of the world, the pressure is even greater. The range of threats includes:

- Pollution – from a huge range of sources, including industrial outflow and sewage. About 3,217 billion litres (850 billion gallons) of untreated sewage flow to the sea through the US's waterways from domestic sources alone. Many developing countries pour 80–90 percent of their sewage out directly onto the coast. Oil spills are hazardous to coastal marine life worldwide (see pages 150–151).
- Power plants – Once-Through Cooling (OTC) systems in coastal power plants draw in vast quantities of ocean water killing plankton, fish, invertebrates, and other marine life. Then, the heated water is released back into the fragile ocean environment. Californian power plants alone take 64 billion litres (17 billion gallons) of water from the oceans every day and kill a terrifying 79 billion fish a year. Fish eggs laid close to the shore are particularly vulnerable. Nuclear power plants in the UK kill half as many young fish as the entire UK fishing industry. When fully operational, Dungeness power station on the south coast of England took in and killed 50 million small fish an hour in its cooling water.
- Litter – plastic litter, especially, can be dangerous to coast-dwelling animals such as birds.
- Coastal development and sea defences – building on the coast may completely destroy or severely disrupt the habitats and lifestyles of many marine organisms. Dredging changes the tidal patterns on which many creatures rely. Landfill destroys fragile wetlands (see pages 76–77).
- Leisure activities – walking and playing on the beach compacts the sand, suffocating beach-dwelling organisms (see pages 68–69).
- Flood defences inland – can deprive beaches of the regular supply of sand they need.
- Invasive species – coasts are especially vulnerable to invasive species (see pages 78–79 and pages 224–225).

Zones on a Rocky Shore

Supralittoral zone (splash zone)	mussels, barnacles, lichens	high water spring
		high tide
Eulittoral zone (intertidal zone)		low tide
	stringy seaweeds	low water spring
Sublittoral zone (neritic zone)	grazers	
		kelp
Circalittoral zone		filterfeeders

The rising and falling of the tide creates distinct zones along the shore or 'littoral' as oceanographers call it. At the top is the supralittoral, the shore above the highest tide, never completely wet but constantly sprayed by breaking waves. Lower down is the eulittoral, the band of shore uncovered once or twice every day by the falling tide, and the sublittoral, the seabed below the very lowest tides, sometimes known as the neritic zone.

SANDY SHORES

Stroll across a beach and it may appear entirely bereft of wildlife, especially in managed resorts where the sand is often imported and sieved to make it clean for holidaymakers. Yet natural beaches are far more lively than they appear; it is simply that all the real activity is going on out of sight, deep in the sand.

Beaches provide virtually no cover on the surface for organisms to hide from predators or the desiccation of sun and wind, and the shifting sands offer few firm footholds to avoid being washed away. But sand is generally soft enough or loosely packed enough for organisms to live beneath the surface in the sand itself.

It might seem, too, that there is little more nourishment for life on a beach than in a desert. But a beach has the tide, and washing in with the tide is not only a regular supply of water but a flotsam of food of both living organisms and organic detritus that more than makes up for the lack of plants. And the organisms that feed on this flotsam, in turn, provide food for others.

MICROLIFE

Many beach organisms are far too tiny to see and live by the billion in the tiny spaces between sand grains. The microscopic plants or microflora include diatoms and algae; the microanimals or meiofauna include ciliate protozoans, polychaete, oligochaete, and nematode worms, as well as tiny crustaceans such as copepods. They may be tiny but they are always on the move, up and down through the sand, responding to changes in the tide, or temperature and light.

There are larger creatures in the sand, too – all expert burrowers. Mollusks and crustaceans in particular seem very much at home there. Mollusks tend to be more abundant on cooler temperate beaches or farther down the beach towards the low tide, while crustaceans are dominant in the tropics or, like sand hoppers, higher up the beach. Tropical beaches often swarm with countless tiny crabs – ghost crabs that pop up suddenly from

the sand whenever food appears, Australian soldier crabs that can march across the beach like a desert army, and sand bubblers that churn up countless tiny bubbles of sand as they sieve it for food.

DINING STRATEGIES

The problem for many of these animals is actually getting their often microscopic meals amid the sand – they have evolved various strategies for this. Some, including polychaete worms and bivalve mollusks such as cockles, take food from the water directly, filtering it out or siphoning it through their bodies. The bivalve mollusk known as the thin tellin has a long siphon like an elephant's trunk that it pokes out of the mud when the tide comes in to suck up food-laden water. Others, such as sea cucumbers and lugworms, swallow sand and all, like earthworms, to get the food as it passes through their bodies before emerging as coiled worm casts that are often seen on beaches with fine sand. Sand dollars are more selective and graze the sand's surface. All these creatures provide food for birds, such as the sanderling, which darts along the beach like a mad cyclist probing the sand for crabs and worms as they come closer to the surface near the tide's edge.

BEACH ZONES

Although sandy shores tend to slope quite gently, the tide still creates marked zones. At the top is the swash or surf zone where waves run up the beach at high tide and break. This is the harshest beach habitat – sprayed by the sea and desiccated by wind and Sun – and the least diverse. It is often dominated by piles of washed-up seaweed, inhabited by sand hoppers and insects. Sand hoppers play a vital role in the beach ecosystem, though, recycling seaweed and its nutrients and providing food for shorebirds and fish.

Farther down in between the tides, mollusks are common, especially bivalves, which have a strong muscular foot that holds them in the sand as the tide washes over them and delivers food for them to siphon. Mollusks also provide food for plovers and oystercatchers when the tide ebbs. Some animals, such as whelks and beach clams, have learned to use their foot as a kind of surfboard and ride the waves to stay where the food is most abundant at the water's edge.

The lower part of the intertidal zone, only briefly exposed at very low tide, attracts the greatest diversity of species, including worms and bivalves as well as sea potatoes, brittlestars, sea cucumbers, and sand dollars. Anemones that live here do not have a basal disk to attach themselves as they would in rocky places but instead burrow into the sand, leaving only their tentacles exposed for feeding. Animals living near the low tide often have to cope with the power of the waves, and clams and razor shells are fast and strong burrowers. Hard clams such as the quahog are oval in shape; razors are long and thin like an old-fashioned razor, which is perfect for tunnelling quickly into the wet sand.

◁ *The beaches of the Shetland Isles are famous for their seaweed, which is traditionally used as fertilizer but only for local crops. However, conservationists are worried that today too much seaweed is being collected for commercial use in fertilizers and for the cosmetic industry.*

△ *Unlike other crabs, the soldier crabs of Australia move forward, not sideways. They emerge from their holes in the sand at low tide and march like an army in their thousands to feed, making it look as if the sand is on the move.*

Vanishing Beaches

Sandy beaches are surprisingly transient features of the world's coastline. Most were formed just 6,000 years or so ago, after the seas rose at the end of the last ice age and washed sand created by the glaciation onto the shore. And they are shifting all the time. They stay much the same shape for long periods only because sand is constantly washed in to replenish sand that is washed away. If the supply of sand is cut off, as it has been in so many places around the world by the construction of sea and flood defences and dredging operations, beaches are washed away quite quickly. A further rise in sea levels due to global warming may drown even more beaches, and there are concerns that sandy beaches around the world may be lost as habitats (not to mention as places of recreation). More than three-quarters of American and European beaches are now suffering serious erosion. A report in November 2009 revealed that Hawaii has already lost many of its beaches – 70 percent of Kauai's once brilliant strands are badly diminished and 25 percent of Oahu's are on the way out.

△ Many of Hawaii's famous beaches – this one is on the island of Kauai – are vanishing fast as the sand supply is interrupted by shore development and as the warming of the ocean raises sea levels.

TURTLE TRAGEDY

THE HATCHING OF BABY SEA TURTLES ON A MOONLIT BEACH IS ONE OF NATURE'S
MOST MAGICAL SPECTACLES, YET IT IS ONE THAT HAS COME UNDER INCREASING
THREAT AS SEA TURTLE NUMBERS DECLINE DRAMATICALLY WORLDWIDE.

YEAR AFTER YEAR, SEA TURTLES navigate thousands of kilometres across the ocean to return to the beach or 'rookery' where they hatched many decades earlier. No one knows how they navigate so precisely, but after mating in the sea with several males, the female hauls herself painfully up the beach to dig a hole in the sand and lay her clutch of up to 250 eggs. She then buries them and returns to the sea, leaving her offspring to fend for themselves. About eight weeks later, the hatchlings dig their way out of the sand at night and head instinctively towards the sea, guided by the pale glow of the water in the moonlight.

While on the beach, the slowly crawling hatchlings are vulnerable to all kinds of predators and the mortality rate is frightening, with barely one in a thousand making it through to adulthood. Nevertheless, the numbers of eggs laid is still large enough – sea turtles have survived for perhaps 120 million years in this way. Now, however, they are in serious danger. Six of the seven species of sea turtles are listed as Endangered or Critically Endangered.

THE DANGEROUS BEACH

The dangers start right at the beginning of their usually long lives, which can be a century or longer. More and more turtle rookeries around the world have been destroyed by beach and other coastal developments. If their home beach is blocked off by a sea wall for example, the turtles will not find another – they simply do not lay their eggs.

Even holidaymakers can have a devastating effect. Sand compaction by vehicles and beach users prevents turtles from digging nests, for instance, and keeps hatchlings trapped in the nests. Shadows from towels, beach furniture, and umbrellas over the nests affect temperatures and so affect the sex of hatchlings – cool temperature results in mostly male turtles, while warm temperature results in mostly females. Beach furniture, umbrellas, and other obstructions also prevent adult female turtles from nesting. Speedboats disorient and even mutilate or kill females waiting to come ashore to lay their eggs. Even noise and light can have a devastating effect, since the hatchlings will simply head towards any light they see when they emerge – often leading them away from the sea. If they are still looking for the sea when the Sun comes up, they are doomed.

The impact of coastal development has been recent and rapid. Florida beaches account for 90 percent of the loggerhead turtle nests in North America, yet numbers here plummeted from more than 80,000 in 1998 to just 45,000 in 2007.

Eggs have also become a target for collectors. Loggerhead turtle eggs have been collected on a vast scale for food in Mexico, Cuba, and Mozambique, while green turtle eggs are plundered in Sarawak by local people who sell them as aphrodisiacs. In 2007, the Philippines government declared egg collecting illegal, but the effect of the law has so far been limited. That same year, a small group of Chinese poachers were picked up with a stash of 10,000 sea turtle eggs.

Climate change could damage sea turtles, too – not simply because rising

▷ *A leatherback turtle crawls up the beach to begin nesting and laying its eggs. But its nesting sites remain under threat and its eggs are still widely collected, despite bans to solve the problem.*

sea levels could drown their nesting beaches, but because sand temperature has a critical effect on the sex of the hatchlings. A change in the sex balance could have a huge impact on the turtle population.

THREATS AT SEA

Life has become precarious even for adult turtles. One of the biggest threats is fishing. Significant numbers of sea turtles are caught deliberately for their flesh and shells. But the main problem is by-catch. Every year, huge numbers of these slow-moving creatures are caught up in nets. Turtles rely on coming up to the surface to breathe and if trapped under the water for any time by nets, they simply drown. Shrimp trawls can be lethal for loggerhead turtles, which feed on the seabed. About 4,000 loggerheads are killed each year by shrimp trawls in the southeastern USA alone. Many Kemp's Ridleys have fallen victim to shark nets off Australia, while drift nets and long lines are a threat to surface feeders such as the leatherback.

Some turtles are deliberately targeted by fishermen who believe, probably wrongly, that the turtles are damaging their nets. A loggerhead turtle was recently found by Greek conservation authorities with its eyes gouged out. Many sea turtles, too, are falling victim to plastic debris that they mistake for the jellyfish on which they feed, and so choke.

THE GOOD NEWS

The news is not all bad, though. In 2009, a previously unknown nesting beach of up to 40,000 leatherbacks was discovered in Gabon in West Africa, potentially doubling the known world population of these Critically Endangered turtles. In many parts of the world, key nesting sites are now protected. Most major nesting sites for the loggerhead in the southeastern USA are now offered some protection, and lighting ordinances have been introduced to prevent the disorientation of hatchlings. The protection of a key

△ *The protection of the Kemp's Ridley turtle hatchery at Rancho Nuevo in Mexico is a success story, and the number of successful hatchings has been slowly increasing, with a consequent recovery in the turtle population.*

Kemp's Ridley nesting site at Rancho Nuevo in Mexico seems to have been strikingly successful. A famous video shot there in 1947 showed the arrival of the turtles in vast numbers – more than 47,000 turtles in one day – highlighting, in contrast, the subsequent collapse of the population to just 200 in the 1980s. But after protection measures were introduced, numbers have recovered, and in 2006, a welcome 7,866 Kemp's Ridley sea turtles nested at Rancho Nuevo.

ROCKY COASTS

CLAMBERING ALONG A ROCKY SHORE and peering into rock pools is a wonderful way to see the richness of marine life at first hand. There are rarely any big creatures there, unless you are in the Galápagos where iguanas splash in and out, or in the Arctic where walruses bask on the rocks. However, they are one of the world's richest and most varied – and most accessible – wildlife habitats.

A closer look at any rocky coast reveals an extraordinary range of small creatures and other organisms. It is a harsh, exacting environment, continually exposed to dessication by wind and sun, doused in an ever-changing bath of chemicals and battered by waves. Yet all kinds of organism have found a way to survive and thrive here. A rocky coast is not comfortable, but at least it offers a firm foothold for those hardy enough to take it.

THE SPLASH ZONE

At the top of a rocky shore, where spray from breaking waves is thrown above the high tide, is the splash zone. Despite continual wetting, there is little water here, but there is plenty of salt and a drying wind, as well as extremes of temperature. Nonetheless, high ledges provide a stable hard-to-reach platform for seabirds, and some organisms, such as lichens, thrive here. Lichens are a remarkable symbiotic partnership between algae and fungi, and the algae in them take energy from the sun while their fungi hold on to moisture. Orange lichens tend to dominate higher up, while black lichens take over nearer the water.

Few animals can take the splash zone – only birds, some insects, and marine mammals such as seals that haul themselves out of the water to bask on the rocks. Yet little periwinkles, with their distinctive twisted shells, seem to thrive. They graze on lichens and breathe through lunglike modified gills, and have an extraordinary ability to withstand both the high temperatures they are often exposed to there, and long periods of dessication.

THE MIDDLE AND LOWER SHORES

Lower down, periwinkles are joined by seaweeds, such as the channelled and spiral wracks that cling on to rocks with rootlike holdfasts. These provide shelter for animals, such as acorn barnacles, sand hoppers, and the wood louselike sea slater. On the middle shore, drying out is much less of a problem. The range of species increases, but staying put against the waves is still a major problem – and organisms still have to find ways of holding on to water. The seaweeds in this zone are typically knotted and bladder wrack, and these, too, provide shelter and food for a variety of animals. Bivalve mollusks, such as mussels, are typically abundant in the middle zone, too, and all of them retain water by clamping their shells firmly shut while the tide is out. Mussels secure themselves to rocks with threads secreted from their muscular foot. More mobile mollusks, such as limpets and chitons, use their powerful muscular foot like a suction cup. Even gobies hold themselves to rocks by suction.

The lower shore, exposed briefly at low tide, shows the greatest diversity of all, with seaweeds such as red algae, plantlike animals such as bryozoans, and sponges and many kinds of anemone. Crevices and large, shaded rock pools provide refuges between the tides for lobsters, crabs, octopuses, and conger and moray eels. The deepest rock pools provide shelter from waves, allowing fragile organisms such as sea slugs, shrimp, camouflage crabs, sea eggs, and small fishes to live on an otherwise exposed rocky shore.

▷ *Rock pools like this one at Kimmeridge in Dorset, England, are water-filled refuges left behind by the falling tide – they are home to an incredible variety of creatures that retreat into the pools to await the next high tide.*

△ *To survive high on exposed shores uncovered by the sea for long periods, acorn barnacles cement themselves to rock with incredible adhesion, only letting out their feathery legs to catch food when they are submerged by the rising tide.*

△ *When the tide falls, marine creatures stop feeding and cling on tight until the next tide appears. That is when the ruddy turnstone moves in and takes its pick of the creatures that are left exposed.*

SEA LION NURSERIES

ALTHOUGH THE HORRIFIC SIGHT OF SEALS BEING BLUDGEONED TO DEATH
ON THE SHORE WITH BASEBALL BATS IS NOW RARE, SEALS REMAIN
VULNERABLE TO A VARIETY OF THREATS.

WITH THEIR WONDERFULLY EXPRESSIVE EYES and their sleek, furry bodies, seals are tremendously appealing creatures. They get their group name 'pinniped,' which means 'fin foot,' from the way they use their short limbs as flippers in the sea and like feet to lumber across the rocks. They are amazingly fast and agile in the water, but once they climb out onto the shore, as they do, to breed, give birth, and feed their young, they are about as agile as their short legs and bulky bodies would suggest. And that has been at the root of their problems.

SEAL SLAUGHTER

When on land, seals have few natural predators, except perhaps polar bears and wolves, but they are sitting targets for humans. They were hunted mercilessly in the 18th and 19th centuries for their popular skins, though hunting is hardly the word. Most were simply bludgeoned to death with clubs and bats in a savagely brutal 'harvest.' The population of Northern fur seals in the North Pacific was reduced in this way from an estimated 4.5 million in 1870 to less than 200,000 by the outbreak of World War 1. Other species suffered similar declines.

The effect was so catastrophic, and the pictures of baby seals left orphaned or simply slaughtered outright so shocking, that seals became among the first marine creatures to receive

a degree of legal protection. Some species began to recover, but for others, especially some species of fur seals, it was all rather too late. The plight of monk seals, which live in warm waters, was already desperate, with 8 out of 12 species being extinct long ago.

MONKS IN DANGER

Then in 1996, the Caribbean monk seal, which once bobbed up onto islands all around the Caribbean and Gulf of Mexico, was formally declared extinct, though the last one was seen as long ago as 1952 on the little island of Seranilla Bank near Jamaica.

The Mediterranean monk seal might soon go the same way. There are only 350–450 of these attractive creatures left in the world, and the populations are so small and scattered that there seems little chance of recovery. Droves of holidaymakers and resorts taking over the shores where the seals used to breed have made their position even more vulnerable. In some places, the seals have retreated to sea caves to find refuge – but getting in and out of these can be a dangerous business, especially for young pups. The fate of the Hawaiian seal is almost as bad with just 1,300 individuals remaining.

Yet, shockingly perhaps, the slaughter is still going on. While monk seals cannot legally be hunted, South African

▽ *This young harbour seal escaped being accidentally trapped in a large fishing net with just an injured flipper; other seals are not so lucky.*

fur seals can. After centuries of slaughter along the coasts of Angola, Namibia, and South Africa, protection in the 20th century allowed numbers to recover – they recovered so well that the population reached more than a million. Then, under pressure from fishermen who believe, wrongly, that the seals are damaging fish stocks, a large commercial 'harvest' of 75,000 a year was authorized in 2000. The result was that in the first year, 60,000 seals were bludgeoned to death – a slaughter captured gruesomely on a film aired on CNN that showed young male seals being clubbed with wooden bats. Annual hunts still go on in parts of Canada, despite protests from animal rights groups.

PIER 39, SAN FRANCISCO

Such culls are now becoming rare, as seals are offered more and more legal protection. Californian seals, celebrated for their acrobatic circus tricks, have recovered in numbers so well that they famously invaded San Francisco dock, Pier 39, and set up camp there under legal protection. The 1,700 Pier 39 seals became a major tourist attraction, though to fishermen and boat owners they were something of a nuisance, being very loud and very smelly. Then they disappeared as suddenly as they arrived. The disappearance remained something of a mystery, prompting rumours that they sensed an imminent earthquake – until a large group of seals was spotted farther north off Oregon, where they had probably migrated in search of food.

Despite such success stories and protection from culls, seals remain vulnerable to the inadvertent side effects of human activities. One study showed that Cornish grey seals were dying in nets meant to catch monkfish, for instance, faster than they

Seal Species

There are 33 species of seals, sea lions, fur seals, and walruses, or pinnipeds as they are known scientifically. They are often divided into the true seals, or phocids, which includes monk seals and common seals; and eared seals, or otarids, which includes fur seals and sea lions; and walruses. The distinction is not always clear, but essentially otarids have external ears, more doglike snouts, and rear limbs that they can turn to use as feet when on land. The phocids are smaller and more agile swimmers with streamlined snouts, but they tend to be clumsy on land. Seals and sea lions are found in all the oceans, and in a few freshwater lakes, including Lake Baikal in Russia, but most species are vulnerable in some ways or places. The Hawaiian monk seal (*Monachus schauinslandi*), the Mediterranean monk seal (*M. monachus*), the Guadalupe fur seal (*Arctocephalus townsendi*), the Saimaa seal (*Phoca hispida saimensis*), and the Steller sea lion (*Eumetopias jubatus*) are listed as endangered by the International Union for the Conservation of Nature (IUCN), or World Conservation Union. The Caribbean monk seal has been officially extinct since 1996.

could reproduce. Australian sea lions, already reduced to barely 10–12,000, are also in decline despite being fully protected by law. No one knows quite why, but entanglement in fishing nets, especially shark nets, is a threat, and there are worries about the siting of fish farms near sea lion 'haulouts,' encouraging the shooting of foraging sea lions, which is legal. Elsewhere, seals seem to be becoming victims to loss of food as seas are overfished, or becoming the prey of killer whales turning to seals as other food sources diminish.

▽ *The spectacle of the Californian seals, which surprisingly made Pier 39 in San Francisco their home, became a tourist attraction – until the seals vanished just as suddenly as they arrived.*

ESTUARIES AND SALT MARSHES

ESTUARIES CAN SEEM BLEAK, DULL PLACES as the wind and rain sweep across the marshes and mudflats that often stretch far out either side of the water. The lonely cry of a curlew rising from the mud or the faint, faint honks of a distant flight of geese seem only to mark out the estuary's emptiness. And yet they are key habitats that play a vital role in the life of the ocean.

Estuaries are usually young features geologically. Many formed barely 10,000 years ago at the end of the last ice age when river valleys or valleys cut by glaciers were drowned by rising seas as the ice melted. The Thames estuary in England is a drowned river valley like this. So is Washington's Chesapeake Bay. The fjords of Norway, Chile, and New Zealand are all valleys cut deep by the ice, then flooded when the ice melted.

FRESH AND BRINY

What makes estuaries so distinctive is the meeting of fresh water and salt water. The rivers flowing into the estuary bring in huge amounts of sediment, which settle as mud as the river meets the sea and slows down. Rich in organic matter, the estuarine muds provide a banquet for creatures able to feed on it, and the sheltered environment, away from the battering of waves, makes a good home for young creatures in particular. But organisms that live here have to be able to adapt to the continual intermingling of fresh water and salt water.

Most aquatic estuary animals came originally from the sea so have little problem coping with salt water. What they must guard against is fresh water, which could easily flood into their salt-rich body fluids. Mollusks and worms can regulate their own internal salt content to suit the water. Fish and crabs take in more water through their gills, or excrete it to maintain the right balance. Plants, however, came mostly from the land, so have special mechanisms to cope with excess salt, like cordgrass, for instance, that excretes salt through glands on its leaves.

DINER AND NURSERY

When the larger estuarine plants die, they are broken down into detritus and colonized by microbes. Phytoplankton provide another ingredient to the rich soup of estuary waters. Countless larger animals feed on the particles in this soup, or on smaller animals that graze on them. Fish such as snook, mullet, jacks, and groupers as well as shrimp, crabs, and oysters are among the many fish that depend upon estuaries. Indeed, a surprisingly large proportion of the world's fish and crustaceans spend some of their lives in estuaries. Three-quarters of the USA's commercially caught fish are at least part-time estuary dwellers.

Many species spawn or breed offshore so that their eggs or larvae are born into estuaries on the tide. The larvae can then grow to adulthood in the comparative safety of shallow water, marshes, seagrasses, and mangrove roots, away from the dangerous attentions of large sea predators. Shrimp, for instance, often spawn offshore and their larvae ride into the estuary on incoming tides, burrowing into the mud at each high tide to save them from being swept out to sea again. Hidden among the grasses of the estuary they are safe from predators that can only

◁ *Estuaries like this one in Torrent Bay on New Zealand's South Island play an important role in the life of the ocean, providing relatively safe nurseries for many young fish to grow to adulthood and leave for the open ocean.*

handle salty water. When they reach maturity, the shrimp return to the sea to live out their adult lives and spawn. Each generation returns to the shelter of the estuary for their adolescence.

THE HUMAN IMPACT

Unfortunately, it is the very same availability of fresh water, shelter, and proximity to the sea that makes estuaries so attractive to wildlife that draws human activity here, too. Many estuaries are the site of heavy industry, such as iron and steel plants, chemical works, power stations, and oil refineries – all of which need a lot of water and easy boat access for bulk materials. They are often the site of extensive housing and leisure development, too. Dredging and filling operations to build waterfronts may seem like improvement on a muddy, scraggy shoreline, but it can destroy the nurseries of young fish and crustaceans – and as the wildlife leave so the water could become foul as well as lifeless.

The subtle and continual shifts between tidal water and river water, fresh water and salt water, mean the estuarine habitat is very finely balanced, and even a slight change to the balance – a new sea wall, which reduces the flow of tidal salt water, for instance – can have dramatic consequences for wildlife.

The estuary is also a focus, or rather a conduit. The finely adjusted balance of wildlife is often upset by the invasion of foreign species, funnelled in by the tide or carried by ships that dock in the estuary's wide, sheltered waters. The river, too, often washes in polluted runoff from cities, farms, and factories – including farm chemicals, raw sewage, and industrial waste.

△ *Endangered Pacific steelhead trout rely on estuaries to adjust to fresh water as they re-enter the rivers of the USA's northwest to spawn, but increasingly they are finding estuaries disturbed or blocked by urban and industrial developments.*

Excess of nutrients can feed an algal bloom – a dramatic growth of algae – that drains the water of oxygen and kills fish.

People have gradually awoken to the need to protect the beautiful wetland habitats of birds that fringe so many estuaries, but the estuarine waters themselves and the extensive mudflats revealed as the tide ebbs are all too often left to be exploited and abused, despite their key role in the life of the oceans.

Salt Marshes and Mudflats

Most temperate estuaries in lowland regions are fringed by salt marshes, covered by water only at the highest tides. Muddy creeks and little islets wind among the clumps of grass. On the highest and driest places, plants such as samphire, glasswort, sea meadow grass, sea aster, and thrift often maintain a foothold, and provide cover for rats, snakes, insects, and birds. Where it is wetter, only plants such as cordgrass can survive the continual submergence under salt water.

Below the tideline, even cordgrass cannot keep a foothold, and the ebbing tide reveals only vast expanses of mud. Mud is much finer and more closely packed than sand, so it is short of oxygen. Nonetheless, vast numbers of worms and mollusks burrow in the mud, notably lugworms, clams, and the minute Hydrobia snail, which can often be found in densities of more than 100,000 per square yard. When the tide is out, flocks of wading birds pick their way over the mud, each species with a bill designed to pick out their own food of choice. When the tide flows in again, in come flatfish, to nip off the siphons of mollusks as they pop them up to feed. Then ospreys in turn feed on the flatfish. Herons and egrets dine on the young fish that make estuaries their nursery.

ALIEN INVASION

AS THE VOLUME OF INTERNATIONAL TRADE BY SEA INCREASES, SO DOES THE
NUMBER OF ALIEN SPECIES ARRIVING AS STOWAWAYS AND MAKING THEIR PRESENCE
FELT IN MARINE ECOSYSTEMS AROUND THE WORLD.

EVER SINCE HUMANS BEGAN to sail the oceans, marine organisms have been inadvertently ferried around the world on boats only to arrive as – usually unwelcome – immigrants in distant waters. But recent decades have seen the numbers increase dramatically.

A major culprit seems to be the ballast water of big ships. Whenever ships are sailing empty or lightly laden, they take on huge quantities of water to stabilize them – and then release the water when they reach their destination. Of course, as they pump water into their ballast tanks, they pump in all the organisms in the water – and then release them as they release the water. The biggest offenders seem to be oil tankers and dry bulk carriers. While container ships sail laden on fixed routes, oil tankers and dry bulk carriers often sail empty to a variety of ports in search of their next cargo, and so carry lots of ballast water to a wide mix of destinations.

UNWANTED TRAVELLERS
Estimates of the impact of this movement vary, but a study by the Nature Conservancy in Arlington, Virginia suggested that there may be 10,000 species in transit in ballast water at any one time, and a major 2009 report by the World Wildlife Fund, entitled 'Silent Invasion,' concluded that 7,000 species are moved in ship ballast water every day. The vast majority of travellers perish en route, or shortly after entering their new home, but the hardiest survive – and of course, it is these hardy ones that have the biggest impact on the places they invade. 'Silent

Invasion' reported that 84 percent of the world's 232 marine eco-regions now have major invasions of alien species, which can overwhelm native species as they multiply away from their natural predators.

American harbours are thought to be home to 800 alien species, and San Francisco Bay is said to be the world's most cosmopolitan habitat with more than half the fish and the majority of seabed animals and plants being immigrants, including Pacific oysters from Japan, killer algae *Caulerpa* seaweed (see page 210) from the tropics, and comb jellyfish.

JELLYFISH AND CRABS
A kind of comb jellyfish known as the sea walnut, *Mnemiopsis leidyi*, is perhaps the most notorious of all invaders. Originally a native of the western Atlantic, it arrived in the Black Sea in the 1990s. Free from competition, it multiplied astonishingly in perhaps one of the most dramatic population explosions ever known and then proceeded to wipe out virtually all local anchovies and sprat in an ecosystem already weakened by eutrophication (see page 18 and pages 222–225). By the mid-1990s, these comb jellies accounted for 90 percent of the total biomass in the Black Sea – a biomass that is more than the total annual fish catch around the world. These comb jellyfish have now invaded the Caspian Sea, the North Sea, and the Baltic.

Another notorious invader is the Chinese mitten crab, which has firmly established itself on both sides of the North Atlantic and is estimated to have caused damage to riverbanks, fishing

Jellyfish Invasion

Volga–Baltic Canal

Baltic Sea

Black Sea

Caspian Sea

Mediterranean Sea

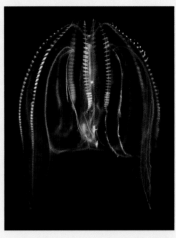

▽ Mnemiopsis leidyi *arrived in Europe in the ballast water of oil tanks, and once there proliferated dramatically in seas where the native species were already weakened by eutrophication.*

After first appearing in the Black and Caspian Seas, the invading American comb jellyfish *Mnemiopsis leidyi* has been spreading through Europe, even reaching the Baltic via the Volga–Baltic Canal through Russia.

gear, and industrial water systems to the tune of 100 million dollars in Germany alone. The mitten crab is a very hardy species, able to survive in heavily polluted areas. It seems to multiply dramatically in its new habitats, but is immensely destructive as it burrows into riverbanks.

THE BLOB

One of the most mysterious invaders, though, is the didemnid sea squirt, often called simply 'the blob.' Made of colonies of tiny animals called zooids, it looks rather like scrambled eggs and grows quickly to smother mussel and clam beds and dock installations. Unfortunately it has no known natural predator. No one knows quite where this filter-feeding menace came from but it is now spreading rapidly everywhere from New Zealand to the Netherlands.

In order to deal with the problem of these invaders, the International Maritime Organization created a Ballast Water Convention to control how ships use ballast water. But of all the world's top ten major shipping nations, only Liberia has ratified the convention and so it remains a deal only on paper. One of the obstacles is what to do. One of the dangers is that ships take on freshwater, and freshwater species, in one place, and dump it in freshwater at their destination. If ships could be forced to dump their freshwater ballast at sea and take on seawater, the freshwater species might not be carried to new places, and saltwater species would not survive in freshwater. But pumping out all the water and taking on a new load mid-voyage would be

time-consuming and expensive. Chemical treatments have been suggested, too. Another idea is to blast the ballast water with microwaves to kill all organisms.

Tasmanian Superstar

In 1986, some strange starfish were found on a beach in Tasmania. At first, experts thought they must be a local species. Then as the numbers of these starfish began to mushroom, it became clear that they were actually North Pacific seastars (*Asterias amurensis*) that had arrived from Japan in the ballast water of ships. As the starfish swarmed up onto Tasmanian shores, the Australian media ran story after story about them, and local people took to rounding them up by hand, thousands at a time, and sending them off for compost. But the tens of thousands picked up barely made a dent in the population, which was soon estimated to be 30 million strong. Unfortunately, they are voracious predators, and may wreak havoc on Australia's shellfish populations – and the billion dollar shellfish industry. As scientists struggle to find a way to control their population, they have spread across to mainland Australia, through Victoria and South Australia.

◁ *Swarms of mauve stinger jellyfish are now often seen in the Mediterranean, thanks to a warmer and saltier sea and the decimation, by fishing, of jellyfish predators such as sunfish and triggerfish, and of smaller fish competing for food.*

THE SMALLEST CETACEAN

THE LITTLE VAQUITA PORPOISE, THE SMALLEST CETACEAN, IS THE WORLD'S MOST ENDANGERED MARINE MAMMAL. AN URGENT BATTLE IS NOW IN PROGRESS TO SAVE THIS CREATURE BEFORE IT IS LOST ALTOGETHER.

THE VAQUITA, WHOSE NAME IS SPANISH for 'little cow', lives exclusively in the warm turquoise and blue shallows of the Gulf of California. No marine mammal occupies such a small territory, and none is so rare. Indeed, it is so elusive that its very existence was confirmed only in the 1950s from the discovery of a skull; and the first confirmed sighting of a live specimen occurred as recently as the 1980s.

Since then, rare glimpses of the vaquita in the wild have become treasured events; it is very shy, avoids boats, and, unlike dolphins, never completely surfaces. Instead, it rolls to the surface to breathe so gently and quickly that the water is barely ruffled, before vanishing altogether. No wonder the capturing of the first live film footage of this little porpoise in November 2008 was a major news event – partly because the footage would be useful in convincing local fishermen that their local porpoise was a reality, not a myth cooked up by scientists.

THE LITTLE COW

By cetacean standards, the vaquita is a tiny creature, being under 1.5 m (5 ft) long. It looks a little like the harbour porpoise of the nearby Californian Pacific, except for its distinctive black eyeliner and lips. But it is actually more closely related to Burmeister's porpoise, which lives more than 5,000 km (3,000 miles) to the south, off the coast of Peru. It is assumed that both these porpoises descended from a common ancestor and became separated a million or so years ago when one branch of the family moved north and ended up in the Gulf of California.

Very little is known about the vaquita's lifestyle because it is so difficult to track, and marine biologists are having to develop special acoustic equipment in an effort to follow its movements. But it is thought that vaquitas live in pairs, or in groups of up to ten. The females, which are slightly larger than the males, mature between three and six years, and give birth in spring every couple of years after an 11-month gestation period. Vaquitas feed on a variety of fish.

VICTIMS OF THE SHRIMP DINNER

It is thought that when they were first identified, there were several thousand vaquitas. But by 1997, when the first proper estimate was made, there were only about 567. By 2007, there were under 150. Marine conservationists concluded that they had just two years to stop numbers collapsing beyond the point of recovery. Now the vaquita is not only listed as Critically Endangered by the IUCN Red List but is also one of the top 100 Evolutionarily Distinct and Globally Endangered (EDGE) species for which conservation is an urgent priority. Perhaps the biggest threat to the vaquita's existence is the nets of local

▽ *A rare photo of a live vaquita, unfortunately caught in a shrimp net, shows its distinctive plump body and almost comical dark eye and mouth.*

fishermen. The fishermen are not targeting the vaquita in the way that Chinese fishermen targeted the baiji; they are simply catching shrimp to earn money to feed their families in an area with few other natural resources. Unfortunately, the shallow-living vaquita gets caught in their gill nets.

The vaquita is now the focus of a last-ditch programme to prevent its extinction, under the auspices of the North American Conservation Action Plan (NACAP), set up by the governments of the United States, Mexico, and Canada. One leading campaigner, marine biologist Lorenzo Rojas Bracho, has stressed how crucial it is to look after local fishermen as well as the vaquita and in a unique scheme, the Mexican government is spending millions of dollars paying the region's 4,000 registered fishermen to give up fishing altogether or switch to a net that does not catch the vaquita. In addition, the Mexican government

△ *Known locally as the Sea of Cortez, the Gulf of California is a unique and rich marine habitat, frequented by many kinds of whales, including the fin, sperm, and humpback whales, as well as the little vaquita.*

has created a nature reserve in the head of the Gulf of California (below left), which may be extended over the vaquita's entire range in which all trawling is banned.

It remains to be seen just how effective these measures are. The worrying thing is, though, that even if all by-catch is stopped, the vaquita is still threatened by water quality. Demand for drinking water from US cities has dramatically reduced the flow of freshwater into the Gulf via the Colorado River – and what does come is sullied by farm pesticides. The vaquita is not beyond hope yet, and its plight is now recognized by both governments and scientists, but its chances remain slim.

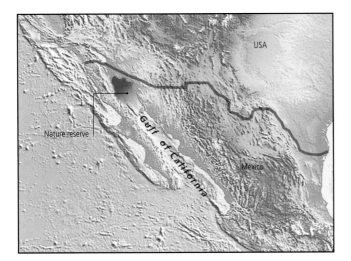

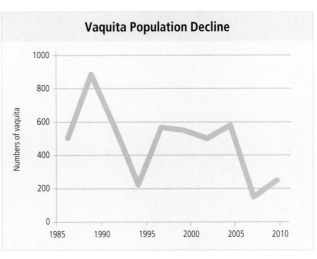

Vaquita Population Decline

OCEAN LIFE ZONES
TEMPERATE WATERS

Dark, dull, and green, the restless seas of the temperate zone could not be more different from the sparkling, crystal blue waters of the tropics. While the clear, sunlit waters of the tropics seem to invite you in and seem very hospitable to life, temperate waters are chilly and forbidding. Even if you brave the cold and dive in, you can often see little life in the murk. But first impressions can be misleading.

The temperate seas, in fact, contain the world's richest marine habitats, and it is partly the sheer abundance of life that makes them so cloudy. While those enticing tropical waters contain few nutrients and little plankton, the temperate sea is awash with nutrients and so flooded with swarming microscopic plant life that it is a living green soup. And all this plant life provides the basic food for a huge chain of other animal life.

The temperate zone is indeed temperate and mild. The water there is rarely very cold but rarely ever warms to tepid, typically ranging from 4 to 20°C (39 to 68°F). But the conditions are intensely seasonal. Winters, though not icy like polar waters, are chill and stormy. Summers, though not tropically hot can be very warm. And the life in temperate zones follows this seasonal pattern, too, with plankton populations exploding every spring in massive blooms that provide a feast for huge numbers of fish, mammals, and birds – some are permanent inhabitants, others are seasonal migrants that winter elsewhere and turn up as the summer banquet begins.

◁ *The huge breakers so famous in the Pacific are the result of the interplay between the wind and the ocean surface over vast distances. Even bigger ocean movements are created by variations in temperature and salinity.*

LIFE IN THE SHALLOWS

THE SHALLOWS OF THE TEMPERATE ZONE are teeming with life. The continuous input of energy from the Sun into the upper layers and the continual supply of nutrients washed down in rivers make sure life is abundant. Though the shallows occupy less than a tenth of the ocean, they are home to the majority of its species – and are the source of 80 percent of the fish catch.

Conditions in the shallows vary enormously from time to time and from place to place, and this variability is reflected in the diversity of organisms that live there. One of the things that makes the shallows so rich in life is the abundance of nutrients. In the deep oceans, the main sources of nutrients in the water are the remains of dead organisms. These are plentiful, but they sink into the abyss beyond the reach of most creatures. In the shallows, however, nutrients can be stirred up from the seabed to a depth of 100 m (328 ft) by waves in winter storms, or the sinking of icy water in the winter months. The rain-swollen rivers of winter pour in extra nutrients, such as nitrates and phosphates. No wonder, then, that spring sees a blooming of life in the shallows that gradually slows down as the summer progresses. In summer, the stirring up of nutrients from the seabed is blocked by the development of temperature barriers in the water called thermoclines, which are created by the limits to which the sun's heat penetrates.

The dramatic seasonality of the 'neritic' zone, the shallow waters of the continental shelf, mean that many of the species there are migrants, swimming in when the food is abundant in spring, then moving on. The fishing there has traditionally been amazingly rich, with herring, mackerel, cod, capelin, pollock, and whiting among the many fish caught in vast quantities. All these fish are migratory, spawning and feeding in different places. Off northwestern Europe, for instance, blue whiting spawn along the edge of the continental shelf from Biscay to the Hebrides, before migrating north in summer to the Norwegian Sea. Each fish has its preferred spawning ground.

SANDY BEDS

Much of the seabed in shallow seas is covered by sand and finer sediment washed down by the rivers and the piled up remains of generation upon generation of marine organisms. In the very shallowest and warmer seas, seagrass may root itself into the sediment. Seagrass is one of the few true plants that grow in the sea, and its meadows provide a rich source of nutrition for an abundance of sea creatures (see pages 106–107). But in most places the sand is too unstable for plants or plantlike organisms to gain a foothold and the sandy bed can seem as lifeless as a desert. Yet though there are few plants, there are countless animals.

There is no cover in the shallows. So many animals hide in the sand – either camouflaged against it on the surface or burrowed right into it, some to avoid predators, others to escape the

△ *All species of sawfish are now critically endangered – they are the victims both of accidental entanglement with fishing nets and deliberate targeting for their rostrum (saw), fins (as a delicacy), and liver (for traditional medicine).*

attention of prey. 'Benthic' fish, such as flatfish and stingrays, may cover themselves in sand as they feed on the seabed. Flatfish, such as flounder, sole, turbot, and plaice, have become so adapted to life on the bottom that, as adults, one of their eyes migrates until both eyes face upwards even though the fish is lying on its side. Many kinds of crab scurry across the surface, while starfish and snails shimmer and slide, never building permanent homes but occasionally burrowing into the sand for safety. Sea pens and anemones anchor themselves in mud, raising sticky polyps and tentacles to catch plankton or ensnare passing fish. Clams, worms, and sea urchins burrow deeper.

ROCKY BEDS

Rocky beds provide a different home. Rocks are somewhere steady to hold on to amid the churning and flowing waters of the shallows. In shallower, sunlit places, forests of seaweed may grip to the rocks, often growing as tall as trees, creating a habitat for other creatures as rich as any forest on land.

In deeper waters, there is too little light for seaweeds, especially brown seaweeds, but there are plenty of plantlike animals, such as anemones and cold-water corals. Deeper down still, the water is more still, and fragile animals, such as sponges and sea fans, can grow quite large. In rock crevices everywhere, numerous creatures lurk, including shrimp and squat lobsters, octopuses and eels,

◁ *The very abundance of life in the shallows fooled us into thinking the supply of fish for the table would be inexhaustible, but large schools like this are becoming increasingly rare due to overfishing.*

and sea urchins, which can often excavate a little niche for themselves. Sea urchins graze the seabed, eating almost everything except hard-shelled animals and corals. Sometimes, when sea urchins are over-abundant, they can graze the seabed so intensively that they leave it like a desert.

The abundance of life in the shallows and its proximity to the coast has made the shallows especially vulnerable to the effects of human activity. The abundance has given the false impression that the ocean shallows are inexhaustible, and so many of the once great fisheries, notably the cod fisheries of Newfoundland (see pages 156–157), have been fished to exhaustion, or nearly so. The rivers that supply the nutrients that make the shallows so rich in life, also wash in pollutants. Sometimes these pollutants consist of a superabundance of nutrients, spilled in the fertilizers of inland farms. This causes such an excessive blooming of micro-organisms that the ocean is choked of all oxygen, creating 'dead zones', which are growing ever larger (see pages 18–19). The pollutants may also simply be toxic chemicals that are consumed by the small organisms at the bottom of the food chain, then concentrated as they move farther up the chain. And, of course, the shallow waters experienced the full range of damaging human activity, from coastal development to the harmful effects of shipping and boating for pleasure.

SEAWEED FORESTS

FOR DIVERS IN THE TEMPERATE ZONE, one of the most wonderful experiences is to dive in a seaweed forest. Weaving in and out of the great fronds as they waft to and fro is like swimming through a magical land. Seaweed forests are as important to the marine world in the temperate zone as deciduous forests are on land. They are home to a multitude of organisms, from countless micro-organisms that live on the weed as it decays, to predatory fish and mammals.

Forests of seaweed like these are found in cool, shallow waters right down the western coast of the Americas outside the tropics, around Western Europe, South Africa, and Australia. They grow no deeper than 30–50 m (100–165 ft), the depth to which the sunlight that they rely on can penetrate. But the fronds of the giant kelp *Macrocystis* can reach to the surface, growing as tall as trees on land, and much faster – almost 1 m (3 ft) a day. The weeds are not plants, but algae. The holdfasts with which they cling to the rocks may look like roots, but they are simply suckers that hold them in place as they climb up towards the light. Most seaweeds have bladders along the frond to buoy them up.

▽ *Long fronds or 'stipes' of giant sea kelp, up to 30 m (100 ft) long, form undersea forests in the shallows that are home to a huge variety of fish and invertebrates and provide vital cover for creatures as big as whales.*

LAYERS OF THE FOREST

Like forests on land, the kelp forests have distinct vertical layers, each home to a different array of plants and animals. Down in the dark at the bottom, among the holdfasts, there are communities of creatures benefitting from the shelter they provide including bristle worms, anemones, such as the Dahlia anemone, urchins, starfish, mollusks, amphipods, and crustaceans. There is also a whole range of fixed filter feeders, such as tubeworms and sea squirts, which could not survive out in the open. Higher up in the twilight above the holdfasts, dwell smaller seaweeds, dwarfed by lack of sunlight and dense growths of red algae.

Lower down, very few creatures graze directly on the living kelp. Seaweeds contain chemicals that make it slightly unpalatable. Instead, they feed on the detritus of broken off and rotting fronds that turns the water around the kelp into an organic soup. Up near the surface, in the sunlit 'canopy', however, various snails such as topshells and pheasant shells, mollusks such as blue-rayed limpets, and crustaceans such as the kelp-curler and the southern kelp crab, feed directly on the fronds. Bryozoans may also form crusts on the fronds.

Sea Otters and Kelp

The keystone species in Pacific kelp forests is the sea otter. Every day, this attractive mammal, one of the few sea mammals with close land equivalents, consumes a quarter of its body weight in herbivorous creatures such as urchins, creatures that could destroy the kelp forest if allowed to multiply unchecked. By keeping urchins under control, the otter plays a key role in the forest's health. In fact, the depletion of kelp forests in the Pacific in the last century was largely due to people's pursuit of the sea otter for its fur, which reduced the otter population from 20,000 to under 2,000 in the 19th century, until the Pacific otters were protected by law in 1911. Otter numbers have now successfully recovered, except in California, where it remains on the brink.

DANGERS IN THE FOREST

Many fish seek refuge from predators among the fronds of the kelp forest, such as, off North America, senoritas, surfperches, garibaldis, and kelp rockfish. Seaweed fronds are sometimes so big that even whales such as the grey whale can hide in there. But that does not stop predators such as blue sharks, sea lions, harbour seals, and killer whales, chasing prey here.

The importance of the kelp forest to marine life in the temperate zone cannot be overstated, yet kelp forests have been dwindling rapidly in the last few decades. A shocking 95 percent of Tasmania's once vast kelp forests have disappeared in the last 30 years. Scientists are keen to find out why. One reason seems to be an explosion of sea urchins, which feed voraciously on kelp. In Tasmania, it is black sea urchins; off North America it is purple sea urchins. Normally, these urchins are kept in check by predators such as lobsters and fish including senoritas and sheephead, as well as sea otters (see above). But overfishing seems to have reduced the numbers of these predators so much that the urchin numbers have multiplied. Another problem may be rising winter sea temperatures, since kelps are happiest in cool water. However, the relationship is not proven yet and some kelps seem to be able to survive in warmer water. A third danger to the seaweed forests could be pesticide-filled runoff from the land. So rapid has the decline been in some areas that practical responses are needed urgently.

Seaweed Forests Around the World

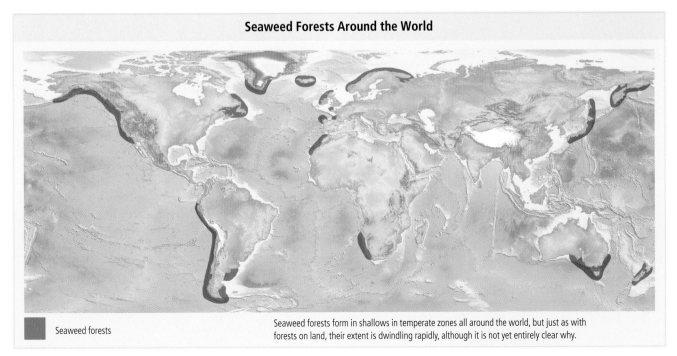

Seaweed forests

Seaweed forests form in shallows in temperate zones all around the world, but just as with forests on land, their extent is dwindling rapidly, although it is not yet entirely clear why.

GOING WITH THE FLOW

THE STRONG SEASONALITY of the temperate zone turns many marine creatures into migrants. Very few creatures stay entirely in the same place all year round, but the journey of some is staggering, particularly birds, pelagic fish, and whales, as they search for the best place to feed, breed, or make a safe home.

Conditions in the temperate ocean change dramatically between winter and summer. In spring and summer, the upwelling of nutrients initiates a bloom of plankton and other

micro-organisms that creates a feeding bonanza. The feast is often at its fullest in the shallows, and there the summer Sun easily warms the water, providing plenty of energy for the processes of life. No wonder, then, that countless fish, birds, and sea mammals head for the shallows at the first signs of spring to make the most of the rich pickings.

The strong tides of Nova Scotia's Bay of Fundy, for instance, stir up a huge quantity of nutrients, and early every spring a host of fish swim in to feed, filling the bay with vast schools of herring, capelin, and sand eel. Close behind come seabirds and mammals including the spectacular finback whale, the world's second largest whale that homes in on the Bay to gorge itself on fish. Hundreds of these great, grey-black giants arrive, and each can swallow 2 tonnes (2.2 tons) of herring a day!

THE FAMILY WAY

Food is not the only incentive for summer migration. Many seabirds, for instance, travel vast distances to reach areas where there is a safe nursery for their young – and enough food for the whole family. Petrels and shearwaters often go on journeys of epic proportions. Small but graceful sooty shearwaters, for instance, fly all the way south from Norway to the Falkland Islands to breed there in the southern hemisphere summer, a journey of some 14,000 km (8,700 miles). Manx shearwaters complete a similar journey in reverse, feeding in the southern hemisphere summer off Brazil, then heading far north to the UK and beyond to breed in the northern summer. One Manx shearwater is estimated to have flown 8 million km (5 million miles) in its half-century life.

Fish, too, can make epic journeys to breed – most notably, of course, salmon, in both the Pacific and Atlantic. After hatching from their eggs far inland in the headwaters of streams, the young smolts head downriver and far out to sea to find the best feeding grounds, changing their bodies as they go to adapt to salt water. A few years of feeding and they head back to the river of their birth, identifying it by the unique smell of the water – and battle all the way upstream to spawn where they first hatched. Many do not make it.

DEEP WINTER

In winter, the shallows that seemed so inviting in summer seem anything but. The thermocline, the temperature barrier that separates the warm upper layers of the sea and the chilly lower layers, breaks down. The upper layers lose heat from the surface and can become bitterly cold. Winter storms churn up the waters and can turn the shallows into a maelstrom. Many fish, therefore, retreat for the winter months to calmer, less chilly deep waters. There may not be as much food, but they can

◁ *Fry of the endangered chinook salmon prepare for their long journey downstream to the sea at the McIntyre Creek hatchery in Canada's Yukon, where conservationists are working to find ways to breed and reintroduce them.*

△ *The basking shark needs to eat huge quantities of plankton and small invertebrates, and swims thousands of miles each year to follow the best supply.*

▷ *Measuring up to 2 m (6.5 ft) across, poisonous golden cow-nose rays migrate in groups or 'fevers' of up to 10,000 as they glide their way towards their summer feeding grounds.*

bide their time in relative peace until the spring comes around and they can return to the shallows to feast again.

Some fish escape winter storms by retreating to sheltered places, such as North Atlantic herring that overwinter in the sanctuary of deep fjords. Others, such as bluefin tuna and seabirds, abandon the temperate zone in winter and travel huge distances to reach the warm waters of the tropics. For polar residents, however, the temperate zone seems positively balmy, even in winter. Many marine mammals that spend their summer in the Arctic and Antarctic, such as Antarctic right whales, head into the less chilly temperate zones in winter to find suitable conditions for breeding. Just as the summer bustle of woodlands yields to winter quiet, so the polar oceans are left to the hardy few.

THE DIRTY SEA

ONCE UPON A TIME, THE OCEANS SEEMED SO VAST THAT WE COULD DUMP JUST
ABOUT ANYTHING IN THEM WITHOUT ANY ILL EFFECTS. BUT IT IS NOW BECOMING
CLEAR THAT ALL THE WORLD'S OCEANS ARE BECOMING BADLY POLLUTED.

AROUND SOME INDUSTRIAL CITIES and ports, the sea now looks and smells so foul because of all the polluting chemicals and rubbish that we will not even go near it, let alone bathe in it. Elsewhere, the vast expanse of ocean looks and smells as fresh and clean as ever. But appearances can be deceptive. There is measurable pollution in every single part of the ocean, and although levels are quite low in some places, even low levels can have a significant effect on the fragile balance of life.

The astonishing and disturbing fact is that nearly every marine organism ever examined in recent years shows some traces of polluting chemicals – and the higher up the food chain, the more concentrated those chemicals become. Polar bears, for instance, which are at the top of the food chain, have levels of some polluting chemicals in their bodies that are three billion times the normal environmental levels. It is clear that organisms can tolerate some of these chemicals, but it is not clear how much. It is clear, too, that some pollutants are already doing tremendous harm.

OIL DAMAGE

Major oil spills from tankers grab all the headlines for their disastrous environmental effects. In fact, millions more gallons of oil end up in the sea every year quietly from non-accidental discharges. More than 1,360 million litres (360 million gallons) of oil are simply thrown down the drain as oil is used then

△ *Sewage discharged into the sea, especially untreated sewage, provides the fertilizer for the algal blooms, which create dead zones and introduce diseases.*

discarded. A further 518 million litres (137 million gallons) ends up in the sea from just the normal operation of ships – not just oil tankers, but cruise liners, too. About 348 million litres (92 million gallons) comes down in the rain after being blown out by vehicle exhausts. In fact, just 5 percent of oil pollution in oceans comes from big spills.

The concentrated effect of a big spill, though, especially if it involves crude oil, can be devastating. Oil destroys the insulating effect of a sea otter's fur, for instance, so that it cannot survive in cold water. It chokes the blowholes of whales, and can poison them as they swallow oil-covered fish. It destroys the feathers of birds, and when they try to clean their feathers, they ingest oil, damaging their livers and kidneys. Bottom-dwelling fish exposed to compounds released after a spill may develop liver and reproductive problems. Even tiny marine organisms such as larval fish, plankton, seaweeds, mussels, and oysters are affected.

TOXIC WASTE

Despite such big oil spills, more than 80 percent of ocean pollution comes from the land. Oil is the major contaminant, but other toxic chemicals are spilled into the oceans every day.

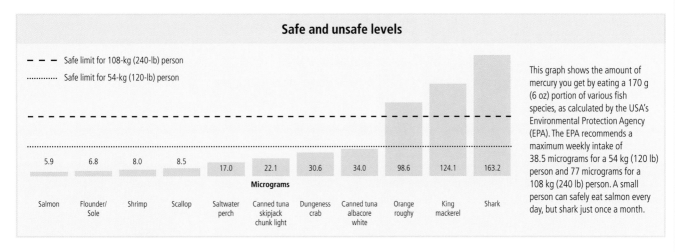

Safe and unsafe levels

– – – Safe limit for 108-kg (240-lb) person

·········· Safe limit for 54-kg (120-lb) person

Salmon	Flounder/ Sole	Shrimp	Scallop	Saltwater perch	Canned tuna skipjack chunk light	Dungeness crab	Canned tuna albacore white	Orange roughy	King mackerel	Shark
5.9	6.8	8.0	8.5	17.0	22.1	30.6	34.0	98.6	124.1	163.2

Microgms

This graph shows the amount of mercury you get by eating a 170 g (6 oz) portion of various fish species, as calculated by the USA's Environmental Protection Agency (EPA). The EPA recommends a maximum weekly intake of 38.5 micrograms for a 54 kg (120 lb) person and 77 micrograms for a 108 kg (240 lb) person. A small person can safely eat salmon every day, but shark just once a month.

Pesticides, chemical cleaners, degrading metals, industrial waste, and many other chemicals leak into the sea, with largely unmeasurable consequences. Deliberate dumping of most toxic chemicals into the ocean was banned in 1996 under the London Convention, but that has only reduced rather than halted the contamination.

It is not just wildlife that is affected by these toxic chemicals. When chlorine is made industrially, for instance, many factories still use mercury, which is discharged into the sea where it is ingested by the fish that we eat such as tuna, sea bass, and swordfish. Eating mercury contaminated fish can have damaging neurological effects on young children and on pregnant women's foetuses. Many chlorine factories no longer use mercury, but the American Food and Drug Administration (FDA) still advises pregnant women to avoid eating certain kinds of fish for this reason. There is mounting evidence that a whole range of industrial chemicals can cause problems to people who eat contaminated fish.

OCEAN WASTED

Ultimately, it may not be obviously toxic pollutants that do the most damage to the marine environment. Fertilizers running off farmland into the sea create blooms of microscopic life that choke the life out of oceans by eutrophication. Such blooms have already created vast dead zones, almost devoid of life (see pages 18–19). Carbon dioxide, pumped into the air by the burning of fossil fuels, is absorbed by the oceans, turning ocean water increasingly acid. The acidification of the waters may completely alter the balance of life in the oceans (see pages 46–47).

There is a huge amount of solid waste thrown into the sea, too, that can pose real hazards to wildlife. Animals drown or get strangled by getting tangled up in everything from discarded fishing gear to old plastic bags, and they may die when they eat plastics and other rubbish.

▽ *The leak of oil from the tanker* Exxon Valdez, *which hit a reef in Prince William Sound, Alaska in 1989, led to one of North America's worst environmental disasters.*

THE BIG CATCH

THE FISHING INDUSTRY IS ON A RAMPAGE THROUGH THE WORLD'S OCEANS
CAPTURING WILD FISH ON A SCALE THAT IS SIMPLY UNSUSTAINABLE.
A CHANGE IN APPROACH IS ESSENTIAL IF WILD FISH ARE NOT TO
VANISH ALTOGETHER FROM THE DINNER MENU.

THE WORLD'S DINERS HAVE BECOME ENAMOURED with fish. Nutritionists tell us it is healthy. Weight-watchers like it because it is free of fat. Gourmet chefs love it for its sheer variety of taste and texture. Many vegetarians who refuse to eat meat are willing to eat the flesh of fish. Specialist fish restaurants spring up in every city and supermarkets have fish counters displaying exotic fish from all around the world.

THERE IS NO CATCH

This newfound taste for fish cannot go on as it is. The scale of fishing in the oceans has become quite simply unsustainable. In the 1950s, the annual fish catch around the world was 20 million tonnes (22 million tons). Now it is probably more than four times as much, at 80 million tonnes (88 million tons). The official Food and Agriculture Organization of the United Nations (FAO) figure is 93 million tonnes (102.5 million tons), but it is thought that the figures submitted by China, which contribute to this figure, may be inflated. Crucially though, the last decade may have seen the annual take decline slightly – not because there has been much let up in the relentless pursuit of fish, but because fish are becoming scarcer.

Fishing quotas have been in place for decades but have not prevented many populations of once abundant fish being fished out. Northern cod, North Sea mackerel, Antarctica's marbled

rock cod, bluefin tuna, and many other populations have all but gone. Ninety percent of large predatory fish, such as tuna, sharks, and billfish, have been removed over the last century. Notoriously, the Grand Banks of Newfoundland (see pages 156–157), once the richest commercial fishing ground in the world, were fished dry in the 1990s and show no sign of recovering. Other major fishing grounds seem likely to follow suit unless there is some dramatic change.

FISHED OUT?

In 2006, Boris Worm, a marine ecologist at Dalhousie University in Halifax, Nova Scotia, Canada presented a study that projected that overfishing was proceeding at such a speed that the oceans would be entirely fished out by 2048. Some argued that Worm was overstating the problem, and one of his critics, Ray Hilborn, joined him on a new study, completed in 2009. Even this study suggested that 63 percent of fish populations were being fished at such unsustainable levels that they will collapse unless there is some change. Only off the coasts of New Zealand and California, where fisheries have long been well managed, does there seem to be a chance of many commercial fish species thriving.

The situation is particularly bad in developing countries. As local fish stocks are exhausted, the organizations of the developed world, such as the European Union (EU), are buying fishing rights from the developing countries for their industrial fishing fleets, which are not only out-competing local fishermen, but fishing these stocks dry, too. This is one of the problems with fishing quotas. They tend to focus on particular fish populations in particular areas, so when fishing boats reach their quota with one fish or area, they simply move on to another. When, for instance, the catching of cod was restricted in the North Sea in an attempt to save the dwindling stock there, many boats switched to catching sea bass, which is now in danger of going the same way. And as fish populations in the inshore waters of the developed countries are fished out, the boats move on to exploit the inshore waters of developing countries, or out into the deep. Commercial fisheries have also been 'fishing down food chains,' which means that once they have fished out big fish, they move on to smaller fish and will eventually be catching jellyfish and plankton.

SUSTAINING THE UNSUSTAINABLE
Fishing quotas, too, tend to be set too high because of competing political pressures. Many quotas still rely on the

△ *Once a staple of the fish dinner, plaice have been so overfished that numbers are declining rapidly. According to the World Wide Fund for Nature, only one of the world's eight populations are fished sustainably.*

concept of Maximum Sustainable Yield (MSY), which seems, on the surface, sensible – it allows fishing boats to catch the maximum deemed sustainable but no more. However, MSY is almost invariably too high, because it assumes that smaller populations will grow faster because they have more food – which is actually the reverse of what happens, because small populations cannot breed fast enough to recover. MSY is still widely used for setting quotas.

Nonetheless, there are grounds for hope. There are places where fish stocks are managed properly, and where there is only a limited amount of illegal fishing. There, fish stocks do seem to show signs of sustainability and even recovery in some cases. Out of ten regions in North America, northern Europe, and Oceania that Worm and Hilborn's team looked at closely, five showed signs of improvement, with diminishing rates of exploitation in recent years. And so, political and government action can make a difference, and so can consumer pressure and choice to alter fishing practices.

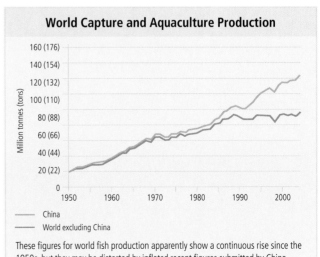

These figures for world fish production apparently show a continuous rise since the 1950s, but they may be distorted by inflated recent figures submitted by China.

◁ *This shoal of pilchards swam unwittingly into a net in the seas off Murcia in Spain and so became part of the huge and needlessly wasteful quantity of marine life that is accidentally caught up as by-catch.*

BED-RIDDEN

DOWN ON THE SEABED IS THE 'BENTHIC' ZONE, named after the Greek for 'depths of the sea'. In the past, it has been neglected, because it has none of the big, exciting creatures that swim in the open waters above. And yet as scientists examine it more closely, it has proved to be a fascinating and varied environment.

Life tends to move slowly on the seabed. There is no need for creatures that live there to dart about in search of food. Most just sit and wait for food to come to them, as it is wafted past by underwater currents. Sponges, sea squirts, corals, and hydroids all sit patiently waiting for food such as plankton to wash by or drift down from above as things die. Then they simply catch, trap, or filter it out using tentacles and various other traps. And when it is time to reproduce, they do not move then either, but just shed their eggs or sperm into the water and let the current do its work.

CRAWLERS AND BURROWERS

There are mobile creatures, of course, especially amid areas of seagrasses and seaweeds in the shallows, but these are only a little more dynamic. Sea urchins creep along slower than snails, grazing on seaweed – they are so numerous that they can devastate a kelp forest unless kept in check by predators such as sea otters. Sea cucumbers are, if anything, slower, relying like the fixed animals on passing plankton and downward drifting decaying matter. The fixed animals themselves provide food for sea slugs, which need to move only a little faster than their immobile prey. Only crabs, lobsters, and starfish show any signs of speed as they scrabble about hunting and scavenging.

Where the seafloor is covered in soft sediments, fixed animals find it harder to gain a foothold, and are vulnerable to being tipped over or buried. So in soft seabeds, many residents burrow. Bivalves and segmented worms are especially well-adapted to the tunnelling life, and there are many thousands of species living down there. Bivalves are often almost completely buried, projecting only their siphons out to get food and oxygen. Ragworms are underground predators, burrowing through the silt in hunt of other worms and crustaceans.

Without plants for food and refuge, animals on the seabed rely on each other more and many interesting symbiotic relationships have developed. Small pea crabs, for instance, live inside the shells of living mussels, a relationship that is described as 'commensal' because only the crabs benefit. Some gobies and shrimp, however, have a genuine 'mutual' partnership, with the shrimp digging a burrow for them both and the goby keeping watch for predators. Anemones that cling to the shells of hermit crabs provide similar protection with their stinging tentacles while at the same time getting a lift to new feeding grounds.

GROUNDFISH

Fish that live on the seabed, known as 'groundfish', do not swim much but simply flap, or hop, along the bottom. They have no need of swim bladders to help them float and their bodies are flat – especially flatfish, such as flounder and sole. As adults, flatfish's eyes migrate around to the 'top' side, to help them keep both eyes open for predators as they lie on the seabed. Predators, such as catfish, need to move a little faster, so have rounder, more muscular bodies, but even they have flattened heads. Some groundfish, such as sculpins and gobies, have their own hooks and suction devices to cling on to the seafloor and avoid being swept away by currents.

THE DANGERS OF TRAWLING

Many flatfish are highly valued as food, and to catch them, fishing trawlers drag nets along the seabed to scoop them up. Unfortunately, this 'catch-all' method of fishing is wreaking havoc on the fragile seabed environment. In recent years, trawl nets have become much bigger and heavier. The weight

Cold-water Corals

Coral reefs conjure up an image of shallow, sparkling blue tropical waters. Yet a decade ago, marine biologists discovered corals living deep in cold water. At first, these cold-water corals were thought to live only in the North Atlantic, but now they have been found off the Galápagos, off Brazil and Angola, and even in Indonesia. They live in cool water between 4° and 13°C (39° and 55°F), at depths between 200 and 1,000 m (655 and 3,280 ft) along the edges of continental shelves, in fjords, and around offshore submarine banks, vents, and seamounts. They are typically found at these depths but can survive as deep down as 6,300 m (20,670 ft). Unlike tropical corals, they do not have communities of algae living with them and feed on plankton and other organic matter. These slow-growing, fragile corals are also refuges for species of snails and clams that were believed by palaeontologists to have become extinct two million years ago.

▷ No sooner were cold-water corals such as these discovered than scientists realized the threat from human activity, especially trawling. Norway has banned trawling on the Røst reef, which was only discovered in 2002.

is needed to keep them scraping the seabed as they move along and the size maximizes the catch. But dragging these huge, heavy nets across the seabed is like dragging an excavator sideways through a meadow. Photographs taken by underwater vehicles reveal great gouges all across the seabed, and seabed communities that have been ripped apart. Unlike communities in shallow water, which are adapted to revive quickly from storm waves, seabed communities in calm, deeper water may never recover from the shock of this kind of disruption. Marine scientists note that virtually every cold-water coral community they have observed has been badly damaged by trawling. Such disturbances do not only pose a threat to the seabed communities themselves, but also to the creatures such as harbour porpoises and seals that rely on them for food.

How Bottom-trawling Works

The benthic trawl nets can be up to 60 m (197 ft) long and 12.5 m (40 ft) in height. The mouth of the net is held open vertically by floats attached to the rope that runs along the upper mouth of the net and weights attached to the rope that runs along the lower mouth of the net. The steel doors scrape along the seabed, making a noise that attracts fish.

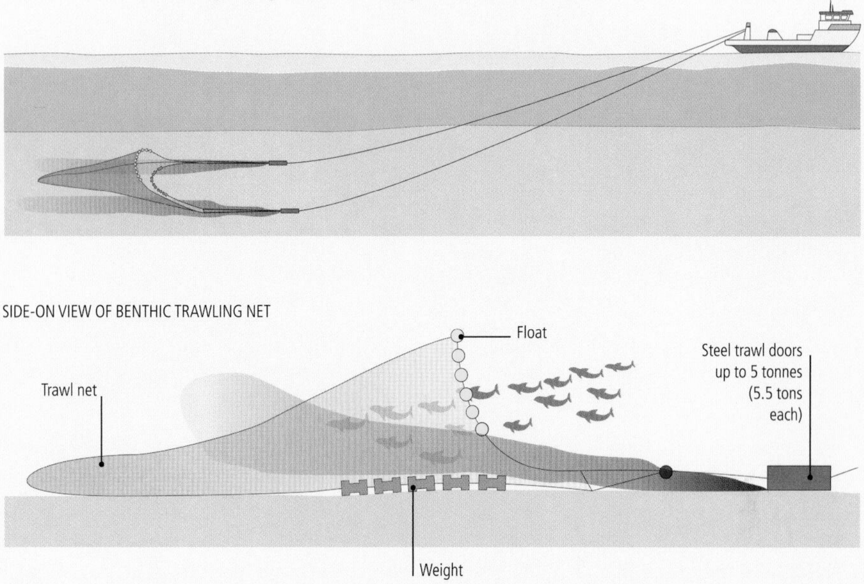

SIDE-ON VIEW OF BENTHIC TRAWLING NET

Float

Steel trawl doors up to 5 tonnes (5.5 tons each)

Trawl net

Weight

▽ *As the massive steel doors used for bottom trawling are dragged across the sea floor, they create gouges that are visible in satellite pictures like this. This process can destroy fragile seabed communities.*

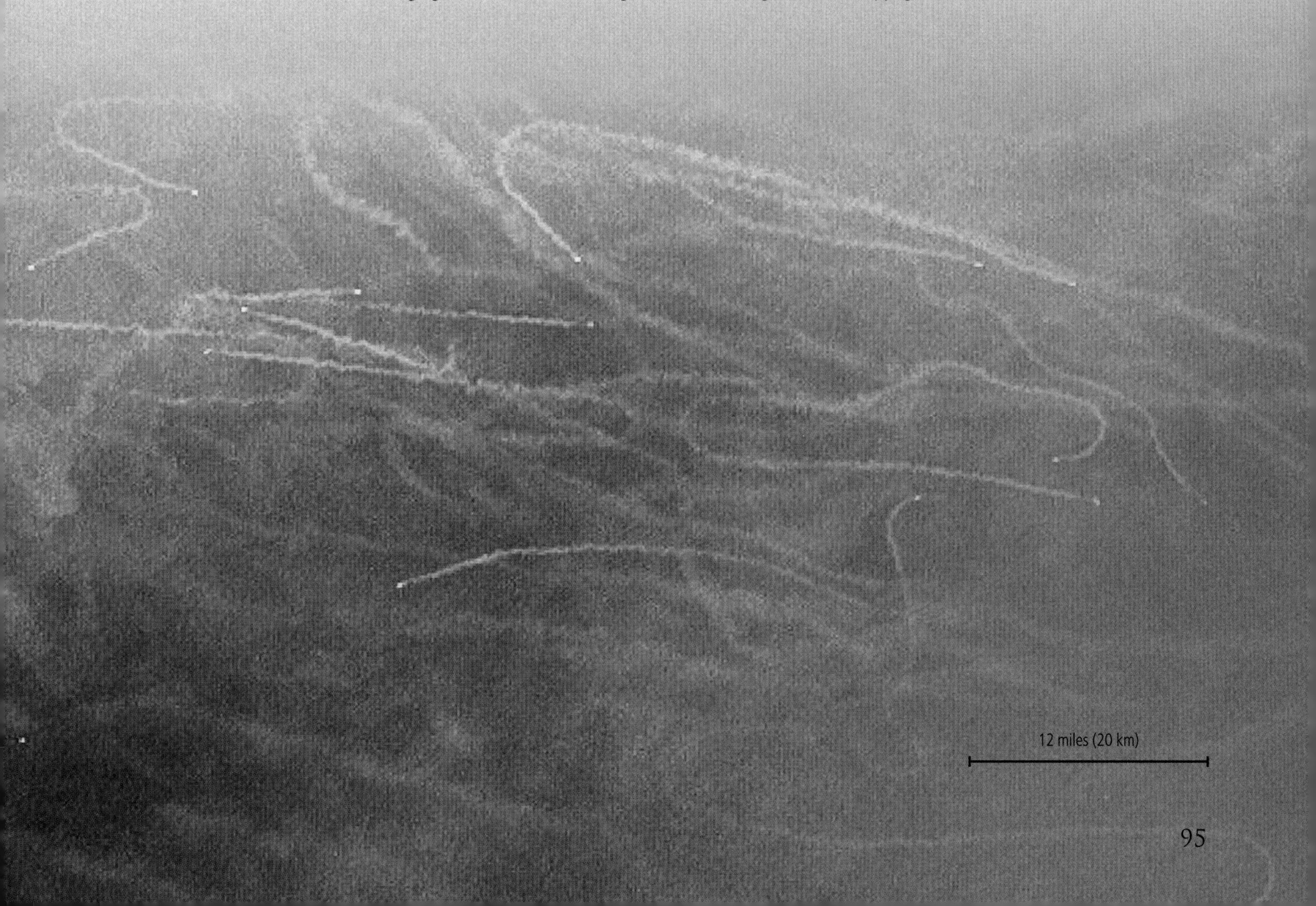

12 miles (20 km)

Ocean Life Zones
Tropical Waters

Undulled by the mass of plankton that fills the temperate ocean, and so often reflecting the cloudless azure sky, the ocean waters of the tropics seem a sparkling paradise, especially close to the coast where white coral sands reflect the light to turn the sea a beautiful turquoise colour.

The very epitome of the tropical marine environment is the coral reef. Coral reefs themselves are among the most beautiful natural sights in the world. Sunlit waters illuminate a fantastic spectacle of corals of all colours and shapes, while in and out of them, through them, above them, and behind them swim an ever-shifting kaleidoscope of brightly coloured fish, from parrotfish to clownfish, angelfish to lionfish – their very names reflecting their carnival aspect. The diversity of life in a coral reef is truly astonishing, with 5,000 species of mollusks alone recorded in the Great Barrier Reef.

Yet these oceanic Edens are in a state of crisis that reflect the environmental problems facing the oceans perhaps better than any other place. The warm tropical waters that seem so pleasant for bathing could turn deadly for corals if warmed just a little too much by climate change. Corals are very, very sensitive to even minor shifts in temperature, and even a slight warming could turn the sea into a boiling pot for them – and with the corals could fall the incredible marine communities that are sustained by them.

◁ *The tropical waters of the mangrove forests of northern Australia are home to the world's largest living reptile, the saltwater crocodile, which can grow up to 6 m (20 ft) long. Here, a young 'salty', as the Australians call it, noses among the mangrove roots.*

THE MAGIC OF CORAL

Like anemones, corals look rather like plants, but they are of course animals. Unlike anemones, most have learned to live together entirely as a colony, so that you very rarely see an individual coral animal or polyp. Instead, they are linked together by living tissue into an astonishing multifaceted community.

Over thousands of years, coral communities can build the great undersea banks known as reefs. Some are just a few feet long. Others are hundreds of kilometres in length. The most famous of them all, the Great Barrier Reef, is composed of 2,900 reefs and 900 islands and stretches for more than 2,600 km (1,600 miles) along the northeastern coast of Australia.

THE CORAL CEMETERY

The remarkable thing about reefs is that they are largely skeletons or graveyards. Only the very top, the brightly coloured soft summit just below the surface is actually the living coral community. All the rest is the dead carbonate skeletons of countless previous generations of corals, built up and up over centuries. Fringing reefs are built out gradually from the shallows along the edge of tropical coasts. Barrier reefs develop as the ocean bed subsides and the reef is left farther offshore beyond a lagoon, so that the corals build up rapidly to stay just below the surface. Atolls are ringlike reefs that form around the sinking summits of extinct undersea volcanoes.

Coral polyps are very simple animals. Although there are thousands of different species, all are basically just a digesting tube or stomach with a mouth at the top surrounded by tentacles. At night, the polyp extends its tentacles farther into the water. Stinging cells or nematocysts on the tentacles stun or kill their prey, which the tentacles then grip and draw into the stomach. For most corals, prey is simply microscopic zooplankton, but large corals may catch small fish. Once digested, the waste is discharged through the back. Meanwhile, the polyps in the colony exchange nutrients with each other, and build their skeleton together, each adding a little more to it with white calcium carbonate crystals every day.

The reef-building corals are, not surprisingly, called stony corals (*Scleractinia*), since the skeletal remains of the coral that form the reef are indeed stony. But there is a tremendous variety. Not only are there up to 2,500 kinds of stony corals, there are also fire corals that are closely related to jellyfish and get their name from their very nasty sting; horny corals, such as sea fans; and thorny corals. And even the same species can grow in a staggering variety of shapes according to the local conditions – wave pattern, light, current, competition for space, and so on. The result is that marine biologists do not always find it easy to identify coral species.

CORALS IN PARTNERSHIP

One of the extraordinary things about corals is just how fast they grow and build reefs when they are healthy. But this only happens with corals in sunlit waters near the surface. Lower down they grow much slower. Corals near the sunlit surface grow up to three times as fast because they have established a remarkable partnership with microscopic single-celled algae called zooxanthellae. The zooxanthellae are harboured right inside the coral polyps' opening and there may be two million of them in every 1 sq. cm (0.1 sq. in). It is these tiny algae that need the sunlight.

The zooxanthellae use the sunlight, like all plants, to produce simple sugars and oxygen – and so provide the coral with a ready-made food and oxygen supply. The coral, in turn, provides the algae with carbon dioxide and nutrients, and also a safe place to live. Without this partnership, corals would probably never build reefs. Besides giving the corals the energy to build their skeletons quickly, the zooxanthellae use up large amounts of carbon dioxide that would otherwise turn the water slightly acidic and dissolve the lime of the skeletons.

BATTERED CORAL

Corals are not necessarily durable structures. They are battered by waves all the time, and they are also undermined by creatures that bore into and weaken the coral in other ways. Bivalve molluscs scrape away at the coral to gain a foothold, while sponges soften it with acids. Parrotfish can bite off huge chunks of coral and swallow the skeleton, excreting the hard remains as fine sand. By these and other means, the coral is broken down into the wonderful, fine sand that characterizes beaches in areas where coral is found.

◁ *The powder-blue tang fish is one of the many stunningly coloured fish of the Indian Ocean coral reefs. But such large numbers are taken for the aquarium trade that its future is far from certain.*

▷ *Schools of brilliantly coloured lyrefish swarm around a coral reef off Fiji. The corals look remarkably like plants, but they are all animals that feed on zooplankton, and occasionally, small fish.*

CORAL SOCIETY

THE EXTRAORDINARY THING ABOUT CORAL REEFS is the diverse community that they support. Unlike ocean waters in the temperate zone, there is not as much nutrition around in tropical seas. However, the reefs act as a focus, like super-oases, concentrating and making the most of what there is. That is why they are so important.

Coral reefs support more species per square metre than any other marine ecosystem by a long way, and the diversity of species is astonishing. There are more than 4,000 species of fish alone – a third of all the world's marine fish. Because of this concentration, though, the competition is intense, and

marine organisms there have developed a huge array of different characteristics and behaviours to cope. There is no other environment in the world where such an extraordinary variety of life strategies is concentrated in such a small space, and the web of interactions between reef species is incredibly subtle and complex. On the reef, the eye is confused not by a camouflage of dull colours but by the dazzling effect of bright colours – the reef presents a fantastic, ever-shifting multicoloured vision. So confusing is the picture that marine biologists believe there may be several million species living there that are still to be identified.

THE CORAL FOOD CHAIN

At the bottom of the food chain are plankton and other micro-organisms. There is not the sheer bulk of plankton that there is in temperate waters, but the reef organisms have found all kinds of ways to make the most of what there is. Little fish such as anthias, for instance, line up in currents that are flowing through the reef with their mouths open to catch plankton, rather than chasing them and expending unnecessary energy. They save even more energy by simply extending their mouths like telescopic tubes and sucking rather than actually moving. But, of course, staying stationary in the current makes these fish very vulnerable to predation by fish such as jacks, so they tend to school together at any sign of risk to confuse potential attackers, and they dash for cover in the reef's many little hiding places.

Corals themselves are animals, but many plants live on the reef, including coralline algae and turf algae, which is a small green seaweed that covers the reef like very short-cropped turf. These plants provide good grazing for a huge range of herbivores, from the diadema sea urchins that graze Caribbean reefs, to fish, such as surgeonfish, damselfish, parrotfish, and rabbitfish. Little fish such as blennies supplement their diet by eating small crustaceans and even the faeces of organisms that feed on plankton. These herbivores are essential for the health of a coral reef. Algae are robust and can choke corals if not kept in check. Caribbean reefs were devastated when disease virtually killed off the herbivorous sea urchin *Diadema antillarum*.

CORAL PREDATORS

All these herbivores also make a meal for the carnivores, including many kinds of invertebrate hunters like slithering flatworms such as *Pseudoceros*, vibrant sea slugs such as the Spanish dancer, and mollusks such as octopuses, cuttlefish and squid, as well as giant clams that can grow up to 1 m (3 ft) across. Anemones here can grow big and colourful, too. In the Caribbean, for instance, pink-tipped, many-tentacled giant anemones (*Condylactis gigantea*) can be up to 30 cm (12 in) across, while elsewhere, the green ruglike Merten's sea anemone grows more than 1 m (3 ft) across. Merten's sea anemone has developed one of the reef's many interesting partnerships – with clownfish. The aptly named clownfish spends almost all its life protected from its predators among the stinging tentacles of the anemone. It escapes identification as food for the anemone with a layer of mucus over its body. The clownfish, in turn, helps protect the anemone from predators such as butterflyfish.

Butterflyfish are among the most common of all the many reef fish and get their name from their vivid colours and flitting butterfly movements. Interestingly, their colours are at their most vivid during the day when they are out feeding on small invertebrates. At night, when they retreat to crevices to rest, their colours often fade. The closely related angelfish may also change colour as it grows.

◁ *Many reefs in the Pacific are threatened by explosions in the populations of crown-of-thorns starfish (bottom right), which prey on corals. The culprit may be farm runoff, which stimulates so much plankton growth that fish that normally feed on starfish larvae do not bother and feed on the plankton instead.*

△ *There is an intricate web of relationships between coral reef species. Fish such as the parrotfish relish the attentions of the little cleaner wrasse, which keeps the parrotfish free of parasites – the parrotfish will roll over and open its gills for a thorough clean.*

GRAZING AND HUNTING FISH

Many other fish on the reef are equally spectacularly hued, including damselfish, such as the vivid blue-green chromis, the lemon-yellow golden damsel, and the striped sergeant major. Some are herbivores, like the damselfish and the parrotfish, which has a parrotlike beak for rasping algae from corals. Others are carnivores like the groupers. Groupers appear docile and so still that they seem harmless, but once a victim comes within range, they lunge quickly to make a kill.

At the edge of reefs, where the water is deeper, barracudas and large sharks, such as the hammerhead, cruise in search of prey, while small sharks, such as the white-tip reef shark and ornate wobbegong, weave in and out of the reef itself. Many fish have developed elaborate defences against larger predators. Scorpionfish, stonefish, and lionfish all have very venomous spines, which can be a real hazard to reef divers. Some fish even resemble their attackers, like the comet fish, whose tail looks like a fearsome moray eel when it sticks its head in a crevice.

The wonderful thing about the reef is that while it provides plenty of rich hunting for carnivores, it also provides countless hiding places for the hunted, and the sheer dazzling array of ever-shifting colours can be very confusing when hunting.

CORAL IN PERIL

IN 2007, THE INTERNATIONAL UNION FOR CONSERVATION OF NATURE (IUCN)
ADDED CORALS TO ITS RED LIST OF CRITICALLY ENDANGERED SPECIES, AND
A GLOBAL REPORT IN 2008 SUGGESTED THAT A THIRD OF THE WORLD'S
CORALS ARE FACED WITH IMMINENT EXTINCTION.

Corals are such a key part of the tropical marine environment that any loss could have incalculable consequences not just for the survival of countless marine species but also for the economic well-being of many communities that rely on the reefs for fishing and tourism. The problem is that despite their diversity and richness, coral reefs are actually incredibly fragile communities, and can be upset by even small changes.

The threats they face are both global and local. The biggest global threat to corals is global warming. The relationship between corals and their algal partners, zooxanthellae, is incredibly sensitive. Corals depend on the presence of these micro-organisms for energy for growth and their vivid colours. If water temperatures rise even very slightly, the corals expel the algae in a stress response and the corals stop growing and lose their colour in what is called a 'bleaching event'. The coral turns white and begins to weaken, making it prone to disease. Sometimes, the coral regains some of its algae and survives. Often, however, bleaching is irreversible and the coral dies. When this happens on a large scale, algal turf smothers both the dead coral and living coral, enabling herbivorous fish and sea urchins to flourish and opening the way to the destruction of the whole reef community.

Bleaching events have become increasingly common in the last decade or so as sea temperatures have risen. Very few corals are now entirely free of bleached sections, and in some places the bleaching is extensive. In April 2009, scientists were relieved to note that sections of the Great Barrier Reef that were ruined by a bleaching event in 2006 had recovered in just a few years. But the worry is that bleaching events will become more frequent as global temperatures increase, and coral's ability to recover may diminish as ocean acidification robs the water of the carbonates that the corals need to build their skeletons.

If, as feared, global warming brings stormier weather, recovery from bleaching events could be further impaired. Research in the Caribbean showed that after powerful hurricanes, coral 'recruitment' (the regrowth of new young corals) drops by two-thirds to three-quarters. Severe storms can damage the skeletal reef itself as it is battered and broken by violent waves.

TAKING FISH FOR TANKS

On a local level, reef communities face pressure not just from overfishing for the dining table but also the capture of fish for the aquarium trade. According to the United Nations environmental programme, 20 million colourful reef fish from 1,471 species, ranging from the sapphire devil to the copperhead butterflyfish, are taken each year. Some 12 million stony corals are taken, too. The spectacular Banggai cardinalfish has been brought to the point of extinction in the wild by demand for it for aquariums, and many other species have been severely depleted.

One especially depressing aspect of the aquarium trade is the use of poison. It is not easy to capture darting reef fish, so many people in the Philippines and Indonesia, often desperate for an income, resort to poisoning the water. Sodium cyanide, squirted

▽ *Even a slight warming of the ocean can cause corals to turn deathly white and stop growing. Such 'bleaching events', like this one here in the Philippines, are becoming increasingly common.*

Threats to Corals Worldwide

ARCTIC OCEAN

Baltic Sea

ATLANTIC OCEAN

Gulf of Mexico

PACIFIC OCEAN

ATLANTIC OCEAN

INDIAN OCEAN

PACIFIC OCEAN

SOUTHERN OCEAN

- ● Tourism
- ● Poison fishing
- ● Over exploitation
- ● Sedimentation
- ● Coral harvesting
- ● Dynamite fishing
- ● Pollution

This map shows the variety of dangers threatening corals in different parts of the world.

from a bottle, immobilizes the fish, making them easy to catch. But it also kills any coral it touches. Even the captured fish die of liver failure in a few months. Some accounts say most aquarium fish from the Philippines are caught this way.

BLOWING UP THE REEF

Even more brutal techniques are sometimes used to catch fish for the dining table. The structure of the reef makes desirable reef fish hard to net, but a stick of dynamite lobbed into the water kills the fish and makes them easy to scoop up from the surface. Unfortunately, the explosion destroys the reef, too.

Even the more subtle methods of fishing can be damaging if overdone. The giant triton sea snail, for instance, is highly prized for its beautiful shell and has been severely overfished. Unfortunately, the triton is one of the key organisms that prey on the crown-of-thorns starfish – one of the few carnivores that

can stomach corals. With the tritons diminished, the crown-of-thorns starfish population can explode without check, with devastating effects for the corals.

Some of the threats to coral are simply down to its proximity to human activity in busy ports and holiday developments – and are even linked to the huge popularity of reefs and reef areas for diving and leisure activities.

Although it needs international agreement to slow the global effects of the planetary warming, action is being taken on a local level at least. Well over a fifth of the world's coral reefs are now within marine reserves and in March 2010, the world's largest reserve, which is about the size of France, was created by the UK around the Chagos Islands in the Indian Ocean. Some felt the park's creation took little account of the wishes of local people, but it will provide a valuable buffer against the destruction of the reefs through development and overfishing.

MUD AND MANGROVES

MANGROVES HAVE NONE OF THE GLAMOUR and colour of coral reefs, and much less than the reef's staggering array of species. Yet their role in the tropical environment is crucial. They act as a unique bridge between the land and the sea, and provide a safe nursery for many of the species that head out to the reef and the ocean beyond for their adult lives.

Mangroves cover vast areas with an unvarying dense mat of foliage and dark tangled roots, all dipping into murky, muddy stretches of water. Even in their most varied regions in Indonesia, there are just 40 different species of mangroves, and only a few more of the other supporting shrubs that live alongside them. No wonder then that they have been neglected, and even exploited as wildlife refuges. But this is a mistake.

THE SEA TREE

Even the mangrove trees themselves are very special plants. They are the only trees that can tolerate immersion in salt water, and survive the almost completely deoxygenated sodden mud in which they plant their roots. They cope with the lack of oxygen in the mud by propping themselves up on high roots that branch off the trunk, or by extending root tubes up like snorkels to take in air through pores called lenticels when the tide is out. They cope with the salinity by keeping their roots partially sealed, and by excreting excess salt through their trunks and leaves. Mangrove leaves taste very salty!

Interestingly, they increase the chances of their offspring surviving to maturity in this very salty environment by allowing seedlings to develop as 'propagules' while still attached to the parent tree, presumably taking care of salt processing and

oxygen supply for their tender offspring. Only after a year or so does the seedling develop its own separate root system – which is why the mangrove swamp is so dense and tangled.

MANGROVE ANIMALS

The capacity of mangroves to cope with tidal seawater and trap mud around their roots enables them to create a unique ecosystem. Some mangrove forests grow alongside sheltered estuaries, but the most extensive often develop along coasts protected by coral reefs. Above the water level and in the drier parts of the forest live many creatures of the tropical forests, including a huge range of insects and spiders, birds, pigs, deer and antelopes, monkeys and mongooses, and even tigers.

Underwater, between the tidal ranges, the root system provides good anchorage points and refuges for a host of marine creatures. Barnacles such as the striped barnacle, oysters such as the enigma, mussels, anemones, sponges, tunicates, annelid worms, hydroids (sea firs), and bryozoans (sea mats) all find places to cling to among the mass of roots. Mollusks such as mangrove periwinkles and common nerites graze on the surface. Piddocks and shipworms burrow right into the roots.

CRABS, FISH, AND REPTILES

Down on the mud scurry countless small crabs, mostly of the related grapsid and fiddler families. As many as 70 of these crabs often live in just a square metre. Grapsid crabs are genuine herbivores and feed on the leaves of mangrove seedlings. Fiddler crabs have a distinctive large right claw and besides for fighting like some bionic machine, they use this claw to scoop up mud

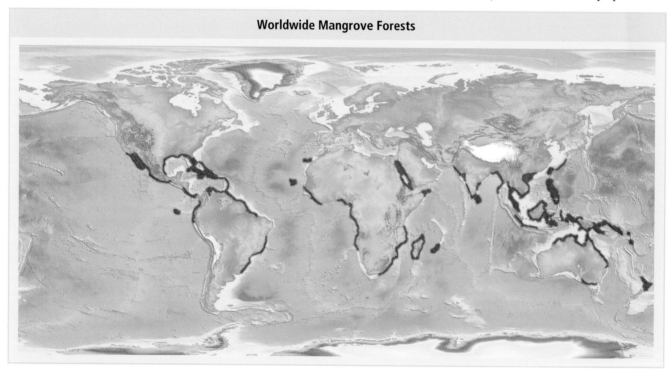

Worldwide Mangrove Forests

to filter through their special mouthparts for food. When the tide is out, though, fiddlers burrow into the mud to escape the attentions of monkeys, herons, and snakes, as well as the odd-looking frog-eyed mudskipper fish that prey on them. Mudskippers get their name because they spend most of their lives out of water on the mud – they hold water in their gills while they are in the air and use their fins almost like legs to haul themselves across the mud. The gold-spotted mudskipper can even climb trees.

When the tide flows in and water floods the root system, it brings with it an array of fish that swim among the submerged roots – jacks and mullets, tarpons and basses, groupers,

cardinal fish, catfish, as well as the young of many reef fish, which use the swamp as a nursery. Amphibians are rare because the water is too salty, but there are reptiles such as water snakes, sea snakes, turtles, and the estuarine or saltwater crocodile, the largest of all living reptiles. Saltwater crocodiles live in the mangrove swamps of northern Australia, eastern India, and parts of Southeast Asia and are thought to grow up to 6–7 m (20–23 ft) long and can weigh a massive 1,300 kg (2,866 lb).

▽ *This photo shows clearly the mangrove's remarkable root system, which enables it to grow in salt water and provide a unique habitat for marine life.*

THE OCEAN'S MEADOWS

AMID THE CONCERN ABOUT CORAL REEFS, the threats to another key marine life habitat – the seagrass beds – are often overlooked. But a report by an international team of scientists published in 2009 showed that these ocean meadows are in swift decline, and the effects could be catastrophic.

Long, waving fronds of seagrass cover vast areas of sandy seafloors in shallow coastal waters with swathes of bright green. Seagrasses are not algae, as seaweeds are, but are flowering plants similar to plants on land. They have adapted to life in the sea with their roots in the seabed, their pollen often carried between male and female flowers by water currents, and their oxygen supply absorbed from the water.

THE SEAGRASS COMMUNITY

These underwater meadows are as important to marine life as forests are to life on land. Countless fish, lobsters, and shrimp find food and shelter in them. A single acre of seagrass can support 40,000 fish and 50 million small invertebrates. Some live among seagrasses all their lives; many young fish spend their juvenile lives in them before heading out to open waters; still others come to the meadows just to feed or spawn. Worms and other invertebrates burrow among the roots; starfish and conches feed on the detritus; sea urchins and seahorses hide among the fronds. Most spectacularly, seagrass meadows play a key role in the lives of dugongs and green turtles that graze on the grass.

The losses reported in 2009 revealed that seagrass meadows are disappearing, if anything, faster than tropical rain forests.

△ *Seagrasses are one of the chief foods for green sea turtles, which eat 2 kg (4.4 lb) of seagrass a day on average – the destruction of their feeding grounds around the world has put the species in grave danger.*

Between 1980 and 2009, 3,300 sq. km (1,300 sq. miles) of seagrass meadow disappeared – and since 1990, 7 percent of the global area has been lost each year. As one of the report's authors put it, 'Globally, we lose a seagrass meadow the size of a soccer field every thirty minutes.'

GRASS DESTRUCTION

Although seagrass meadows are in decline all around the world, the dangers they face are probably not global – like those faced by corals – but local. The problem for seagrass is that it lives in

Current Distribution of Seagrass Beds

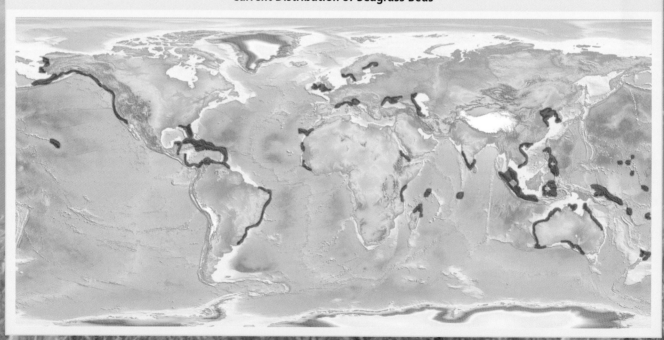

shallow waters close to the coastlands where almost half the world's population live. Damage from the churning of boat propellers, land reclamation projects, hard sea defences, and coastal industrial and residential development have all played their part, but perhaps the biggest single threat to seagrass is pollution. Far too many of the world's rivers have become drains – conduits flushing vast quantities of farm chemicals, industrial effluent, and human waste out into the sea, where it is dumped right on the very places that these priceless meadows grow. The effect of the losses of seagrass ripple far beyond the meadows, since they provide spawning grounds and food for species that spend much of their lives farther afield.

The impact on human sources is significant, too. When disease wiped out 90 percent of a kind of seagrass called eelgrass in the North Atlantic in the 1930s, the mid-Atlantic scallop fishery was finished for good. Unfortunately, the destruction to the meadows goes on, out of sight and out of mind of those contributing to pollution. The need to protect them continues to be a difficult message for conservationists to get across.

▽ *It is not only those creatures that feed directly on the grass that are affected by the loss of seagrass meadows. Predatory mammals, such as dolphins, find many a meal among the fish that live around the beds.*

△ *Living up to their name as sea cows, dugongs are the world's only truly herbivorous marine mammals, and they graze entirely on seagrass. They need to consume more than 40 kg (90 lb) of seagrass every day, and the loss of their seagrass habitat is proving devastating.*

SHELLFISH MOTIVES

SHRIMPS AND PRAWNS HAVE BECOME THE BIGGEST FISH FOOD SUCCESS STORY
OF RECENT YEARS, WITH MILLIONS OF CONSUMERS AROUND THE WORLD
ENJOYING THIS 'LIGHT AND HEALTHY' EATING OPTION.
BUT WHAT IS THE ENVIRONMENTAL COST?

Shrimps and prawns have been popular foods for thousands
of years, but in the last few decades consumption has boomed,
partly as people in the Western world have become accustomed
to the light and healthy eating benefits of Asian-style cooking.
Shrimp production around the world almost trebled between
1987 and 2006, and the rate is still rising rapidly, with the
European Union and the USA the largest single consumers.
Some of this avalanche of shrimps has come from a substantial
increase in the wild catch, but the bulk of it is from newly
established farms, and farmed shrimps now account for well
over half of all global consumption.

INDUSTRIAL SHRIMP

By far the majority of the new shrimp farms are in Southeast
Asia (notably China, Thailand, and Vietnam) and South
America, and the boom has had a huge impact on local
economies – and the local environment. Shrimps have been
farmed in Asia for thousands of years in a low-key traditional
way. But what has happened recently has been the coming of
industrialized fish farming on a gigantic scale. So lucrative is
the business for the biggest producers that huge areas of the
coastal margins have been ponded in with vast concrete tanks
where access to salt water is easy.

Industrial shrimp farms produce two or even three crops a
year, raising the shrimps from their tiny postlarval stage to
full-size in just two or three months. Originally, the postlarval,

Loss of Mangrove Swamps

This pair of Landsat satellite images of Honduras shows the scale of the loss
of mangrove swamps by the startling growth of shrimp farms – rectangular
features – in only a decade, between 1987 and 1997.

▽ *This aerial shot of the landscape south of Bangkok, Thailand,
reveals the huge extent of the shrimp farms and their pools, dug
out where mangrove swamps once stood.*

or PL, shrimps were caught wild. Now most are produced from eggs in hatcheries and sold to the farm for cultivating.

△ *Shrimp farming provides a vital income for many poor people. Here, people are sorting tiger prawns in a shrimp farm in Bangladesh's deprived Sundarbans region.*

PRAWN COCKTAIL

While traditional farms could rely on natural growth to keep the shrimp fed, the forced production of industrial farms demands that artificial food is fed into the tank continually. This is either in liquid form or as pellets, which need to be scattered into the tank four or five times a day. One of the problems with pellets, although they are much cheaper than liquid feed, is that they are never fully eaten by the shrimpss, and a sludge builds up and rots on the tank floor, eventually making the tank unusable.

Chemical growth stimulants are often added to the pond to increase growth rates along with pesticides and anti-fungals, while antibiotics are frequently used on some farms to combat the disease that often breaks out in the crowded tanks. Many farms have had to be abandoned because diseases, such as yellowhead and white spot, have got out of control. Demands from both consuming countries and producers have encouraged better standards of farming, but many people still report that the conditions in some tanks, with their mixture of rotting feed, chemicals, and antibiotics, are foul. After barely ten years, many tanks are so badly contaminated that they are unusable and have had to be abandoned and new sites found – leaving the old tanks to continue leaking pollution with potentially devastating effects on the local ecosystem.

MANGROVE LOSS

Establishing these industrial-scale shrimp farms has already taken a huge toll on the environment simply because the obvious location for them is in mangrove swamps. Mangrove swamps, which once seemed to have little economic value, suddenly became gold mines. Vast areas of mangrove swamps have been stripped away to make way for shrimp farms. Estimates vary but it is thought that more than a third of the world's mangrove forests have been lost in the last few decades, mostly to shrimp farms. And as, of course, shrimp farms have to be abandoned after their comparatively short life, further areas of forest need to be cleared in order to set up new farms.

It is hard to be sure what effect this has on the marine environment and as yet there has been little conclusive research done. However, besides their own environmental worth, mangroves act as nurseries for many sea fish, including both coral reef and commercially fished species. Therefore it seems likely that this massive loss of mangrove could have a huge impact on the marine environment even beyond the impact on the mangrove forests themselves.

There is no doubt that in some places, shrimp farming practices are dramatically improving in response to growing pressure internationally, both to make the shrimp themselves a better, more healthy product and to reduce the impact on the environment. Some people argue, indeed, that the problems outlined here are simply teething problems of a young and potentially valuable new way of farming that has simply grown too fast. If handled properly it could bring much needed jobs and income to some of the world's poorer countries. But the record has been less than perfect so far.

THE FISHING MACHINES

THE DAYS WHEN MOST FISH were caught by small boats sailing out locally from quaint fishing villages are long gone; most commercial fishing is now a global business carried out on an industrial scale.

In the early 20th century, the whaling industry was transformed by the arrival of large factory ships in which the whales could be brought on board and processed without returning to port. At first, the whales were just stripped of useful parts before the carcass was dumped in the sea. Later on, ways of using all the carcass were developed. Such was the brutal efficiency of these killing machines that the world's whale population was quickly decimated.

FACTORY TRAWLERS

As whale catches declined, some companies had the bright idea of using the same techniques for fishing. In 1953, the first factory trawler, *Fairtry*, was launched in Aberdeen, in Scotland. At more than 85 m (280 ft) long and weighing 2,600 tonnes (2,866 tons), this giant fishing boat had a stern ramp just like the whalers, but *Fairtry*'s ramp was used for hauling on board not whale carcasses but giant nets filled with any fish caught up in its mesh. The stern ramp allowed *Fairtry* not only to use bigger nets, but also to operate in stormy weather that was far too

dangerous for traditional side-hauled nets. Equipped with the latest technology – radar, sonar, fish finders, and echograms – *Fairtry* could track down schools of fish in any conditions. Once on board, the fish could be fed into automated filleting machines and a fish meal rendering factory and quickly chilled in giant freezers. *Fairtry* could fish around the clock for weeks on end before returning to its home port of Hull, in the UK, with a massive haul of fish.

Such was the chilling effectiveness of the *Fairtry* that it soon spawned imitators. By the 1970s, the Soviet Union had 400 factory trawlers, Japan 125, Spain 75, West Germany 50, and France and the UK 40, with dozens more operated by smaller countries. Between them, these boats scooped up vast quantities of hake in South Africa, krill in Antarctica, pollock off Alaska, and northern cod on the Georges Banks and the Grand Banks of Newfoundland.

On the Grand Banks, the factory ships caught as much fish as had been caught in decades in earlier years, in just a few years, and before long this once unimaginably abundant fishing ground was entirely fished out. This setback has not stopped the factory ships. When fishing quotas or depletion of stocks limits catch in one fishing ground, they have the range to move on and hunt farther afield.

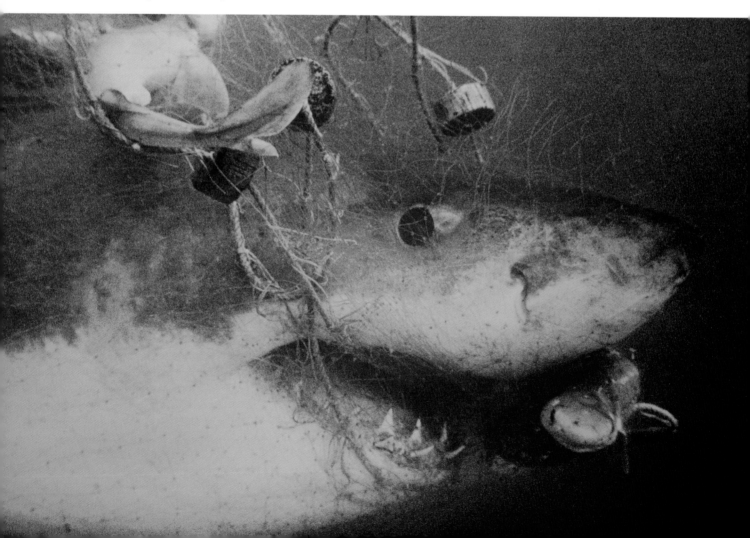

△ These unwanted dead starfish, dumped from fishing boats on a quay at Hokkaido, Japan, may provide a great meal for the slaty-backed gulls, but marine life is being devastated by this waste.

THE BIG FISHOUT

The world's biggest factory trawler is the 144-m (472-ft) long, 7,700-ton (7,000-tonne) monster once known as the *Atlantic Dawn* and now called the *Annelies Ilena*. This giant trawler can haul on board hundreds of tonnes of fish an hour, and on a single trip can net enough fish to feed the entire population of Tokyo for a day. When it was first launched, it became the focus of controversy because the European Union would not grant it a licence to fish in European waters. So instead, the boat fished off Mauretania in Africa, where it was said to be catching the same amount of fish as 7,000 traditional fishermen. Today, it is trawling in the South Pacific.

Factory trawling arouses controversy not just because of the vast quantity of fish that it catches, but because of its indiscriminate nature. To get the large numbers of cod they needed to fill their nets, for instance, factory trawlers would home in on the fish as they gathered to spawn, sweeping them away before they could produce their offspring.

Fishing Methods

- Longline fishing: involves trailing a line many kilometres long with hundreds or even thousands of baited hooks. Surface lines catch tuna and swordfish. Demersal lines catch seabed fish such as halibut. It can also catch albatross and sea turtles that try to feed on the bait, but is less damaging overall than trawling can be.
- Midwater (pelagic) trawling: involves towing a cone-shaped net either from a single boat or between two boats (pair-trawling) fairly high in the water to catch pelagic fish such as anchovies, shrimp, tuna, and mackerel. The main problems are by-catch.
- Bottom trawling: involves dragging a net along the seabed (benthic trawling) or just above (demersal trawling) to catch groundfish, such as sole, flounder, and halibut, or demersal fish such as cod, rockfish, squid, and shrimp. It can have a very damaging effect on seabed communities, especially slow-growing coldwater corals such as *Lophelia pertusa*, which can take hundreds of years to recover.
- Seine fishing: uses a weighted seine net that hangs from floats. Purse seines draw the bottom of the net together like a purse to catch sardines, mackerel, herring, and anchovies, as well as some kinds of tuna.

◁ This great white shark, caught inadvertently in nets off New Zealand, makes up just a small part of the million tons of unwanted 'by-catch' caught up and dumped back in the sea to die every year by the global fishing industry.

BY-CATCH

Another problem is 'by-catch'. Colin Woodard in his salutary book *Ocean's End* describes the practice of 'high-grading' on the cod fishing trawlers in the 1980s, which meant catching everything in the net and then discarding the unwanted. 'Crabs, flounder, redfish, starfish, juvenile cod, sharks, and a hundred other unwanted creatures – the so-called by-catch – would be sent overboard through special discard chutes; for every 3 tons of fish that were processed, another ton or more of other creatures were killed in this manner.'

The waste is just as high today. Each year, nearly 27 million tonnes (30 million tons) of by-catch is dumped in the sea – a quarter of the entire global catch. Shrimp trawlers are the worst, killing up to 20 kg (44 lb) of unwanted fish for every 1 kg (2.2 lb) of shrimp caught. Shrimp fisheries take just 2 percent of the world fish catch but a third of all its by-catch, and shrimp trawlers are the main killers of adult endangered sea turtles, hauled up indiscriminately with the shrimp on which they feed. In theory, they should be thrown back, but they rarely survive. Dolphins and whales are also victims of industrial fishing vessels. If they are spotted in the nets, they should be released, but they usually drown long before they can be put back.

▽ A sea turtle, lying lifeless on the deck amid the catch of fish, is a stark reminder of the threat posed by fishing even to non-targeted species. But the right fishing gear, such as turtle excluder devices, can help decrease by-catch.

OCEAN LIFE ZONES
POLAR WATERS

The Antarctic and Arctic are places of incredible, awe-inspiring beauty, with their towering peaks of ice, their glistening snowfields, and their turquoise seas, illuminated every now and then by raking sunlight of gorgeous pale peach. But they are also the bleakest, most unforgiving environments on Earth. It is almost inconceivable that much wildlife can make it their home, and yet it does, in surprising abundance, and especially in the oceans.

The low angle of the sun in the polar regions ensures they are never warm. Even during the summer months, when the poles enjoy the midnight sun and daylight 24 hours a day, temperatures rarely climb much above 5°C (41°F). Winter brings the polar night, when there is only a faint glow of daylight during the middle of each day – and close to the poles not even that. Winter temperatures in the Arctic plunge to –50°C (–58°F) and even lower. In Antarctica, temperatures in the interior can drop to –70°C (–94°F). And the winter winds in both regions are unimaginably chill.

What both polar regions have is oceans. The Southern Ocean surrounding Antarctica, and the Arctic Ocean around the North Pole are very different in character. But they play a vital role in reducing the chill, and so create a food supply that sustains a surprising variety of creatures both in the oceans themselves and on the surrounding solid ice and land.

◁ *Adelie penguins live farther south than any other birds and have to cope with very cold conditions. They are helped by short, stocky bodies and short, densely packed feathers as well as an underlying layer of insulating fat.*

ICY SEAS

ALTHOUGH THEY SHARE BITTER COLD, ICE, and polar nights, the Arctic and Antarctic are very different. The Antarctic is a small mountainous continent surrounded by oceans, with the tip of the nearest land, South America, more than 1,000 km (620 miles) away. The Arctic, however, is mostly ocean, enclosed by the vast continental landmasses of North America and Eurasia, and dotted with just a few large islands, such as Greenland, Baffin Island, and Ellesmere Island.

By comparison to the Arctic, the Antarctic is isolated. It is not simply the distance away of the nearest land. It is also the impassable nature of the ocean inbetween to all but the hardiest. Around it, like a vast icy river, flows the Antarctic Circumpolar Current that completely cuts off the Antarctic from warm ocean waters. The lack of land also means that winds roar through the surrounding Southern Ocean creating some of the world's stormiest seas.

Almost the entire Antarctic continent is smothered with a vast, thick, and ancient ice sheet that is more than 5 km (3 miles) thick in places, but in summer

there is only a small shelf of ice on the sea around it and small pockets of sea ice in sheltered bays such as the Weddell Sea. Only when winter begins to take hold in March does the sea begin to freeze over and the ice push out over the waves to cover an area of ocean more than twice the size of the continent itself by September. In the following months, as the Antarctic spring arrives, the sea ice largely breaks up and melts away.

In the Arctic, however, there is only the equivalent of the Antarctic's vast, land-based ice sheet on Greenland, and it is a tiny fraction of the size. Most of the Arctic's ice floats on the sea and is under 8 m (26 ft) thick, even at its thickest. About half of the floating Arctic ice surrounding the North Pole remains solid, year after year, and is known as multi-year ice. It melts a little in summer and grows back in winter a small amount each year. Every winter, though, a layer of thinner ice spreads right across the ocean to join up with the shore. The adjoining landmasses not only bring the Arctic warmth, preventing it from ever getting quite

▽ *Walruses are well-adapted to life in the Arctic – they haul themselves out of the sea onto ice floes to rest and bear their young. These Pacific walruses are in the Chukchi Sea north of Siberia.*

as stupefyingly cold as the Antarctic, but they also bring a much wider range of plant and animal species that have been able to adjust to the slightly less severe conditions. The largest resident in the Antarctic that does not rely entirely on the sea for food is a kind of midge, while the Arctic has polar bears, foxes, and hares, even though the northern sea is almost entirely oceanic. It is the oceans, though, which are the key to life in both polar regions.

CHILLY WATERS

Unlike the sea elsewhere, the polar oceans do not separate into temperature layers. They are almost evenly cold throughout – bitterly cold at the surface, and bitterly cold right down into the depths. While the surface layers of the ocean warm up considerably in the summer months, they never do in the polar regions. Even in summer, sunlight glances off the ocean surface at such a low angle that much of its heat is lost. And in winter, of course, the sea is often cold enough to freeze. The cold keeps salinity here low, and the water only has to drop to −1.8°C (28.7°F) to freeze – not much less than a few degrees below its average year round temperature of just under 0°C (32°F).

Although the polar oceans are cold, they are not too cold for life there to flourish. The coldness of the oceans ensures the waters are rich in oxygen. In the Arctic, rivers bring a steady supply of nutrients, phosphates, and nitrates, too. In the Southern Ocean around the Antarctic, meanwhile, the meeting of the icy Circumpolar waters with the warm ocean waters from the north,

along the boundary called the Antarctic Convergence, creates continual upwellings that bring nutrients to the surface. In summer, the extra light in these nutrient-rich waters both in the Arctic and Southern oceans ensures a bloom of phytoplankton, providing the basis for the entire polar sea food chain.

△ Wolffish, or sea wolves, look fearsome, but their strong jaws are used only for getting into the shellfish that they eat. Natural antifreeze keeps their blood flowing in chilly Arctic seas. But these unusual fish are now under severe threat from overfishing and by-catch.

Surviving the Chill

Life in the polar regions is dominated by the cold. Every animal and plant that lives there has to find a way to cope. Although it is cold all year round, it is the bitter chill of winter that presents the real challenge. For some creatures, the challenge of the polar winter is just too much and when the polar fall comes, some creatures simply leave for warmer places. Those that stay through the winter, and even those who arrive only for the summer, have their own cold survival techniques.

FAT AND FUR

Mammals can generate their own heat from food, and their biggest problem is how to avoid losing it. One way is for them to grow large and rotund to keep the surface area for heat loss at a minimum in comparison to their body volume. Thick fur or fat, or both, provides insulation. Fur works well on land by trapping insulating air, and polar bears, Arctic foxes, and most other Arctic land mammals have warm, thick fur. Fur does not work so well in the water, especially deep down where the pressure is greater and pushes the air out of the fur. So most marine mammals, such as whales, seals, and walruses encase themselves in a thick layer of blubber. On some whales, this can be up to 20–30 cm (8–12 in) thick, enabling them to live comfortably in temperatures as low as –40°C (–40°F). Seals, which also spend some time out of the water, also have a layer of fur so warm and silky smooth that humans have killed seals for it for thousands of years.

Penguins are among the most remarkable of all survivors of the cold, with some able to sit out on the ice in the open through the worst of the Antarctic winter. They have special short, overlapping feathers that retain heat, and a thick layer of fat for extra insulation. Their rounded body shape also keeps their surface area down, and they have very small feet and wings. Their unique blood circulation keeps the heat that is sent to the extremities, such as the feet, to a minimum, so penguins have cold feet but warm bodies. In the bitterest weather, the penguins also huddle together for warmth, with each penguin taking its turn to warm up in the middle.

AMAZING ICEFISH

Fish, too, have their own cold adaptations. One group of fish in particular, the Notothenioid fish, has its own remarkable proteins, which combat freezing in icy waters, earning them the name 'icefish'. Normally, a fish's body fluid freezes at –1°C (30°F), but Notothenioid fish can live in waters that are –1.9°C (28°F) or even colder and full of ice crystals. If the fish swallows ice when feeding, the ice crystals could coat the fish's stomach lining in ice and kill it. But icefish secrete a protein called antifreeze glycoprotein (AFGP) into their stomachs, which plugs any tiny holes in the crystals that encourage the growth of bigger crystals.

There are eight families of Notothenioids in the Southern Ocean, and their freeze-fighting strategy is so successful that they are virtually the only fish in the seas around the Antarctic. But fish in the Arctic, such as white flounder, sculpins, and herring have antifreeze proteins that evolved independently, and these either prevent freezing altogether or allow freezing without damage.

SLOWING DOWN

Antifreeze is not the only way icefish combat the cold. They are all ghostly white because their blood has virtually no red haemoglobin. Haemoglobin is normally used to transport oxygen through the blood, but the Antarctic waters are so rich in oxygen that the haemoglobin is unnecessary. Icefish can slow their heartbeats and their metabolic rates right down to minimize their energy demands. As a result, icefish seem incredibly sluggish.

Other fish have developed their own ways of slowing down to cope with the cold. Shrimplike krill, remarkably, regress to childhood – while most crustaceans moult their shells to grow bigger, in winter, krill shed their shells to shrink back to their juvenile size and cut their food intake by 95 percent and their metabolism by up to 50 percent. Limpets in the Antarctic hide in crevices and smother themselves with antifreeze mucus, while periwinkles in the Arctic simply dry out to shed water that might otherwise form ice crystals.

◁ *Notothenioid fish, like this emerald notothen swimming past a sponge under the Antarctic ice, survive the polar chill because their bodies contain a natural antifreeze, glycoprotein, that enables them to survive even in half-frozen water.*

▷ *The Weddell seal lives farther south than any other mammal, living in McMurdo Sound just 1,300 km (808 miles) from the South Pole. A thick layer of fur and blubber enables it to survive the extreme cold.*

THE VITAL KRILL

VAST SWARMS OF SHRIMPLIKE KRILL ARE THE STAPLE FOOD OF THE ANTARCTIC
OCEANS, AND WITHOUT THEM MANY SPECIES OF FISH COULD NOT SURVIVE.
BUT CAN THE KRILL SURVIVE A HUMAN ONSLAUGHT?

Such is the importance of krill to life in the Antarctic oceans that these creatures are described as keystone species, forming the crucial link in the food chain between the phytoplankton on which they feed and the countless carnivores above them. A huge range of creatures depend on them for food, either eating them directly, or eating other animals that feed on the krill. Squid, fish, seals, whales, penguins, and seabirds all depend on krill. Baleen whales, such as minke, eat them in vast quantities. So do manta rays, whale sharks, and crabeater seals. At the top of the food chain are big sea mammals such as leopard seals and killer whales that consume large amounts of krill inbetween dining on small seals and penguins that in turn also feed on krill.

There are 11 species of krill in Antarctic waters, and there are 85 altogether worldwide, but it is just one species, the Antarctic krill, *Euphausia superba*, that is key in Antarctica. It is hard to be sure just how many Antarctic krill there are, but acoustic surveys suggest that somewhere between 100–500 million tonnes (110–550 tons) of these krill appear each summer in the Southern Ocean. When the ice melts and the warmer weather comes, the krill gather in vast swarms of many miles across with densities of up to 30,000 individuals in a cubic metre. Swarming is a defence mechanism, confusing the picture for the smaller predators that try to pick out individuals. Nevertheless, that does not prevent a feeding frenzy when a swarm is spotted coming up to the surface to feed.

Antarctic krill can swim a little, and when attacked, can dart backward rapidly in an action called lobstering. But swarms are largely at the mercy of currents and are swept along where the currents take them. All they can do is come up to the surface to feed at night when they are less likely to be hunted by diving birds, then descend to safer depths during the potentially dangerous daytime. Even so, millions are eaten every day.

Typically, krill spend the winter under the ice. The sub-ice water is a nursery for juveniles that feed on the diatoms that live in cracks in the ice. It is also a dormitory for the adults that revert to juvenile size and shape, and cut down their feeding rate and metabolism dramatically. When spring comes around and the phytoplankton blooms, the adults start feeding voraciously and soon return to their full size.

△ Antarctic krill grow up to 6 cm (2.4 in) long and are the most successful animal species in terms of biomass, weighing in at a total of some half a billion tonnes. They provide food for many species in Antarctic waters.

◁ Millions of krill school together into a boiling pink mass called a krill ball, here being fed upon by mackerel over Nine-mile Bank off San Diego, California. As many as 30,000 can crowd together in a cubic metre.

CATCHING KRILL

Until recently, krill fishing was relatively small in scale. The krill are too far away for most people to be economically viable to transport to the dining table, although up to 200,000 tonnes (220,000 tons) are caught annually for fish food. In addition, once they are caught, they decay quickly because of enzymes they contain. But all that is beginning to change. As food prices climb and other fish stocks dwindle, krill may become a target for human consumption. Moreover, advances in technology mean krill can be easily processed and preserved aboard ships.

Like fish oils, krill oil is high in omega-3 oils – which are seen as having health benefits for humans – as well as the antioxidant astaxanthin, and the oil is now being marketed as a dietary supplement for those worried about heart disease. Since krill has not been fished on a very large scale before, no one knows what the impact of this sudden interest will be. Marine biologists worry that taking too many krill could threaten the survival of baleen whales and the Adelie penguin that eat them, as well as creatures higher up the food chain, although it seems unlikely that Antarctic krill will be targeted. The USA is considering a ban on krill fishing in American waters.

Krill numbers have dropped since the 1970s, maybe by up to 80 percent. Some scientists believe the cause is global warming. How many are left remains uncertain. The British Antarctic Survey estimates 100 million tonnes (110 million tons); krill harvesting companies say it is 400–500 million tonnes (440–550 million tons). Under the Convention on the Conservation of Antarctic Marine Living Resources, the annual allowed krill catch in the Southern Ocean is 3.5 million tonnes

△ *Humpback whales are gulp-feeders. They swim then gulp large mouthfuls of water and prey, rather than filtering their food continuously. The whales look for the huge swarms of Antarctic krill that provide their chief food.*

(3.8 million tons). Until now only a tiny fraction has been caught, but the demand for omega-3 oils could change all that. Conservationists hope that in future scientific observers are mandatory on all boats catching krill in Antarctic waters.

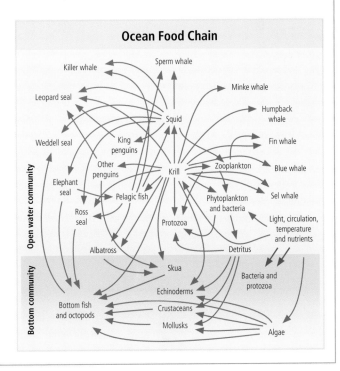

Ocean Food Chain

Killer whale · Sperm whale · Minke whale · Leopard seal · Squid · Humpback whale · Weddell seal · King penguins · Fin whale · Other penguins · Krill · Zooplankton · Blue whale · Elephant seal · Pelagic fish · Phytoplankton and bacteria · Sel whale · Ross seal · Protozoa · Light, circulation, temperature and nutrients · Albatross · Detritus

Open water community

Skua · Bacteria and protozoa · Echinoderms · Bottom fish and octopods · Crustaceans · Mollusks · Algae

Bottom community

Polar Migration

I N SUMMER, THE BLOOM OF PLANKTON turns the waters of the polar oceans into a feast that draws in millions of creatures for a feeding frenzy. But so harsh are the polar winters, and so impossible is it for some creatures to obtain food once the sea freezes, that the coming of autumn signals the start of an exodus.

WHALE JOURNEYS

Whales are great polar migrants, and the journeys made by baleens are probably the longest made by any mammal. Grey whales have been recorded travelling over 8,000 km (4,970 miles) from the Bering Sea to Baja, California in five months, while humpbacks have been tracked for 8,330 km (5,176 miles) from the Antarctic Peninsula to Colombia.

In summer, baleen whales such as the blue, the humpback, and grey head off to where the krill and other fish are. In the south, baleen whales head for the Antarctic. In the north, they head into the Arctic Ocean. All summer, they feed greedily, eating huge quantities of krill each day to build up a store of blubber ready for winter. Then, in the autumn, as the food supply dwindles and the waters begin to get even colder, they assemble and head away from the poles for warmer waters. It seems they find milder, more sheltered places for mating and breeding, and the warmth means they can probably get by on

▽ *Southern right whales generally tend to make their long migration to their summer feeding grounds off Antarctica alone, although females may be accompanied by a calf, like this one. They only get together in groups in the winter and spring, when they return to their breeding areas.*

Southern Right Whale Migration Routes

⟷ Migration routes
▪ Breeding areas
▪ Feeding areas

Every winter, some southern right whales make the journey back from their summer feeding grounds around Antarctica to the coasts of New Zealand and Australia to mate and calf in places such as Doubtful Bay and the Head of Bight.

△ *Arctic terns mate for life, and tend to return to the same colony every year. In between, they are on the wing almost continually, dipping down into the ocean every now and then to catch small fish close to the water's surface.*

heading either along the African or the South American coast, before ending up in the Weddell Sea. On the return trip north, they take a different route, flying in a huge S-shape up the middle of the Atlantic and crossing the Caribbean. In a year, the tern flies up to 81,600 km (50,700 miles). Since terns are thought to live well over 30 years, an average Arctic tern will fly some 2.4 million km (1.5 million miles) in its lifetime.

These birds are on the wing nearly all their lives – feeding, sleeping, mating, and doing nearly everything else in the air. They catch their food by dipping down and catching prey at the ocean surface. They land just once every few years in the north to nest and breed. As soon as they have finished nesting, they are off on another long polar migration, this time joined by the fledglings. Just three months after being ringed as an unfledged chick in Northumberland in the UK, one young Arctic tern was spotted in Melbourne Australia, 22,000 km (13,670 miles) away.

In the Antarctic, the tern are there for the explosion of krill that happens every spring after the bloom of phytoplankton. In the Arctic, they come for the schools of capelin and herring that arrive in the spring to make the most of the summer's feeding opportunities, as well as krill in places such as the Newfoundland Basin. Some observations suggest that global warming means Arctic terns are having to fly farther and farther north to find the right conditions for nesting, and the journey may prove too much. Others suggest that they may be hampered in the south, too, as the reduction of winter ice reduces the krill.

less food. Some baleen whales seem happy to vary the winter destinations. One group of humpbacks wintering in Hawaii was spotted the next year in Mexico, and one whale was seen in both Hawaii and Mexico in the same winter!

Toothed whales may also migrate long distances sometimes. In spring, for instance, some populations of beluga whales and narwhals follow cracks or 'leads' that open up in the receding ice to push farther north to find new feeding grounds.

THE FANTASTIC TERN

The greatest migrants are seabirds such as the Arctic tern. The Arctic tern flies all the way from the Arctic to the Antarctic and back to catch the summer and avoid the winter at each end of the world. It is a medium-sized bird, less than 40 cm (16 in) long and with a wingspan of about 80 cm (31 in). Yet when autumn comes to the Antarctic, it flies literally halfway around the Earth to arrive in the Arctic in time for spring in May or June. And when the Arctic summer is over, it heads off south in August or September on the other half of its yearly journey. This incredible voyage is not direct, since the bird has to visit feeding grounds en route, and on each trip it covers 19,000 km (11,800 miles) or more. One study of 11 terns published in January 2010 showed them travelling south through the Atlantic towards the Azores, then

Arctic Tern Migration Routes

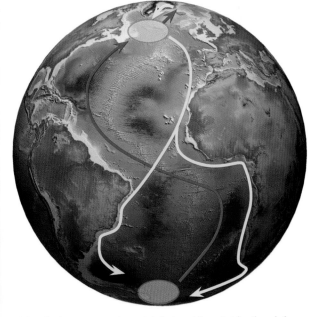

 Southern migration

 Northern migration

A recent study showed the route taken through the Atlantic by the Arctic tern on its amazing annual journey from pole to pole. It flies south down the coasts of South America or Africa, but returns north on a huge S-shaped loop through the mid-ocean.

OCEAN GIANTS: THE WHALES

DESPITE HUGE ATTENTION AND PUBLIC INTEREST,
THE FUTURE OF WHALES HANGS IN THE BALANCE, AND
AT LEAST TWO SPECIES ARE CRITICALLY ENDANGERED.

In late March 2010 whale experts from around the world met to discuss a perplexing problem. In the previous five years, 300 southern right whales had been found floating dead in the waters off Patagonia, one of the most important breeding grounds for the species. Die-offs like this have happened before, but never in such numbers. Some experts believed the problem was the accumulation in their bodies of toxic pollutants, concentrated because the whales are at the top of the food chain. Others suggested a shortage of krill, their essential prey. Another idea was that they were suffering from disease.

It is this lack of certainty that is causing so much concern. Whale populations were decimated by hunting in the 19th and 20th centuries (see page 192). Some populations are now extinct, including the grey whales of the North Atlantic and the bowheads of Spitsbergen, Norway. Two species, the blue whale and the northern right whale, are – perhaps critically – endangered worldwide, with a population of less than 3,000 blue whales and 1,100 northern right whales altogether. Although whaling bans have done a lot to halt the decline in numbers, the numbers of most whale species remains pitifully small, and just a tiny fraction of what it was in pre-whaling days. The small size of these populations exposes whales to a host of new threats.

THREATS TO WHALES

Climate change seems to be emerging as a major problem because the melting of sea ice and the changes to the ecology of the polar seas in recent years threatens the feeding patterns as krill populations fluctuate or decline. Whales that live in the Arctic all year, such as the bowhead, beluga, and narwhal, may be affected by the changes in conditions.

But smaller toothed whales seem to be falling victim to another threat – by-catch. The vast nets now used by fishing boats, especially the big trawl nets hauled between two boats in pair-trawling, catch up not just the fish they intend to take but also toothed whales as they home in on the schools of fish gathered by the nets. In theory, fishermen are supposed to release any mammals caught accidentally, but most drown long before they are brought to the surface. Dolphins and porpoises are especially frequent victims, but even sperm whales can be entangled. Some estimates suggest at least 300,000 dolphins, porpoises, and whales are killed in this way each year. Fishing may threaten the survival of whales by taking the food out of their mouths. Fish stocks are dwindling rapidly around the world as the annual catch continues at unsustainable levels, and whales may already be facing famine.

NOISE AND DIRT

Noise is another problem. Whales depend on incredibly sensitive hearing and sound for communication and navigation, but the oceans have become increasingly noisy. The oceans are filled with the nonstop throb of ship's engines. To this has been added the unknown but worrying effect of naval sonar weapons. In 2000, the US navy admitted that the deaths of six whales found bleeding on a beach in Bahamas was attributable to a tactical sonar exercise. Seismic tests can also badly damage whales' hearing. The effect of all this noise is uncertain but some suggest that whales may become disorientated and lose their way.

When such threats are combined with the effects of toxic pollutants such as oil and gas, and the destruction of whale habitats by human activity, it is clear that whales face an uncertain future. While bans on whaling and whaling quotas may seem to halt the decline, numbers have reached such a low they may be badly affected by any new threat that comes along.

▷ *The biggest creatures that have ever lived, blue whales have been pushed to the very brink by whaling, and there are no more than 5,000–12,000 of these great creatures left around the world, despite the complete ban on hunting them.*

Baleen and Toothed Whales

Whales are the largest of all marine mammals. Like mammals on land, they breathe air, taken in at the water's surface through the blowhole in the tops of their heads, which seals off to let them dive deep down for long periods.

There are about 80 species of whales, including true whales, dolphins, and porpoises. They are divided into two groups: baleen and toothed whales. Most of the baleens are huge and include the blue, fin, common minke, sei, and grey. They feed entirely on plankton, mainly krill, which they sieve from the sea with the brushlike baleens in their mouths (below). Some gulp in water and catch the krill in their baleens as they push out the water. Others sieve the water as they swim along.

Toothed whales, such as sperm, pilot, and killer whales have teeth, not baleens, and feed on larger prey, including seals. Dolphins and porpoises are also classified as toothed whales. Though sperm whales are huge, most toothed whales are small hunters that stay in much the same place all year round and have no need to go on long migrations in search of food. The toothed whales have not been hunted as ruthlessly as baleens, either, since they are faster, harder to catch, and offer much less meat and blubber when they are caught.

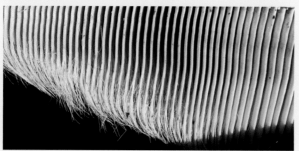

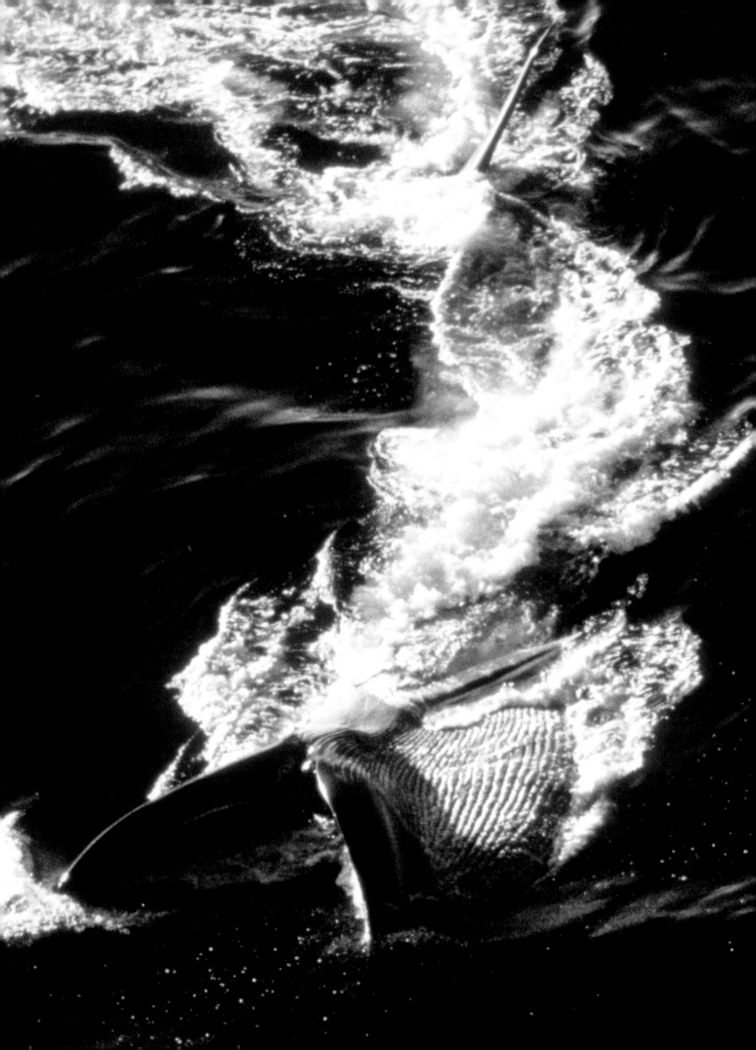

OCEAN LIFE ZONES
OPEN WATERS

Only on the very margins of the ocean is land within sight or even a few hours sailing distance away. Most of the ocean is a vast expanse of open water where nothing is visible but sea as far as the horizon in every direction. Not only is the open ocean remote from land; it is deep, too. You can sink 4,000 m (13,000 ft) or more before you touch bottom. And the very deepest places are nearly three times as deep.

The sheer size of the open ocean is staggering. It covers more than 70 percent of the Earth and holds 99 percent of its water. It is easy for even the biggest creatures, whales, to seem very, very tiny in such a great volume of water. There are vast expanses of the open ocean that are so empty they seem like a desert. This is not just an illusion; some of the ocean is indeed fairly empty of life at certain times. But such is the huge volume of the open ocean that the organisms that live there, known as 'pelagic' organisms, vastly outweigh all the rest of the world's living things put together.

There are few landmarks in the open ocean, of course, to act as focuses for life. Instead, here and there, currents in the water bring nutrients up from the deep. These nourishing fountains draw fish and other animals from far and wide across the ocean to make the most of the feeding opportunities. Then the supply dwindles and the fish are forced to journey on to another feeding ground.

◁ *The rough waters of the open ocean, whipped up by the wind into huge swells, seem inhospitable to humans, yet beneath the surface lurks a vast amount of life, more than any other habitat on Earth.*

OCEAN LAYERS

THE OPEN OCEAN MAY BE FEATURELESS for thousands of kilometres in every direction, but it is not a uniform habitat. It is actually divided into vertical layers that create different living conditions and attract particular creatures and lifestyles.

The very top metre or so of the ocean is special chemically and biologically. Known as the 'neuston' layer, it is in some ways the cream of the open ocean, enriched by light, oily nutrients that drift up from below – amino acids, proteins, and fats excreted by plankton and oils oozing from larger animals when they die. In calm conditions, the neuston layer may settle into an even more concentrated cream on the surface that is just a few centimetres thick, known as the hypo-neuston layer.

Bacteria, protozoans, and microscopic algae flourish in this rich mix. Jellyfish live here, too, floating on the surface to take advantage of food sources. But every day, masses of plankton and other creatures drift up here, too, to take advantage of the nutrition and the sunlight.

Sunlight shines down no farther than the top 100–200 m (328–655 ft) of the ocean, which is known as the photic zone.

▽ *Despite their name and vast size of more than 5 m (6 ft) across, the devil rays of the eastern Atlantic and Mediterranean have come on to the endangered species list, being unlooked-for victims of dragnets intended for swordfish.*

Indeed, red light only penetrates down to about 10 m (33 ft). Below this, red things look dark and everything else is bathed in grey or silver because all the red light has been filtered out, leaving only green and blue, then just blue. In cloudy water, this sunlit zone is even shallower. All the phytoplankton that rely on sunlight for photosynthesis live within this top layer, and the zooplankton that feed on them must follow them there, too. And where the zooplankton go, so do other animals – the fish such as lanternfish that feed on them, and the great hunting fish such as sharks and billfish that feed on those fish – so that most life in the open ocean is focused on this sunlit zone in the top few hundred metres.

THE TWILIGHT ZONE

Below the sunlit photic zone you enter the twilight zone, which extends down to about 1,000 m (3,280 ft). It is murky, and many animals seek refuge here to avoid being caught in the glare of the sunlit zone. But there is still just enough light for animals with sensitive eyesight to hunt. So creatures that live in this zone, both predators and prey, are in a constant battle to see and avoid being seen, in a place where there is no cover but twilight. The result is a ghostly world of shifting, faintly visible shapes that flit momentarily into vision then vanish. Many animals make

△ *Leatherbacks are the largest of all sea turtles but remain highly endangered, both from threats at sea and threats while hatching. This embryo was probably killed when its egg was moved, long before researchers opened it.*

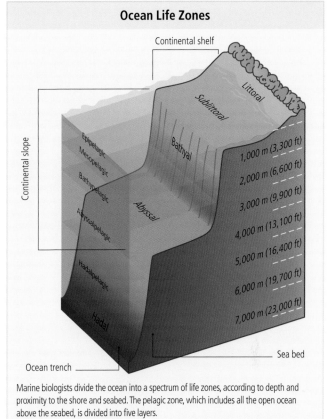

Ocean Life Zones

Marine biologists divide the ocean into a spectrum of life zones, according to depth and proximity to the shore and seabed. The pelagic zone, which includes all the open ocean above the seabed, is divided into five layers.

themselves almost invisible by being translucent so that they cast virtually no shadow. Others are wafer thin to reduce their silhouette, so that predators will not spot them.

THE LOWER DEPTHS

No light at all reaches below 1,000 m (3,280 ft), and the lower depths are pitch-black. The cold is intense and the pressure immense in this dark zone, yet there are plenty of creatures who are adapted to living here – many more than was once thought. There is no need at this depth for a swim bladder, the gas pocket that provides fish with buoyancy. By replacing compressible gas in their bodies with incompressible liquid, deep-living fish become relatively immune to the effects of pressure. They cope with the cold and lack of resources at depth by moving slowly, growing slowly, and living long, just waiting for nutrition to drift down from above or for prey to come their way. Hunters in the deep, therefore, do not have muscular bodies built for the chase, but instead huge, gaping mouths for trapping prey and, in the case of anglerfish, dangling lights to lure prey in.

This dark zone is divided into the abyssal zone, which covers the lower depths of the ocean above the abyssal plain, down to the ocean bed at about 4,000–6,000 m (13,000–19,700 ft), and the hadal zone. The hadal zone is the water in the ocean deeps, where the seabed plunges into trenches far below the abyssal plain, from 6,000–11,000 m (19,700–36,000 ft). Only a few craft have ever managed to penetrate this black, icy, crushing-pressured region, yet those that have have proven that there are animals, including fish and shrimplike amphipods, even at this great depth. Some creatures glow slightly on the underside, so from below they vanish against the brighter water above, rather than showing up as shadows.

▷ *Despite 'dolphin safe' practices, Atlantic spotted dolphins continue to be threatened by tuna fishing activities, as they are caught up in nets.*

OCEAN COMMUTERS

EVERY NIGHT WHEN THE SUN GOES DOWN on the open ocean, there begins the biggest mass movement of organisms on the planet. During the day, only the phytoplankton stay in the surface layers to make the most of the sunlight they need for photosynthesis. But for zooplankton, the vast mass of minute creatures, such as copepods, that feed on phytoplankton – and each other – the bright, surface layers are far too exposed and dangerous in daylight hours. So, during the day, they sink to the relative safety of the murkier depths. Only when night falls and the upper layers are dark do they rise to the surface again to dine. And as the plankton rise, so the larger animals that feed on them follow, triggering an upward migration of life in the ocean that is on a truly staggering scale.

THE NIGHT SHIFT

During the day, the surface layers of the ocean contain barely 10 percent of all the life in the ocean, as countless creatures descend into the twilight zone to find refuge. What makes daylight especially dangerous in the surface layers is not just that marine predators see prey better, but so do diving bird predators. The vast open ocean appears almost lifeless as most larger animals seek safety in the twilight zone, where three-quarters of all marine life lurks during the day. But when night falls, the amount of life at the surface multiplies by four, and in the darkest hours of the night, the ocean surface is teeming with animals of all kinds. Then, with the dawn, this vast wealth of life descends to the depths again in what is rather dryly described by marine biologists as 'vertical mass migration'.

The smallest zooplankton only move up and down about 10–20 m (33–66 ft). But at just 20 m (66 ft) down, the light levels are low enough during the day for some degree of safety for such small creatures. Larger copepods, though, can migrate 100 m (328 ft). Jellyfish such as siphonophores, krill, arrow worms, pteropods, ctenophores, and the plankton-feeding larval young of fish migrate a similar distance.

FISHING IN THE DARK

Schools of fish, such as mackerel and anchovy, that feed on plankton move up and down a few hundred metres or even more. Most of these fish need light to help them see their prey, so they feed most actively at dusk when the plankton are near the surface but there is still a little light, or at dawn. When food is scarce, they may be forced to stay at the surface for longer, despite the risk of being spotted by birds and other predators. Lanternfish, however, have found a way to feed at the surface at night.

Although little known, lanternfish are the most abundant fish in the sea by a long way, making up two-thirds of the entire biomass of fish in the deep sea, so the strategy is clearly successful. Lanternfish not only have very sensitive eyes to help them see in the dark; they have also developed the lights to illuminate their prey, and this earns them their name. All but one lanternfish species have light-producing organs called photophores that emit a pale blue, green, or yellow glow. The pattern varies, but in the Diaphus family, a pair of photophores is located on either side of the fish's eyes, like headlights. Since they have all night to feed, lanternfish can afford to descend far deeper into the twilight zone during the day. They also need to shield their sensitive eyes. So at sunrise, most lanternfish dive to depths of at least 300 m (980 ft) and some as much as 1,500 m (4,900 ft), to ensure that they spend their entire lives in darkness.

Lanternfish are a major source of food for a huge number of species, including whales, dolphins and seals, tuna, sharks, marlins, grenadiers, squid, such as the jumbo squid, and a wide range of seabirds. So the feeding habits of these species are often dictated by the diurnal migration of the lanternfish. Larger sea mammals and fish follow the same daily commute to the upper surfaces and back as the plankton, following not just lanternfish but other schools of fish, such as mackerel and herring, up and down.

◁ *This scuba diver is studying salps. These are remarkable creatures that look like jellyfish, but because they have a spinal cord (although no backbone), they actually have more in common with humans.*

> ### Turtle Dives
>
> It has long been something of a mystery why turtles, such as the leatherbacks, dive so deep. They feed at the surface, on jellyfish, and their bony armour means that they are not especially in danger of predation. Yet leatherbacks are capable of diving 500 m (1,640 ft) or more downwards in just ten minutes. It was speculated that, for instance, they might just be trying to cool off by diving deep, but the cooling benefits of going this deep are minimal. A recent study by scientists from Swansea University, in the UK, suggests that what is really going on is that the leatherbacks are diving to check out the colonies of the jellyfish on which they feed at depths of 600 m (1,970 ft) or more during the day. Having spotted a colony, the turtles bide their time until nightfall when the jellyfish come to the surface to feed – and then make their move.

▷ *Great white sharks are one of many predators that take advantage of the daily concentration of life near the ocean surface, sometimes leaping out of the water as they take seals.*

THE MULTITUDINOUS MASS

OFTEN ALMOST INVISIBLE except under a magnifying glass or even a microscope, plankton are the most important and abundant organisms on the Earth. Not only do they make up more than half the biomass of the ocean and underpin every ocean food chain, they also produce more than half the world's oxygen. Without plankton, very little life on the Earth would be possible.

The word plankton comes from *planetoi*, the Greek for 'wandering', and plankton get their name because they simply drift through the ocean with very little control over where they are going – unlike other animals in the sea that are collectively known as 'nekton' and can swim and choose where to go. However, plankton multiply and dwindle in response to local conditions, so they are not simply flotsam washed around by ocean currents and waves, and zooplankton can swim vertically to get into the surface layers to feed on phytoplankton at night.

SOLAR FOOD
Like plants, phytoplankton make their own food by using the energy from sunlight – photosynthesis – and it this energy input from the Sun via phytoplankton that ultimately fuels all life in the ocean. To build the food, phytoplankton also need certain nutrients, notably nitrates and phosphates. Some are washed in by rivers – sometimes in such excessive quantities that they can generate the runaway local 'blooming' that causes eutrophication and creates 'dead zones' (see pages 18–19). But mostly, nitrates and phosphates are the product of a vast and continuous chain of ocean recycling.

EFFICIENT RECYCLERS
The phytoplankton absorb the nutrients as they multiply; the zooplankton consume the phytoplankton along with the nutrients; nekton, such as fish, consume the zooplankton; and in time all of them die and bacteria decompose them and release the nutrients again. The released nutrients, though, tend to sink out of reach to the bottom of the ocean. That's why plankton growth is concentrated in those parts of the ocean where the surface is cold, allowing cool water to rise from the depths and bring the nutrients up again.

The two most common phytoplankton by far are diatoms and dinoflagellates. Diatoms are single-celled algae that take an astonishing variety of forms. There are 100,000 or more species,

▽ *A typical male ocean sunfish weighs more than 1,000 kg (2,205 lb), making it the heaviest bony fish in the world. Yet it gets all its bulk just by eating tiny plankton and jellyfish – in gigantic quantities.*

which each look very different under a microscope where they look like a fantastic collection of designer buttons. Although a few grow up to 2 mm (0.07 in) across, most are too small to be seen by the naked eye. Yet altogether, diatoms generate 45 percent of all organic materials in the ocean. Dinoflagellates are tiny, longish organisms with two tiny tails or flagella that they whip to move themselves short distances. Most survive by photosynthesis, but a few species wrap themselves around food and absorb it.

ANIMAL PLANKTON

Zooplankton are the plankton that feed on other plankton. They are usually larger than phytoplankton and range from tiny copepods under 1 mm (0.03 in) long to jellyfish and colonies of salps that can be many metres across.

Meroplankton are the larvae of fish and other animals who only spend the early part of their lives as plankton, to avoid competing with adults. Almost all pelagic fish spend their early days as meroplankton. Zooplankton known as holoplankton spend their entire lives as plankton. Copepods, krill, larvaceans (related to sea squirts), some sea snails and slugs, salps, and jellyfish are all holoplankton. Copepods are tiny organisms that look like transparent woodlice and together may weigh more than any other group of animals on the Earth, though the weight of all the krill put together may come close. Copepods and krill are both

▽ *Although only properly visible under a microscope, plankton include many thousands of different species such as these diatoms, with their extraordinary geometric forms, and dinoflagellates, which have double whiplike tails that they lash to propel them through the water.*

crustaceans – a group that includes young lobsters, crabs, and shrimp – and are the most abundant zooplankton by a long way. Salps and larvaceans are almost entirely clear-bodied to reduce their chances of being spotted by predators.

What is amazing about the role of plankton in the oceans is the sheer range of animals that rely on it directly for food, not simply indirectly through other smaller animals, such as mackerel and lanternfish, that feed on plankton. Indeed, the ocean's biggest creatures bulk up entirely on plankton. These are whale sharks up to 14 m (46 ft) long, manta rays with 5 m (16 ft) wings, and the biggest baleen whales, such as the blue and the fin. Imagine a lion surviving entirely by eating ants and you can see just how astonishing this is. The key is the sheer mind-blowing abundance of plankton. These giant creatures can simply gulp in a lot of seawater from near the surface and know that they will get all the food they need by sieving out the plankton by the bucketload.

Plankton Blanket

For the last decade or so, some scientists have argued that one way to reduce global warming is to stimulate massive blooms of plankton that will soak up the excess atmospheric carbon dioxide. Like plants on land, phytoplankton use atmospheric carbon dioxide to make their food when photosynthesizing. The absorbed carbon would then sink to the bottom of the ocean out of harm's way when the plankton die. So scientists have been experimenting with fertilizing patches of the ocean with iron to stimulate blooms. Recently, however, they found that, as always, nature's response is a lot less predictable than this simple solution would suggest. When the sea is fertilized with iron, it seems, it stimulates the growth of one major species of plankton in particular – one that produces a chemical that is toxic to both fish and humans.

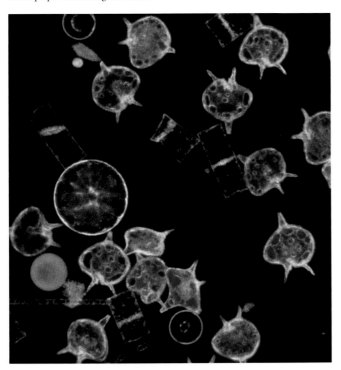

▷ *Sunlight reflects as bright turquoise off the chlorophyll in massive swirls of plankton, showing up clearly in these satellite views of the sea off New Zealand's South Island. The brightness of the colour suggests that the plankton are probably coated with calcium carbonate (white chalk).*

SHARKS IN DANGER

SHARKS CAN BE SUCH FEARSOME KILLING MACHINES, THAT IT IS
HARD TO IMAGINE THAT THEY COULD EVER BE ENDANGERED. YET THAT IS EXACTLY
WHAT THEY ARE. SHARK NUMBERS HAVE PLUMMETED IN THE LAST FEW DECADES
AND MANY SPECIES ARE IN IMMINENT DANGER OF EXTINCTION.

So limited is the public appeal of sharks that the devastation that has been wrought on shark populations by overfishing passed by almost unnoticed by the media until an eye-opening report by the International Union for Conservation of Nature (IUCN), published in 2009, made headlines around the world. The report suggested that a third of all the world's open-ocean (pelagic) sharks are in danger of being wiped out, and the IUCN put sharks on their Red List of endangered species for the first time. Indeed, they redlisted 64 species of sharks, including scalloped hammerheads, which are classified as 'globally endangered' – that is, near to becoming extinct altogether.

What is so shocking is the speed at which shark numbers have dropped. Scallop hammerheads have dropped in number by 99 percent in just 30 years, and other species have shown declines almost as rapid in certain areas. Overall, shark numbers in the northeastern Atlantic, for instance, have been cut by anything between 50 and 90 percent since the 1970s. It is not just numbers that have shrunk; so too has the size of sharks. In some species, sharks are less than half the size they

were only a little while ago – a sure sign that they are not getting the chance to mature properly.

SHARK KILLS

The big problem is fishing. Sometimes sharks are just the unfortunate by-catch of fishing activity. And sometimes they are deliberately targeted, since shark meat and, in particular, shark fins, have become increasingly popular as a delicacy, especially in China. All too often, sharks are caught, their fins sliced off, and their bodies thrown back into the sea. This process is known as 'finning'. Estimates of numbers vary because by-catch and illegally taken fins go unreported, but it is thought that anywhere between 100 and 200 million sharks are killed every year, with maybe 10 million blue sharks alone killed for their fins. Particularly vulnerable are sought-after species such as the porbeagle and the shortfin mako. The fins of a million or more shortfin makos are traded each year in the Hong Kong fin market.

Any species would have problems with this level of reduction, but sharks are especially vulnerable because they can take decades to mature and then only produce relatively

▷ *The strange head extensions of hammerhead sharks, like this great hammerhead, one of the two endangered hammerhead species, have always been a puzzle. But scientists may now have found the answer. The wide-set eyes give the sharks amazing binocular vision and enable them to see above, below, and behind.*

△ *Strict regulation of fishing quotas in Canadian waters of the Atlantic since 2000 has given the porbeagle shark a fighting chance of recovering there, after overfishing reduced the population by 80–90 percent.*

few young. The decimated global dusky shark population, even though it is now protected, may take 400 years to recover, if it ever does, because these sharks take 20 years to mature and produce only one offspring at a time.

TOP PREDATORS

Despite the killer image, only 12 of the 450–500 or so species of shark ever pose any threat to humans – and there are less than ten fatal shark attacks every year around the world. Moreover, even the killer sharks play a key role as top predators in the marine environment. The dramatic reduction in shark numbers in the eastern Atlantic, for instance, allowed the population of cownose rays on which they preyed to explode. These cownose rays then wreaked havoc on the scallops on which they feed, almost ending the scallop industry in this part of the world. Similarly, some tropical sharks prey on big fish that eat smaller fish that eat algae, which can quickly smother coral unless kept in check by regular grazing.

Governments around the world have begun to recognize the problem. The USA has long had controls of shark fishing in its waters, and in 2003 the European Union banned the practice of finning. But at a key meeting of the Convention on International Trade in Endangered Species (CITES) in April 2010, the assembled governments failed to reach an agreement on regulations that would have afforded some protection to a handful of very vulnerable species including hammerheads. For some sharks, time is running out.

Mighty Hunters

Estimates of the number of shark species varies. Today there are thought to be 460 or so, but they have been so little studied that marine biologists believe there may be well over 500. Despite their popular image, they vary tremendously in size and feeding habits. They range from the herring-sized dwarf lantern shark up to the whale shark – the world's biggest fish, which can grow to 13 m (43 ft) long or more. And while some sharks hunt and attack seals and dolphins (and humans), such as the tiger, bull, and great white, the huge whale shark is a filter feeder that strains the water for plankton and crustaceans, and the angel shark prefers to lie on the seabed waiting to snap up passing molluscs. Unlike other fish, sharks and the related rays are cartilaginous, which means instead of a bony skeleton, they have a supporting structure of rubbery cartilage, which is so light that they do not need a swim bladder to help them float.

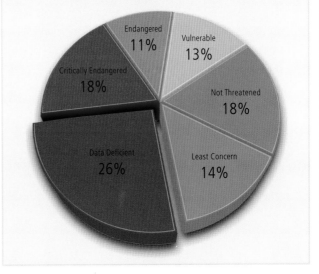

DEEP HAUL

As fish stocks run low in the once teeming continental shallows, the fishing industry has been plundering farther out and deeper down and catching fish not even known a few decades ago.

Most of the fish we know from the dinner table – cod, haddock, hake, flounder, sole – are caught in the continental shallows. However, over the last few decades, catches from the shallows have been shrinking as the fish become scarcer and as quotas come into play. In order to evade the quotas and find new hunting grounds, fishing trawlers have been venturing farther into the ocean to hunt new quarry.

THE WHITING ON THE WALL

One of the victims of this oceanward expansion has been the blue whiting. Although little known as a fish for eating, it is caught in ever-rising quantities as feed for fish farms, and in 2006 was the fifth most important caught fish. It is a fish of the continental slopes, living some way out from the shores of northwestern Europe and northeastern North America. It is very abundant in the northeastern Atlantic and is therefore an important link in the marine food chain, feeding on planktonic crustaceans and small fish and being prey to a wide range of predatory fish, squid, and marine mammals. It descends to around 1,000 m (3,280 ft) by day, then migrates each night to the surface to feed. On average it lives at a depth of 200–400 m (655–1,300 ft) – and therein lies its problem.

At that kind of depth, it tends to live just off the continental shelf, just outside the 320-km (200-mile) limit of different countries' jurisdiction. It falls in no-man's land, and countries took a long time to reach an agreement on quotas. In 2002, the International Council for the Exploration of the Sea (ICES) estimated that a sustainable catch of blue whiting was around 600,000 tonnes (660,000 tons). The following year, a record 2.3 million tonnes (2.5 million tons) were caught in the Atlantic. In 2007, the countries around the Atlantic agreed to impose a quota, which meant substantial cuts in their catch to 1.25 million tonnes (1.38 million tons). This is progress, and estimates suggest that numbers are recovering, but the future of the blue whiting, until recently one of the world's most numerous edible fish, stays uncertain.

▽ *Gigantic shoals of migrating sardine not only tempt bluefin tuna, as here, but fishing boats too. But as sea temperatures rise, these spectacular migrations seem to occur less and less.*

DEEP PROBLEMS

It is the deep-sea fisheries farther out that may be in worse trouble. Until a few decades ago, the waters here, out beyond the continental shelf in the deep ocean, were little known, and many of the fish had only recently been discovered. Yet now they are the target of a massive fish hunt involving industrial-scale trawlers. These trawlers are dragging huge nets thousands of metres down far out into the ocean – way beyond, crucially, the jurisdiction of most countries. Ironically, many of the trawlers are heavily subsidized to fish this far out, and it is often only the subsidies that make it viable to use the fuel to get there.

Deep-sea fish are quite different from shallow water fish. Deep-sea fish such as the orange roughy, grenadier, and scabbard fish all have large heads and tapering bodies, which means that much younger deep-sea fish get caught up in nets that shallow water youngsters would slip through. Even more problematic is the fact that deep-sea fish are slow-growing, take a long time to mature, and only have a few offspring. It is thought that the orange roughy may live up to 150 years – twice as long as most humans – and is not ready to reproduce until it is at least 30 years old. Roundnose grenadiers, too, are long-lived and slow to mature. That means that they are deeply vulnerable to overfishing. If even slightly too many fish are caught, there is little chance of recovery for a very long time. Some experts believe there is no sustainable level of catch for deep-sea fish – fishing simply has to stop altogether.

Deep-sea fish are not that numerous, and the only reason they can be caught in viable numbers is that they tend to gather around a few places in the deep ocean, such as the summits of seamounts, where the upwelling of water provides extra food for breeding and spawning. So the trawlers home in on these places, which are often focuses of life in the mid-ocean.

ROUGHY TIMES

The orange roughy was the boom fish of the early years of deep-sea fishing, but the boom was short-lived. In many places, fishing began just a few years after the fish was discovered. In Australia, the roughy was discovered in the mid 1990s. By 2008, the population was reduced by 90 percent. Fishing for the orange roughy began in British waters around the Hatton Bank and Rockall in 1991. That year, there was a great haul, but within three years, the catch had plummeted by 75 percent. It was off the coast of New Zealand, though, where the orange roughy was really big business, with 100,000 tonnes (110,000 tons) a year

△ Organizations such as Seafood Watch recommend that people avoid eating orange roughy. This particular fish grows slowly and reproduces late in life, and so is vulnerable to overfishing – also, the bottom trawling needed to catch it wrecks seafloor ecosystems.

being caught in the 1980s. As the catch began to plummet, the New Zealand government began to introduce quotas limiting the catch to what their experts argued were sustainable levels. But with the roughy taking so long to reproduce, it is hard to see what a sustainable level is, and quotas have been slashed every year as New Zealand tries to keep this fishing industry going.

Many environmental organizations argue that the orange roughy is so close to the edge that it should not be on anyone's menu. Roundnose grenadiers and scabbard fish may be in just as much danger. Deep-water sharks such as the spurdog, porbeagle, and basking shark are getting close to the edge, too, and ICES recommended that they should not be caught at all. Spurdogs are one of the few sharks with catch limits imposed by the European Union, but fishing for these is still over the limits and the species is now critically endangered. The brief boom years of deep-sea fishing are in danger of turning to bust, with unknown consequences for the open ocean ecosystem in which these fish play a key role.

▽ The striking black scabbard fish, Aphanopus carbo, has long been a favourite to eat on the Portuguese island of Madeira, where it is known as espada. But it is now being fished intensively by deep-sea trawlers, and is in danger from overfishing.

Deep scars

Deep-sea trawling is not simply reducing the numbers of deep-sea fish; it is having a profound and direct effect on deep-water habitats. The vast nets that are dragged across the seabed weigh 15 tonnes (16.5 tons) or more. In a few hours, they can destroy deep-sea cold-water corals and sponge beds that have taken centuries or millennia to grow. The great gashes that they carve across the seabed are so marked that they are often visible through the water from space.

MIGHTY HUNTERS

THE OPEN OCEAN IS THE PROVINCE of the great hunters of the marine world – sharks and rays, billfish, and tuna. Catching prey in the vastness of the ocean is not easy. Potential meals may be not just hundreds but thousands of kilometres away, and locating them in so much open water is a very demanding business.

In water, vision is of little use in spotting prey except at very close range. Instead, big hunting fish are equipped with amazing detection systems as sensitive as a modern attack submarine. One of these systems is chemical. As they swim through the water, their prey leave a faint telltale trace of chemicals behind them – proteins, faecal pellets, and so on. Many fish are sensitive to traces of chemicals, which they sense with olfactory cells in their nostrils, but the acuity of the hunting fish is truly astonishing. When sharks and rays were tested in a laboratory, tales of them being able to detect a faint drop of blood 0.4 km (0.25 miles) away proved to be less than adequate. Skates belonging to the family *Rajidae* could actually detect chemicals when there were just ten molecules of them in 1 litre (0.25 gallons) of water – the equivalent of finding a grain of sand in an Olympic swimming pool. Whenever a shark or ray picks up just the faintest whiff of prey on the current, it follows the current to home in on its target.

ELECTRIC SENSE

Sharks have electrical receptors, too, located in rows of little cells in their faces called the ampullae of Lorenzini after the Italian anatomist who first described them in 1678. Like human ears, these cells have minute hairs, but instead of reacting to sound waves, they react to tiny changes in electrical polarity – electrical changes triggered by the muscle movements of their prey. Great hammerhead sharks can detect stingrays dug into the seabed by

▽ *As they sift the sea for other fish, drift gill nets accidentally catch swordfish. Juveniles that cannot be legally caught are put back in the water, but their chances of survival are slim.*

sweeping their heads from side to side like metal detectors.

Even once located, it is far from easy to catch prey. There may be nowhere for prey to hide in the open ocean, but the same is true for the hunter. So the hunting fish need to be very, very fast swimmers. Billfish are indeed exceptionally fast. They are built for speed, with sleek, streamlined bodies and stiff fins that tuck into grooves on their bodies when cruising at speed for minimum drag, and only come out again when the fish are manoeuvring. Sailfish are perhaps the fastest fish in the world and among the fastest creatures on the planet, which is astonishing considering they achieve their speed through water. Sailfish have been recorded reaching speeds of up to 130 km/h (80 mph) in short bursts, which is faster than a cheetah.

IS IT FAIR GAME?

All these fish – swordfish, marlin, sailfish, and sharks – are magnificent hunters, the ocean's top predators. They are the jaguars and tigers of the deep, and it is no surprise that they, like their counterparts on land, are 'big game fish'. They are the target of recreational anglers who relish the challenge of landing such strong creatures. Sport fishing tournaments around the world see hundreds of these fish hooked as competitors vie for the biggest fish. But recently there have been increasing calls to ban such events.

The problem is that these great fish, once so abundant, are facing an astonishing decline in numbers. The tournaments themselves are not the major culprits but the threats to these fish are so immediate that actually hunting them for sport seems wasteful. The decline in numbers in the Atlantic has been little short of catastrophic. The problems with blue fin tuna are well publicized. Less well-known are the almost equally severe decimation of white marlin, down 96 percent from their levels in 1960; blue marlin, down 80 percent; swordfish, down 64 percent; and sailfish, down 54 percent.

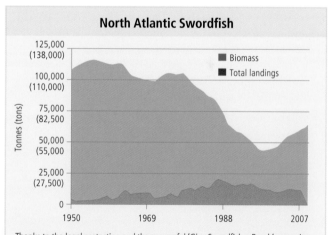

North Atlantic Swordfish

Tonnes (tons)

125,000 (138,000)
100,000 (110,000)
75,000 (82,500)
50,000 (55,000)
25,000 (27,500)
0

■ Biomass
■ Total landings

1950   1969   1988   2007

Thanks to the legal protection and the successful 'Give Swordfish a Break' campaign that saw the fish removed from many US restaurant menus, the biomass of the North Atlantic has now partially recovered.

Recent surveys suggest that the biomass of white marlins in the Atlantic is now barely 5 percent of what is needed to sustain a healthy stock.

THE END OF THE LINE

So what is behind this decimation? The answer is industrial fishing. Longline fishing in particular targets these fish in vast numbers – fishermen laying out heavy lines up to 40 km (25 miles) long to which hundreds or thousands of dropper lines are tied, each armed with a baited hook. Sometimes, longliners attach chemiluminescent plastic 'light sticks' to attract big fish in the dark sea. But it is not just the targeted fish that are victims. Both longlines and drift gill nets pick up huge numbers of juveniles that are too small to be legally sold. Nearly half of all the swordfish caught are juveniles. These young fish are thrown back in the water, but most are dead or will die soon after. The USA prohibits its commercial vessels from keeping Atlantic marlin and Atlantic sailfish of any size, but 30 percent of the white marlin and 25 percent of the blue marlin are already dead by the time they are brought on board.

Since a groundbreaking report by Ransom Myers and Boris Worm was published in 2003, showing that 90 percent of all the ocean's large fish have been lost in the last half century, the threats have been all too clear. But attempts to restrict catches or have the fish listed as endangered have been repeatedly caught up in the tangled nets of international negotiation. The International Commission for the Conservation of Atlantic Tunas (ICCAT) wants to collect data for five years before it will act, while sports fishermen have fought, successfully, against attempts in the USA to have the white marlin listed as endangered. Meanwhile, the ocean's biggest fish are going the same way as their hunting counterparts on land.

▽ *Sailfish are the fastest fish in the ocean, reaching speeds of 110 km/h (68 mph). Sporting fishermen prize them for their size and the tremendous fight that they put up when hooked. As yet, sailfish are still abundant in the oceans.*

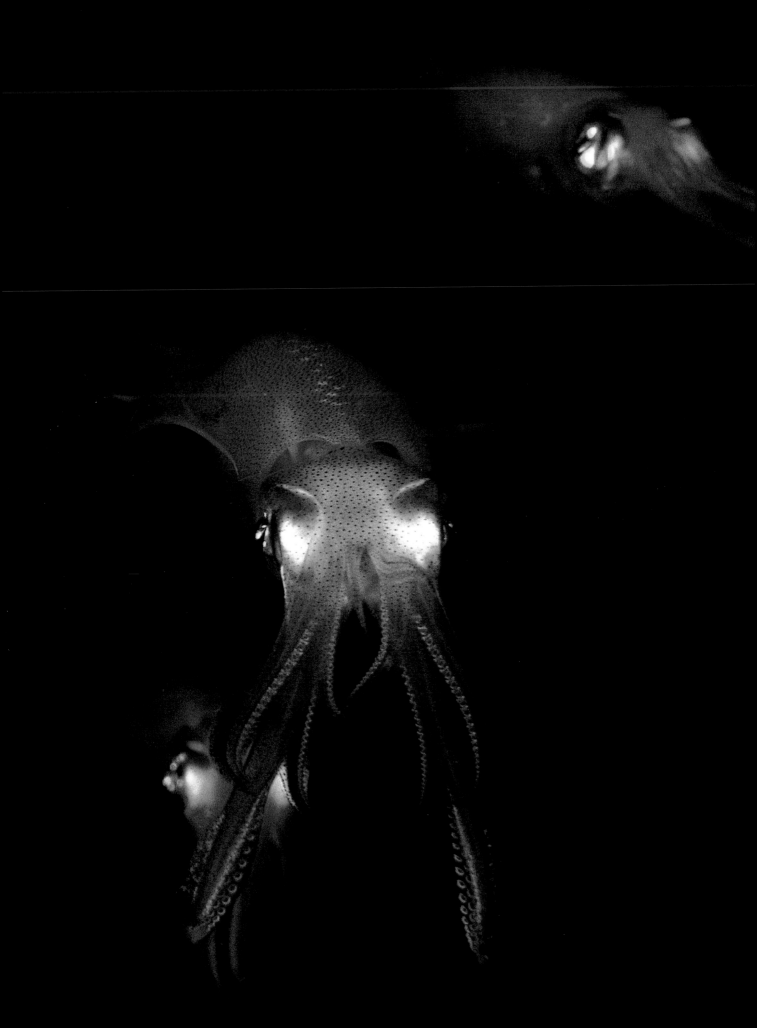

Ocean Life Zones
The Ocean Deeps

The deep ocean is the ocean below the photic zone, the top 150 m (490 ft) or so of the ocean where sunlight can penetrate. Below this is a gigantic dark realm, the biggest habitat for life on the Earth. It is not just that the deep ocean occupies a huge area of the planet's surface – more than two-thirds – it is the sheer volume of this deep water. In fact, the deep ocean provides 160 times more space for life than all the world's land surfaces put together.

It is often said that the ocean deeps are less known than the surface of Mars or the Moon, and this is partly true. Fewer explorers have made it down into the deepest parts of the ocean than have travelled into space, and marine biologists have studied barely 3 percent of the ocean floor, if that. Yet each year the deeps are giving up more and more of their secrets.

Not so long ago, marine biologists believed that this vast dark realm was almost devoid of life. Life here is certainly challenging. Down to about 1,000 m (3,280 ft), there is a faint glimmering of light, which is why it is called the twilight zone. But beyond that there is utter darkness. It is icy cold, too, all the way through. There is none of the variation in temperatures that is found on the surface; below 1,000 m (3,280 ft) it is between 4°C and –1°C (39°F and 30°F) everywhere. Most telling of all, though, the pressure at these depths is intense. Even 1,000 m (3,280 ft) down, the pressure is 100 times the pressure on the surface, at more than 254 kg per sq. cm (1,400 lb per sq. in). In the deepest trenches, 10,000 m (32,800 ft) down, the pressure is a crushing 1,000 times that on the surface at more than 1 tonne per sq.cm (6 tons per sq.in). Yet, although life is not as abundant as near the surface, recent discoveries have revealed that life in the deeps is more rich and varied than ever imagined – and often very weird indeed.

◁ *Like many creatures of the ocean deeps, the bigfin squid glows in the darkness, with its own natural light known as bioluminescence. This may act as a light to hunt other species, or as a decoy to distract predators, or as a communication with other squid.*

DEEP LIFE

DURING DAYLIGHT HOURS, A VERY FAINT GLIMMER of light can penetrate down as far as 1,000 m (3,280 ft) below the surface – the twilight zone. But beyond about 150 m (490 ft) down, the light is faint, and the water so gloomy that there is not enough light for phytoplankton to photosynthesize, but for a few small and unusual red algae. Many creatures descend to the safe cloak of this twilight zone during the day and commute daily to the surface layers to feed in the hours before dawn (see page 128), but there are many creatures, too, that live down here permanently. These creatures of the twilight zone are engaged in a constant game of hide and seek. Without plants to feed on, it is an entirely carnivorous world, and predators and prey face a continual struggle in the gloom to see and avoid being seen.

BUG EYES

Good vision is essential for hunters in the twilight zone, and many creatures that live here have large eyes. The fish *Winteria* has such enormous protruding, cartoonlike eyes that it looks like a bug-eyed bush baby. The eyes are tilted upwards, and help the winteria see the faint silhouettes of their prey against the lighter water above. The *Winteria*'s eyes are not eyeballs like fish elsewhere (and indeed other vertebrate animals) but are tube shaped. Many fish in the twilight zone seem to have these tubular eyes, such as all the barreleye fish (of which the *Winteria* is one), that have eyes that stick up from their heads like binoculars, and tubular eyes seem especially good for capturing what little light there is in the gloom.

It used to be thought that the barreleye's tubular eyes could only look up and gave only a 'tunnel vision' of whatever was above its head, but it was discovered recently that the eyes can rotate within a transparent shield covering the fish's head. This shield may protect the fish's eyes as it ducks in among the stinging tentacles of jellyfish such as siphonophores to stalk prey.

Jellies, including comb jellies (ctenophores), jellyfish, and siphonophores, are abundant in the twilight zone and are both important predators and prey. Jellies avoid being seen in the gloom by being virtually transparent. Their shapeless, jelly outline makes them even harder to spot. Transparency is a technique used by the vast majority of creatures in the twilight zone, and the zone seems like a realm of floating glass animals. The amphipod *Cystisoma* looks like a giant glass shrimp, while *Phronima* looks like a miniature perspex model of the creature from the movie *Alien*. Other creatures are silvery to match the twilight. Still others, such as hatchetfish, are simply very thin so that their silhouette is hard to see end on.

LIGHT SHOWS

But the business of staying hidden in the twilight zone is clearly more complex than simply being invisible. The vast majority of animals in the twilight have their own personal light shows, known as bioluminescence. Some make their light with special enzymes called luciferins in cells called photophores; others

◁ *When the Pacific blackdragon opens its mouth, it reveals a set of long, dagger-sharp teeth. Drooping from its lower jaw is a barbel tipped with a glowing lure that the fish sways to entice prey. Its body is also lined with luminescent cells that confuse other fish in the dark.*

control the oxygen supply to glowing bacteria that live on them.

Bioluminescence seems to work in several ways. It may act as camouflage, breaking up a creature's outline. Some species, for instance, have photophores on their undersides, perhaps so that their silhouette then disappears against the dim light from above. With some crustaceans and jellyfish, photophores may be like a burglar alarm, suddenly flashing on when danger approaches – either illuminating predators and making them visible to other predators, or simply confusing them with flashing lights. Some predators may use them like searchlights to seek out prey, while others, such as viperfish, use them as lures to lead their prey into their gaping mouths. Siphonophores such as *Erenna* use just a few gently glowing lights to lure small fish into their tentacles. Bioluminescence may also be a form of communication, a come-and-see me lure for potential mates.

BIG MOUTHS

Food is so scarce in the twilight zone that for those that do not make the daily commute to the surface it is not worth the energy spend of hunting far afield. These twilight-dwelling fish generally have rather weak muscles and lead a rather idle existence, simply waiting for food to pass by. But to make the most of infrequent opportunities, they have larger mouths and large stomachs so they can quickly swallow anything that comes their way – even if it is bigger than them. Once prey are unfortunate enough to end up in one of these twilight zone monster mouths, they cannot be allowed to escape. So most of the twilight zone predators have extraordinarily long fangs, not for chewing but for shutting tight like a gintrap. That is why so many fish here, such as the aptly named fangtooth or ogrefish, have gigantic fearsome-looking heads and mouths, and small weak tails.

◁　*The alien-like* Phronima *creates its own spaceship of the deep from the body of a salp. After catching the salp, it eats away the inside of the creature, makes an entrance, and crawls inside. Then it glides through the deep in its ship, waiting to emerge and pounce on unsuspecting prey.*

DEAD ZONES

ELOW 1,000 M (3,280 FT) OR SO IN THE OCEAN, there is utter darkness, and it is aptly called the dark zone. It is perpetually cold – not more than 1 or 2°C (34 or 36°F) – and the pressure is immense. It is the least known and least explored part of the ocean, and only in recent years have a few research trips ventured deep enough to learn about life here. What they have found is truly fascinating.

MONSTERS OF THE DARK

Despite the challenging conditions in the dark zone, scientists are finding that a much wider range of creatures live here than they ever imagined. Although surface creatures would find conditions such as the pressure fatal, the creatures that live here are adapted to the challenges – and this is what makes studying them especially hard. Animals that live here, for instance, are built to cope with pressure that is 100 or even 1,000 times what it is at the surface. But though they can survive in the deeps of the ocean, most of these deep-sea animals die instantly if they are brought up for study.

Many creatures that live in the depths have truly monstrous appearances and have acquired suitable names, such as sea devil, devil fish, and dragonfish, although most are actually tiny. They have some of the adaptations of animals that live in the twilight zone, but taken to extremes. If the fish that live in the twilight zone have big mouths, then those that live in the dark zone have mouths that are truly gigantic. The extraordinary gulper eel is pretty much all mouth, and has a jaw that is so loosely hinged it can gape much, much wider than its head. And its stomach is so elastic that it can swallow prey many times its normal size.

ANGLERS AND DRAGONS

The predators in the dark zone have bioluminescent lures that are even more impressive than those in the twilight zone. The best known examples are the aptly named anglerfish that 'fish'

for food using a glowing lure on the top of a 'pole' sticking out of their heads. The anglerfish dangle this lure in front of their gaping, fanged mouths – softly flashing it to draw curious victims in, then suddenly dart forward to snap them up. Some anglerfish have lures on very long 'rods', while *Thaumatichthys* has a lure right inside its big mouth. *Thaumatichthys* got its name, 'wonderfish' in Greek, because Danish oceanographer Anton Bruun (1901–1961) rightly described it as 'altogether one of the oddest creatures in the teeming variety of the fish world.'

But if the lures of the anglerfish are impressive, they are nothing in comparison to those of some dragonfish. The armoured heads of dragonfish are truly fearsome, having a mouthful of knife-sharp fangs. But the barbeled dragonfish has another weapon – barbels that hang beneath its jaws with a lure on the end. The barbels vary enormously, but one 15-cm (6-in) long dragonfish has a 2-m (6.5-ft) long barbel. That means that it can sweep a large frontal area in its hunt for prey, though no one knows exactly how it uses its lure.

The Deepest Fish

In his book *Seven Miles Down*, Swiss oceanographer Jacques Piccard described his historic trip with Don Walsh in the bathyscaphe *Trieste* in 1960. They travelled to the bottom of the Mariana Trench, the deepest place in the oceans, 10,910 m (35,794 ft) down. Piccard wrote that, just before touching the bottom, he spotted a type of flatfish that must be the deepest living fish ever seen, but his sighting could not be verified. So the official record for the deepest fish is held by *Abyssobrotula galatheae*, which was dredged from the bottom of the Puerto Rico Trench at a depth of more than 8,370 m (27,460 ft) in 1970. However, it was dead by the time it reached the surface. The deepest fish ever confirmed alive was the weird, pale pink *Pseudoliparis amblystomopsis* filmed in 2008 by Oceanlab's HADEEP project 7,700 m (25,262 ft) down in the Japan Trench, in the Pacific.

▽ *The viperfish's fangs are so long that they will not fit inside its mouth and curve back towards its eyes. It uses the fangs to impale its prey like a harpoon, and its top vertebra acts like a shock absorber to cushion the impact.*

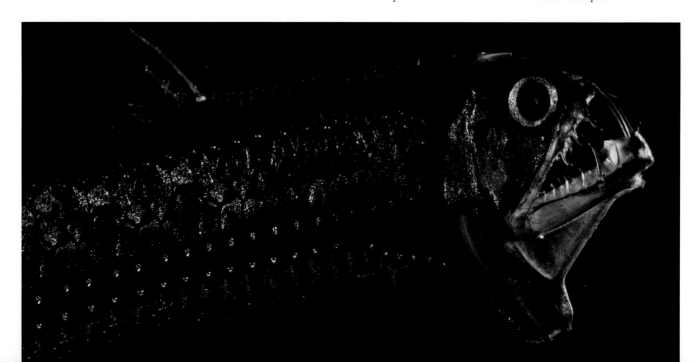

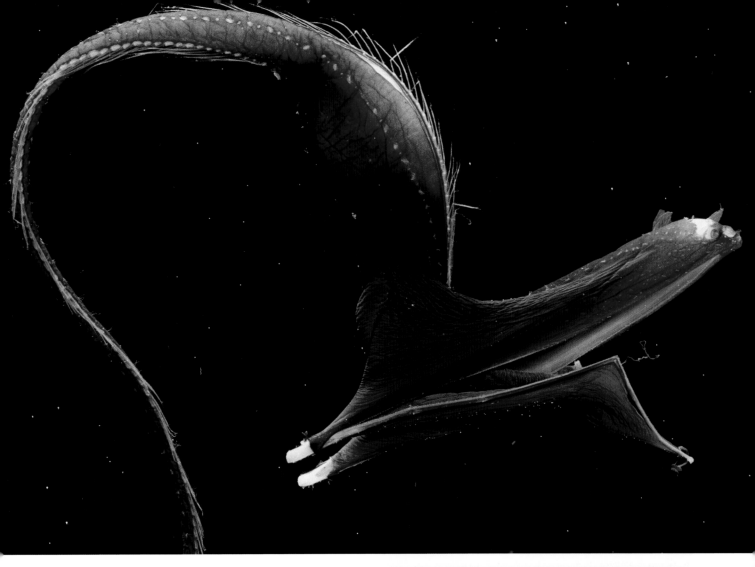

△ *The extraordinary big-mouth gulper eel doesn't swim much, but then it does not need to. With a mouth this big, it just glides slowly along and opens its gigantic jaws to swallow prey that is even larger than itself.*

THE DARK SIDE

Although some of the features of animals in the dark zone are those of the twilight zone writ large, dark zone animals have their own unique features, too. With not even the faint glimmer of the twilight zone down in the utter darkness, there is no point in the transparency or silvery colours that twilight zone animals use to vanish into the twilight. Down in the blackness of the dark zone, the animals are simply black – or dark red, which in the darkness may as well be black.

The utter darkness also means that there is no need for the large, light-sensitive eyes of animals in the twilight zone. No amount of light sensitivity will make things visible, so animals here have small eyes and rely on other senses to find things in the dark. Many, for instance, have incredibly sensitive receptors that can pick up even the faintest trace of movement. Hairy anglerfish are absolutely bristling with antennae-like hairs that can detect the tiniest of movements in the dark. Like many deep-sea fish, the hairy angler has a giant expandable stomach for making the most of passing prey.

▷ *This anglerfish, photographed 660 m (2,000 ft) down off the coast of Australia, can lure the prey it wants with the glowing light on top of its head.*

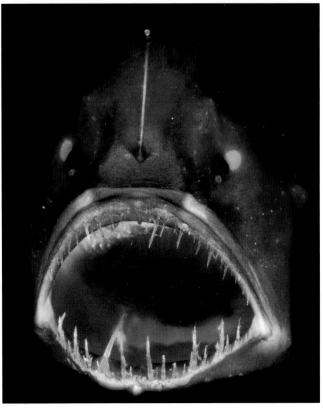

THE WORLD'S OCEANS AND SEAS
THE ATLANTIC

The Atlantic Ocean, which gets its name ultimately from the ancient Greek Titan Atlas, is the world's second largest ocean, covering almost a quarter of the planet to an average depth of just under 4,000 m (13,000 ft).

The Atlantic winds in a giant S shape between the Americas and Europe and Africa and varies between 3,000 and 5,000 km (1,900 and 3,000 miles) across. On either side, the continents slope slightly towards it and as a result, more fresh water drains into it than any other ocean, as great rivers such as the Amazon and Mississippi, the Rhine, the Congo, and the Niger, deliver their vast loads.

Of all the oceans it is the most intensively studied. The real mapping of the ocean floor began in the Atlantic in the 1950s, and it was here that the configuration of the ocean floor with its extraordinary submarine mountain range revealed the reality of ocean spreading (see page 30). Climatologists revealed the power of water movements in the Atlantic that drive weather all around the world. Today, expedition after expedition is beginning to yield some of its secrets, from the special nature of life on seamounts, such as the Bear, to previously unknown species on the abyssal plain.

The Atlantic is also the most intensively used ocean. Millions of people live close to its shores in vast cities such as New York, São Paulo, and Buenos Aires. A vast quantity of shipping plies across the ocean or drives through its continental shallows. The fishing industry fishes it with such intensity that some areas are now bereft of fish entirely. And huge amounts of effluent from industry and farms are emptied daily into Atlantic waters, which are now proving that they are not so vast that they cannot be badly damaged by human activity.

◁ *The waters of the Atlantic Ocean meet the land along more than 111,000 m (365,000 ft) of coast, and this vast coastline provides a rich habitat for myriad creatures. Yet, though there is plenty of sand here in northwestern Africa, more than two-thirds of the Atlantic's beaches are being worn away by slowly rising seas.*

THE ATLANTIC BASIN

Despite its vast size, the Atlantic Ocean is the second youngest, if not the youngest, ocean on the Earth – only the Antarctic Ocean may have formed more recently.

It was only about 170 million years ago in the Jurassic – the first age of the dinosaurs – that a line of volcanoes began to burst apart the supercontinent of Pangaea to start opening the North Atlantic, with the continents of Laurasia (North America and Eurasia) on one side and Gondwanaland (Africa and South America) on the other. It was not until the Cretaceous period (140–65 million years ago) that South America and Africa began to unzip and open up the South Atlantic. And it was barely 55 million years ago that Laurensia finally broke free from Eurasia to form North America and open up the northern end of the North Atlantic. This means that North America and Eurasia were joined together throughout the age of the dinosaurs.

THE MID-ATLANTIC RIDGE

Even today, the Atlantic is getting steadily wider, at anything up to 10 cm (4 in) a year, and New York is getting measurably farther away from London. It is all happening along the most remarkable feature of the Atlantic seafloor, the Mid-Atlantic Ridge. This great mountain range winds for 20,000 km (12,400 miles) all the way down through the Atlantic in a giant S from Iceland into the Southern Ocean. There are sharp canyons and jagged crests all the way down this range, but its most marked feature is a deep cleft or rift valley right down the centre. This is where hot lava wells up from the Earth's mantle and cools quickly in the chill water to solidify into new seafloor. This in turn slowly pushes two halves of the Atlantic seafloor apart and makes the Atlantic ever wider. Here and there, volcanoes along the Ridge have been tall enough to project above the surface and create islands such as the Azores and Tristan da Cunha. The Ridge itself appears above the surface in Iceland, which sits astride the rift. This is why Iceland is one of the world's most volcanically active places.

Most of the Atlantic's other islands are higher features of the continental shallows, such as the British Isles and Newfoundland. Some of the volcanoes that once erupted along the Ridge have long since gone quiet to form undersea mountains, scattered across the seafloor as the seafloor spreads, such as the Great Meteor Tablemount and New England Seamounts, which stretch in a line 1,500 km (932 miles) east from New England. Each seamount is a focus for undersea life (see page 30).

ABYSSAL PLAINS AND VENTS

As the ocean floor spreads, the ridges and crests that are carried apart create valuable variations on the abyssal seafloor before they are, eventually, buried by sediment. These variations create important niches on the otherwise featureless abyssal plains for

▽ *Despite the battering by storm waves, the rocky shores of the Atlantic are swathed in marine life. Here, red algae turns the wave-splashed rocks rich brown along the tide mark and while another algae turns them yellow higher up.*

▷ *The Mid-Atlantic Ridge is clearly visible on this image of the world's ocean floors, snaking down the middle of the Atlantic from Iceland in the north right around through the Southern Ocean to the south of Africa. The large patches of dark blue either side are the abyssal plains.*

wildlife, from sea cucumbers to necrophage fish, such as grenadier fish, cusk-eels, and synaphobranchoid eels, that feed on the carcasses of dead animals that drift down to the seabed. There are a dozen or so of these plains on the seafloor, including the Porcupine Abyssal Plain (PAP) southwest of Ireland, and the biggest Atlantic plain, the North American Basin, which stretches from the Grand Banks of Newfoundland to Puerto Rico.

There are hydrothermal vents in the Mid-Atlantic Ridge, too. Vents were once thought to occur only in the Pacific, but in 1985 one was found on the seabed far east of Miami, and in the 1990s, US oceanographer Peter Rona observed creatures such as shrimplike *Rimicaris exoculata* (the 'eyeless rift dweller') living right next to the vents' superheated jets. Then in 2000, scientists discovered a spectacular vent field on an undersea mountain that they dubbed the Lost City because its tall pillars and spires looked like a gothic cathedral. Here, dense mats of microbes live under mineral disks in water as hot as 160°C (320°F). In 2008, scientists discovered vents at the southern end of the Ridge that were heating water to a 'supercritical' temperature of 464°C (867°F), hotter than water anywhere else on Earth.

ATLANTIC HOT SPOTS

Here and there in the Atlantic, there are regions that are especially abundant in sea life. Off southern Africa, for instance, the cold Benguela Current flowing north along the west coast creates nutrient hot spots where it mingles with two warm currents – the south-flowing Angola Current and the Agulhas Current from the Indian Ocean. Here, species such as jackass penguins, pilchards, Cape horse mackerels, Cape fur seals, southern right whales, and the rare Heaviside's dolphin can be seen making the most of the blooming plankton, or the organisms that feed on it.

Similarly, where the cool Canary Current flows southwest along the northwestern coast of Africa, upwelling creates a nutrient-rich environment in which deep-sea fish and lobsters flourish far out and humpback whales breed. In Chesapeake and Delaware Bays, it is the great rivers – the Susquehanna, James, Potomac, Patuxent, and Chester – that bring the nutrients that make the bay so rich in wildlife, especially shellfish, such as American oysters, soft-shelled clams, hard clams, and marsh periwinkles, and a host of birds from the clapper rail and the Atlantic brant to the oldsquaw and the bufflehead. But this region has suffered, like so many, from urban development and pollution from agriculture, and this has caused algal blooms and encouraged invasive species, such as the rapa whelk.

▽ *The tarpon is one of the Atlantic's great hunting fish, growing to over 2 m in length, and with the strength and spirit that makes it a real challenge for gamefishers. Game fishermen must usually throw back any tarpon they catch, however.*

THE GULF AND THE CARIBBEAN

IN THE LARGE GULF BETWEEN NORTH, Central, and South America lie the warmest tropical offshoots of the Atlantic Ocean – the Gulf of Mexico and the Caribbean Sea.

The Gulf of Mexico is almost entirely enclosed by the southern USA, Mexico, and Cuba. The seabed is an ancient sunken ocean plate, that dates back 300 million years. Just over 40 percent is taken up by continental shallows – and in places off Mexico's Yucátan Peninsula the water is so shallow you can walk many kilometres out to sea. But beyond that it plunges to an abyssal plain, the Sigsbee Deep, up to 4,000 m (13,000 ft) down. It is in the Gulf that one of the world's key currents, the Gulf Stream, originates as the Loop Current and runs clockwise around the Gulf to exit between Florida and Cuba before beginning its long journey northwest to Europe.

The northern margin of the Gulf of Mexico has a warm temperate climate and the coast is fringed with oyster reefs and saltmarshes, while out beyond the estuaries, seagrass meadows grow. The southern edge is more tropical, and mangrove swamps and lagoons line the coast. To the west, the coast is lined by Texas' uniquely salty Laguna Madre lagoon, while to the east are the Florida Keys, a remarkable cluster of about 1,700 islands built from ancient coral. It is one of the most biologically diverse regions for marine life with more than 15,000 species, including Kemp's Ridley sea turtles, manatees, and whale sharks.

▽ *The Florida Everglades are one of the last refuges of the once widespread manatee or sea cow, but even there where they are protected, they are frequently injured or even killed by speeding boats, and conservationists worry if their numbers will ever recover.*

THE DEAD GULF

The Mississippi River system collects water from a huge proportion of North America and delivers it to the Gulf. Fresh water, sediment, and nutrients washed down by the river have contributed to the Gulf's unique richness of marine life as well as remarkable coastal wetlands along the Gulf's northern coast. But the river also drains the farms of the USA's heartlands – over half of all the USA's farms – and carries down with it a huge quantity of fertilizer that seeps through the soil and into the rivers.

As this superabundance of nutrients hits the Gulf, it stimulates a massive 'algal bloom' every spring – an explosive growth of phytoplankton that spreads far around the mouth of the Mississippi. Zooplankton eat the algae, excreting pellets that sink to the bottom like tiny stones. Seafloor bacteria multiply to feed on all this faecal matter and consume from the water much of the oxygen in the water on which countless sea creatures rely. As creatures die and the bacteria release sulphur, the seabed turns black, and the water begins to stink like rotten eggs.

The result is a Dead Zone in which there is very little marine life. The Dead Zone tends to recover in October when cooler weather slows the algal growth and storms mix up the water, but the Gulf's Dead Zone has been growing bigger each year since it was first noticed in the 1970s. It now covers about 20,700 sq. km (8,000 sq. miles). In recent years, some people have grabbed nets and poles to catch the fish and shrimp that seem to gather on the Gulf shore in the spring, but this is not a sign of nature's bounty – just the desperation of creatures that are trying to escape the suffocating sea.

Urchin Loss

In 1983, Caribbean reefs were devastated by a sudden calamitous loss of 97 percent of the population of the lime urchin, *Diadema antillarum*, to disease. Along with parrotfish, this grazing urchin kept algae levels down and prevented them from smothering the coral. Without the urchins, parrotfish are now the only grazers of seaweed on many Caribbean reefs, but parrotfish have been heavily fished. With too few parrotfish grazing, corals cannot recover after major disturbances such as hurricanes and become much less healthy as a result. This is why some conservationists argue that parrotfish should be taken off the dinner table menu.

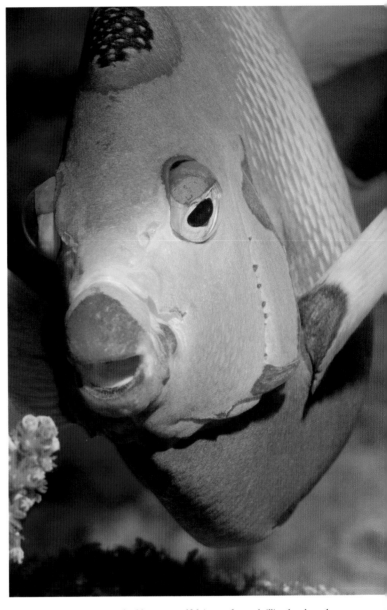

△ *The stunning turquoise and gold queen angelfish is one of many brilliantly coloured fish that grace the coral reefs of the Gulf of Mexico and Florida's Atlantic coast. It feeds mainly on sponges, but may also eat sea squirts and graze on algae.*

THE CARIBBEAN

Underlying the Caribbean is an entirely separate tectonic plate. Geologists disagree about the plate's origins, but it is only a few tens of millions of years old at most. Along its northern edge it meets the North American plate along the Puerto Rico Trench, the deepest part of the Atlantic, and plunges to a depth of 8,400 m (27,560 ft). The Caribbean plate is moving westward, like the North American plate, but much slower, and it is the friction between them that makes the region so prone to earthquakes such as the terrible one that hit Haiti in January 2010.

The Caribbean is a rich marine habitat, home to a huge range of species including countless fish, various sea turtles, and the humpback whale. But the sea's jewels are its coral reefs. Nine percent of the world's tropical reefs are in this small sea. The most spectacular of all is the Mesoamerican Reef that stretches 720 km (447 miles) from the tip of the Yucatán to Honduras, and is the second largest reef in the world after the Great Barrier Reef off the coast of Australia. But it is not only its size that is special but its diversity. The Mesoamerican Reef is home to 65 species of stony coral alone, as well as more than 500 species of fish, 350 kinds of molluscs, and various sea turtles.

In recent years, though, the alarm has been sounded for the Caribbean's beautiful reefs. Some experts believe that almost two-thirds of the reefs are facing a serious threat from ongoing human activities. It has become clear that the reefs are struggling to cope with overfishing and pollution, including the sugars in untreated sewage and farming runoff. Bleaching caused by warming waters, disease from new pathogens, and hurricane damage also cause their own problems. A recent survey showed that 75 percent of the Caribbean's reefs have lost their structure and become flat compared to 20 percent in the 1970s. This loss of reef architecture poses a major problem for many animals that rely on it for hiding from predators. Scientists now believe that fish numbers have declined dramatically in the last 15 years in the Caribbean reefs because of this loss of coral structure as well as overfishing.

SPILLED OIL

IN 2010, THE USA SUFFERED ITS WORST MARINE OIL DISASTER AS MILLIONS OF BARRELS OF OIL POURED INTO THE GULF OF MEXICO AFTER THE *DEEPWATER HORIZON* ACCIDENT. BUT AS THE DEMAND FOR CHEAP OIL CONTINUES, MORE SPILLS ARE LIKELY.

On 16 April, 2010, a BP manager emailed, 'Who cares, it's done, end of story, will probably be fine.' He was talking about the decision to cut corners when cementing shut the newly drilled pipe into a deep undersea oil reserve beneath the Gulf of Mexico, ready for later opening. He was utterly wrong. It was the start of the story, it was not fine, and a lot of people care very much.

The huge pressures in the oil reserve proved too much for the skimped back-up systems. On 20 April, methane gas powered its way up the pipe to BP's *Deepwater Horizon* drilling rig and exploded catastrophically, killing 11 people.

Soon oil was pouring out from the seabed. First estimates suggested that it was 1,000–5,000 barrels a day. But as attempt after attempt to cap the gush failed, and other experts chipped in with advice, BP were forced to revise the figure upwards dramatically. By mid-September, when the crisis was finally ended with the drilling of a relief well to take the pressure off an emergency cap dropped into place in June, over 4 million barrels may have gushed out – 13 times as much as the 1989 Exxon Valdez disaster in Alaska. Although the surface oil quickly dispersed, it had already had a devastating effect on Louisiana coastal communities and marine life.

OIL AT SEA

The irony was that, a few weeks previously, US president Barack Obama, bowing under pressure to satisfy America's voracious need for cheap oil, had given the go-ahead for further drilling in the Gulf, saying, 'oil rigs today generally don't cause spills.'

When his words came back to haunt him, it is no wonder he was enraged. Yet he was partly right; until recently, oil rigs were involved in only a few spills. Most major spills are from oil tanker groundings or broken pipelines – although even these account for only a tiny portion of oil leaking into the ocean (see page 90). Tighter regulations and the wider use of double hulls to prevent breaching in case of accidents have actually been bringing down the number of bad spills dramatically. In the 1970s, there were more than 25 major spills a year, but in the last decade there were barely three. In 2008 there was just one, and in 2009 there were none at all.

Yet, just as tanker spills are declining, so the unstoppable demand for oil pushes companies to drill offshore in evermore extreme conditions. The risk of blowouts like the *Deepwater Horizon* may be increasing. In 2009, Australia suffered one of its worst oil disasters at the Montara rig in the East Timor Sea. There is also a concern that if, in the aftermath of *Deepwater Horizon*, drilling in the Gulf is restricted, oil companies will satisfy demand for oil by drilling out of sight of the media in places such as Nigeria, where lack of regulation mean the oil industry has already brought human and ecological tragedy.

AFTER THE SPILL

When oil is spilled from tankers at sea, most floats out in a slick that thins to a rainbow-coloured sheen as it spreads. Creatures that touch the surface – birds and mammals – are the most obvious victims. The oil gets in birds' feathers, for

▽ *After the explosion on the* Deepwater Horizon *rig on the 20th April 2010 which claimed the lives of 11 men, firefighters battled to put out the fire for more than a day before the rig finally sank.*

△ *This brown pelican was just one of the many bird victims of the Gulf oil spill along the Louisiana coast. Even if the bird was cleaned by rescue workers, it would soon have died from ingesting the toxic oil.*

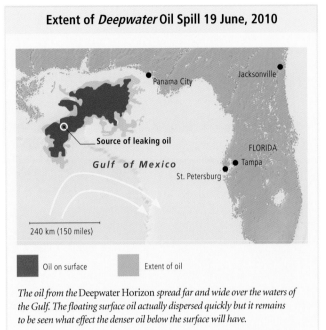

Extent of *Deepwater* Oil Spill 19 June, 2010

Panama City
Jacksonville

Source of leaking oil

FLORIDA

Gulf of Mexico

Tampa

St. Petersburg

240 km (150 miles)

Oil on surface   Extent of oil

The oil from the Deepwater Horizon spread far and wide over the waters of the Gulf. The floating surface oil actually dispersed quickly but it remains to be seen what effect the denser oil below the surface will have.

instance, making it impossible for them to fly. Worse still, as they try to get clean, they ingest the oil and toxic substances and this causes fatal liver failure. After an oil spill, desperate attempts are made to clean oiled birds, but most cleaned birds die from the toxins within a few days of being released.

The clean-up process may be more damaging than the oil itself. After the *Exxon Valdez* disaster, the worst damage to shore life was caused by steamcleaning the shore, effectively rendering it sterile. Similarly, chemical dispersants may appear to clean the sea by breaking the slick into globules that sink out of sight, but they add toxic chemicals to the water, which can do more harm than the oil. With the Gulf spill, 3 million litres (800,000 gallons) of dispersant were poured on and into the sea in an attempt to stop oil reaching the surface and the shore. Dispersants have never been used in this volume before, and they include Corexit 9527, which is toxic to marine life.

The combination of coagulated oil globules from dispersed oil and gushing oil held underwater by deep-water pressures is thought to have created underwater plumes and clouds. These may be devastating for huge numbers of marine creatures that swim into them, or seabed life as they settle in the water. Also, plankton and shrimp coated in oil and the toxic chemicals will be eaten by fish, thereby passing the effect up the food chain. Worryingly, these plumes fell on fish spawning grounds at a crucial time, and might be the death knell for the endangered Atlantic bluefin tuna, which spawns exclusively in the Gulf.

There is a temptation to blame corporate greed and carelessness for oil spills, and it is true that the treatment of the environment by the big oil companies around the world has often been shockingly cavalier – especially out of sight of the world's scrutiny in the world's poorer countries. But maybe ultimately the problem lies just as much with our unquenchable thirst for cheap oil.

Ten Worst Oil Spills At Sea

Disaster	Location	Date	Volume in barrels
Gulf War oil spill	Persian Gulf	19–28 January, 1991	6,000,000–8,000,000
Deepwater Horizon	Gulf of Mexico, USA	20 April, 2010– 15 July, 2010	4,100,000–4,300,000
Ixtoc I	Gulf of Mexico, USA	6 June, 1979– 23, March 1980	3,329,000–3,520,000
Atlantic Empress	Trinidad and Tobago	19 July, 1979	2,105,000
Nowruz Field Platform	Persian Gulf, Iran	4 February, 1983	1,907,000
ABT Summer	Angola, offshore	28 May, 1991	1,907,000
Castillo de Bellver	South Africa, Saldanha Bay	6 August, 1983	1,848,000
Amoco Cadiz	France	16 March, 1978	1,635,000
Haven	Italy	11 April, 1991	1,056,000
Odyssey	Canada, off Nova Scotia	10 November, 1988	968,000

THE SARGASSO SEA

RIGHT OUT IN THE OPEN ATLANTIC TO THE SOUTHEAST OF BERMUDA IS A PATCH
OF OCEAN THAT IS SO EXTRAORDINARY THAT IT HAS ITS OWN NAME, THE SARGASSO
SEA, SOMETIMES SAID TO BE THE ONLY SEA WITHOUT A COAST.

The Sargasso Sea was given its name by the sailors on the famous voyage of discovery by Christopher Columbus in 1492. On their return across the Atlantic, they were becalmed there for days, and were amazed to see a mass of floating vegetation that looked like a carpet of tiny yellow grapes, which is why they called it *sargaço* after the Spanish word for grapes. Columbus rather liked the area. 'The weather is like April in Andalusia,' he wrote. 'The air is soft as April in Seville, and it is a pleasure to be in it, so fragrant it is.'

FLOATING GARDENS

The fragrant smell must have been the aroma of two species of brown seaweed, *Sargassum natans* and *Sargassum fluitans*, and the 'grapes' were the tiny bladders that keep these weeds afloat. Seaweeds normally grow close to the shore where they can attach themselves to the seabed, but in the Sargasso, they float free, supported by the bladders, in a great tangled mass out in the open ocean. The reason they can do this is that the Sargasso, despite being in the middle of the ocean, is as calm as a millpond. It is at the still centre of a vast eddy or 'gyre' in the Atlantic circulation, bypassed by the Gulf Stream and North Atlantic Current to the west and north, and the Canary and North Equatorial Currents to the east and south. It rotates slowly clockwise but the movement is barely detectable. Winds are light, too, and in earlier centuries sailing ships entering it were often becalmed, earning it the reputation of being a Bermuda Triangle.

The light winds, mild weather, and still water, however, allow a remarkable community of little animals to flourish – animals that are normally associated with coasts, but survive here clinging to the thick mat of weed that floats undisturbed by violent water movement. Millions of tiny plants, fish, crabs,

sea slugs, barnacles, hydroids, and other little creatures find a home on the weed, clambering about within the fronds. Some are unique to the Sargasso, such as the Sargassum pipefish, which is coloured yellowish brown like the weed, and is such a peculiar knobbly shape that it almost looks like weed as it clambers rather than swims about, using its fins to grip. Other unique species include the Sargassum snail, the Sargassum anglerfish, and the Sargassum crab, all of which are adapted to blend in with the weed.

ATLANTIC SERVICE STATION

The fishing industry was apt to regard the Sargasso as something of a desert because it seemed to lack the nutrients to support the plankton on which large, commercially important fish depend – hence the Sargasso's vivid, clear blue waters. But, in fact, a great deal of plankton is produced here, and its calm waters and many hiding places mean that it acts as a mid-Atlantic service station for many species such as tuna, dolphin, wahoo, and billfish. Seabirds such as shearwaters, boobies, and tropicbirds rest here and forage. And young sea turtles struggle out here from the shores of North America, and nestle among the seaweed fronds while they gain

enough strength and size to brave the open Atlantic Ocean.

Most famously, the Sargasso is the spawning ground of European and North American eels. Between the ages of 4 and 18 years old, European eels live far from the sea in freshwater lakes and rivers inland in Europe. When they reach maturity, they head off downriver to the ocean, where they quickly adapt to life in salt water and head south, first following a roundabout route via the Azores, before swimming out westward across the Atlantic, using the flow of the Equatorial Current to help them on their way. Eventually, they reach the calm of the Sargasso, where they meet millions of other eels and spawn in the cool water deep down. The adults die, but the young, transparent, leaflike 'leptocephali' tarry in the Sargasso for a few years before launching themselves back into the Gulf Stream to the north of the Sargasso and snaking their way gradually back across the Atlantic. As they reach the estuaries of their European homes, they transform into elvers and transparent 'glass eels' to wriggle up the rivers where they become adults.

FINDING GENES IN THE OCEAN

Recently, the geneticist Craig Venter, famous for his work on the human genome project, which mapped all the genes in human DNA, revealed another aspect of the Sargasso to the world. It was in the Sargasso in 2004 that Venter and his crew, aboard the *Weatherbird*, did the pilot study for an ongoing global voyage to discover the full range of microbial life and genes in the oceans, which he believes is much, much more abundant and diverse than anyone has suspected. In the Sargasso study, Venter astonished the scientific world by discovering 1,800 species of microbes, including 150 new species of bacteria, as well as more than 1.2 million previously unknown genes.

The North Atlantic Garbage Patch

Scientists have long been aware of the vast floating mass of discarded plastic in the Pacific known as the Great Pacific Garbage Patch (see page 169). In March 2010, a similar patch was reported in the North Atlantic, right in the Sargasso Sea. Although its true extent is not yet known, the North Atlantic Garbage Patch has, in places, plastic concentrations as high as the Pacific patch, with more than 200,000 bits of rubbish per 1 sq. km (0.4 sq. miles) – the trash includes fragments of consumer products from landfill sites and careless discards. The full impact on the natural environment of all this floating plastic is uncertain, but scientists already know that the plastic is mistakenly eaten by countless marine organisms and seabirds as it mingles with the Sargassum weed.

▷ *Like many Sargasso species, the Sargassum sea slug,* Scyllaea pelagica, *is camouflaged so well that it is often impossible to spot among the weeds. It spends all its life attached to the floating weed.*

◁ *The floating seaweed of the Sargasso has its own species of crab, the Sargassum crab,* Portunus sayi, *which has been forced to learn to swim. Its mottled carapace blends so perfectly with the weed it is hard to see unless it moves.*

THE GULF STREAM

WITHOUT THE GULF STREAM, living on the East Coast of the USA and in northwest Europe would be very different. This ocean current carries warm water from the tropics up past Florida and Carolina on and out east over the Atlantic to wash the British Isles in a warm bath, giving them one of the most comfortable climates in the world. Without the Gulf Stream, Florida, which basks in almost tropical warmth, would be quite cool, and Britain would have a climate as chilly as Alaska, which is on the same latitude. And the Gulf Stream is even more important for marine life in the North Atlantic.

△ *In January, surface temperatures (orange) reach 30°C (86°F) in the Caribbean. The Gulf Stream still takes the chill off the sea as it flows on past Cape Hatteras.*

△ *By June, warm seas have spread into the Gulf, and the Gulf Stream brings temperatures (dark blue) up to 10°C (50°F) in the farthest north of the Atlantic.*

△ *These images, created using microwave data from NASA's Aqua satellite in 2007, show clearly the Gulf Stream's effect on temperatures in the Atlantic throughout the year. Notice the dramatically cooler temperatures in the lee of Cape Hatteras, sheltered from the Stream's northwesterly flow, especially in the autumn (bottom image).*

RIVER OUT OF AFRICA

The origins of the current lie in central and north Africa, where the equatorial sun beats down all year. As the air warms, it plumes up, drawing in streams of air beneath it from far to the north and south as Trade Winds, which are deflected to the west by the spinning of the Earth. As the Trade Winds blow westward across the Atlantic, they drag the surface waters with them to generate a westward flow along the Equator – the North and South Equatorial Currents. It is the North Equatorial Current that drives the Gulf Stream, hitting South America and then, forced around in a great loop by the land masses around the Gulf of Mexico and the Caribbean, curling back round the southern tip of Florida to run out into the Atlantic again.

From here, the Gulf Stream flows like a giant warm river up the East Coast of the USA, sweeping along an estimated 80 million cu. m (2,800 million cu. ft) of water per second. Various eddies and counter currents split off as it drives on north to pass near the Grand Banks of Newfoundland, where it is deflected northeast across the Atlantic towards the British Isles. Where it begins off Florida, the Gulf Stream water is a balmy 23°C (73°F), and even as far north as Newfoundland it is still more than 17°C (63°F). When viewed on heat-sensitive infrared satellite pictures it shows up as a great red ribbon streaming northeastward. It is the largest and fastest warm current in the world, and a very special habitat for wildlife, delivering both warmth and nutrients.

THE SUSTAINING STREAM

Many species, such as sea turtles, use the Gulf Stream as a travelator to carry them swiftly along migration routes. Many, too, use it because of the way it generates food, as its eddies and collisions with cold water stir up the nutrients that stimulate plankton growth. That is why the summer waters off Carolina, that project right into the Gulf Stream at Cape Hatteras, are famous for their 'sport' fish, such as yellowfin tuna, grouper, rockfish, snapper, mahi mahi, and especially blue marlin, which all come to feed on the fish, such as baitfish, that in turn feed on the plankton. Where the northern edge of the Gulf Stream washes into the cold Labrador Current south of Newfoundland, the mixing of the waters creates what was once the world's greatest fishery on the Grand Banks. The coastal waters of the British Isles are similarly enriched by the intermingling of the warm Gulf Stream and the colder Arctic waters, and species such as loggerhead and leatherback turtles journey here in the summer to take advantage of the bounty, hitching a ride on the Gulf Stream.

But the Gulf Stream is not such a permanent feature of the

◁ Fragile and beautiful seahorses, like this short-snouted seahorse, are particularly vulnerable to habitat degradation, and they are now only seen rarely on the coasts of Europe.

▽ Mutton snappers that live on the tropical Atlantic coast of the Americas are popular fish for the dinner table. Sold as 'red snappers', they are too popular for their own good and numbers have declined dramatically.

oceans as its importance would suggest. About 13,000 years ago, for instance, it suddenly changed direction for a while, plunging northwestern Europe into an Ice Age, and dramatically altering the distribution of ocean life. There are increasing concerns among scientists that global warming could trigger another change. If global warming heats the Arctic quickly enough to melt a substantial amount of the ice cap all year round, it could flood the North Atlantic with cold fresh water and stall the flow of the Gulf Stream in a matter of months. If so, the northeastern USA and northwestern Europe could be snapped into an icy time lasting decades or even longer. Some scientists believe they have already detected a slight slowdown in the Gulf Stream, though others dispute their findings. The change, though, could come suddenly and without warning.

▽ The Gulf Stream keeps the British Isles unusually mild for their latitude. Any change in the current could make rare snow coverings like this on the famous Seven Sisters cliffs on the southeastern coast of England, in January 2010, much more common.

ONCE GRAND BANKS

THE GRAND BANKS OF NEWFOUNDLAND WAS ONCE THE WORLD'S RICHEST FISHING
GROUND, BUT ITS TEEMING SHOALS OF COD AND OTHER FISH HAVE BEEN ALL
BUT OBLITERATED BY INDUSTRIAL FISHING.

The Grand Banks of Newfoundland, along with similar banks nearby, are a vast range of low hills undulating on the seabed off Newfoundland. Cod once arrived in the early months of every year to spawn in vast numbers, their young finding plenty of food and cover among the rocky outcrops and pebbles, and the adults finding a feast in the even vaster numbers of smaller capelin fish that spawned here. When the Venetian explorer John Cabot (Giovanni Caboto, c.1450–c.1498) reached Newfoundland from Bristol in 1497, he discovered an astonishing resource that became fundamental to Britain's maritime future. Cod and other fish teemed here in such abundance that sailors were awestruck. Even a century later, skippers of the English fishing boats who followed Cabot told of cod schools 'so thick by the shore that we have hardly been able to row a boat through them.' For centuries, this cod cornucopia provided perhaps the main source of cheap protein for poor people in western Europe. It was dried and salted in Newfoundland, then shipped back in boatload after boatload across the Atlantic. Newfoundland thrived and great mansions were built in the Grand Banks.

THE BANKS IN CRISIS

In 1954, it all began to change. That was the year the *Fairtry* arrived over the Grand Banks. Four times the size of a large trawler, the *Fairtry* was the world's first factory-freezer trawler, a ship able to sweep the sea for fish on an industrial scale. With a ramp at the stern, she could haul aboard astonishing quantities of fish – and go on doing so hour after hour, week after week without cease as the on-board processing plant filleted the fish automatically, rendered the waste into fish meal, and froze it all. And with sonar and radar to locate schools, fish had little chance of escape.

The *Fairtry* was followed by hundreds more industrial fishing ships, each generation bigger than the last. One reason for their chilling effectiveness was that, instead of longlines, they used vast gill nets. These were dragged along the seabed, where they scooped up everything in their path – including vast quantities of 'unwanted' creatures that were swept up and dumped. Their vast nets stripped the Grand Banks, pulling out nearly 816,000 tonnes (900,000 tons) of cod in 1968 alone – more than triple the biggest annual hauls in pre-factory ship days. Then suddenly, hauls began to plummet. Just nine years later, they could only land 143,000 tonnes (158,000 tons). Indeed, not just cod, but other groundfish such as haddock, halibut, and flounder had been plundered too far.

Disturbed, the Canadian government extended its territorial waters and slapped a ban on foreign factory ships – only to begin building its own fleet while allowing foreign ships to continue fishing on licence. By the early 1990s, catches had dwindled further and surveys showed the cod stock had all

but vanished. There are scientists who blame warm seas and global warming for the decline of cod in the North Atlantic, but for others, the cause was clear.

A CODLESS PLACE

A moratorium was called on all direct fishing of cod here in 1992, but many fear it came far too late. The unthinkable may have happened and the once seemingly inexhaustible cod schools of the Grand Banks may be gone forever. The problem is not only that there may be insufficient cod to build up schools, but that the cod's spawning grounds may have been utterly wrecked by the factory ships as they dragged their vast 1-km wide (0.6-mile) weighted nets along the seabed. Without the spawning grounds, there are no nurseries for young fish to feed and grow safely to maturity.

Worse still, with cod stocks exhausted, the fishing industry turned its sights on the capelin, the little fish that in its vast numbers provided the cod with its main food. For a while in the 1990s, capelin hauls went up massively. Then they too collapsed just as suddenly, being victims of the same rapaciousness as the cod. Without their main food prey, there is even less chance of cod stocks recovering. Many biologists argue, too, that the cod's

◁ *Sights such as this – a plentiful catch of cod on the deck of a small trawler – are now merely a memory of better days in the North Atlantic waters off Newfoundland.*

△ *Picturesque Petty Harbor is one of many Newfoundland fishing villages that have been left high and dry following the collapse of the cod stock on the Grand Banks of Newfoundland. As the cod have vanished, so the human population has decreased.*

decline has been so dramatic that it has lost its ecological niche irredeemably, as other less palatable creatures, such as snow crabs, have multiplied to take advantage of its absence. The derelict fish factories on the shores of Newfoundland may soon be the only memorials to the richest, most astonishing fishing ground the world has ever known.

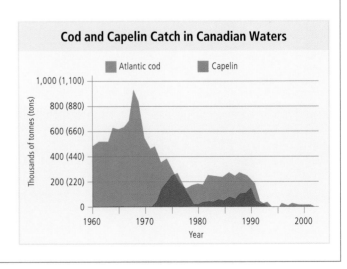

Cod and Capelin Catch in Canadian Waters

■ Atlantic cod   ■ Capelin

157

THE WORLD'S OCEANS AND SEAS
THE PACIFIC

From far out in space above its midpoint, the vast, shining blue expanse of the Pacific Ocean seems to cover the entire Earth. It is the biggest ocean by far, twice as big as the Atlantic and covering almost a third of the globe.

Everything about the Pacific is vast. At more than 155 million sq. km (60 million sq. miles), its expanse is so huge that it could swallow all of the world's continents. At its widest point, it stretches halfway around the world. This ocean contains half of all the world's water, a staggering 700 million cu .km (167 million cu. miles). It is more than 4km (2.5 miles) deep on average, and at its deepest point at Challenger Deep in the Mariana Trench, which is nearly 11,000 m (36,000 ft) down, it could engulf Mount Everest. There are more than 30,000 islands in the Pacific, a greater figure than the total number of islands in other parts of the world.

The Pacific was given its name by the Portuguese navigator Ferdinand Magellan on 28 November, 1528. He named it in relief when his battered ship finally emerged from the tortuous Straits that bear his name and found a still blue ocean opening before him. But Magellan had no idea how vast his 'peaceful ocean' is, nor how violent it can be.

Although at times it is indeed as calm as a millpond, such is the enormous energy contained in all this water and the air above it, that the Pacific is the world's prime storm generator – it frequently lashes the coasts of the western ocean with furious typhoons and giant waves tens of metres high. Such, too, is its vast fetch – the distance that winds blow over the ocean – that even in good weather, huge waves crash against the California and Australia coasts to delight surfers. And the Pacific's climatic influence is felt around the globe, through, for instance, the changes in ocean circulation that create El Niño, the collective name for the atmospheric conditions that bring drought to Africa and bushfires to Australia.

Within this gigantic, ever-churning pool live and die a staggering range of wildlife, from the countless phytoplankton that give us much of the oxygen we breathe, to rare and fascinating creatures, such as the killer whale and the dugong, and magical living coral. The scale of it all seems so vast that it is difficult to imagine humans could ever have much impact, but is the unthinkable now happening?

◁ *The tropical Pacific is dotted with stunningly beautiful coral islands such as these, the Rock Islands of Palau. Palau is a pioneer in the protection of Micronesia's coasts, and in 2009 created the world's first shark sanctuary, banning all shark fishing within its coastal waters.*

THE PACIFIC BASIN

AS WELL AS BEING THE LARGEST OF THE OCEANS, the Pacific is also the most ancient. Some of the Pacific floor at least dates back some 200 million years, and was part of the seabed of the original universal ocean that surrounded the supercontinent Pangaea. All the same, new ocean floor is being generated all the time, so there are parts of the seabed that are very young indeed. The Pacific is also shrinking.

It has no great central ridge like the Atlantic's Mid-Ocean Ridge from which new ocean floor is generated. Instead, it has the shallow East Pacific Rise that runs up the eastern side of the ocean to meet the land at Baja, California. This is the Pacific's spreading ridge. Volcanoes along the Rise, such as those on the Mid-Atlantic Ridge, generate new plate material and the Pacific plates are spreading by at least 20cm (8 in) every year. But much less material is generated compared to the Atlantic's spread zones, and there is no great seabed landscape of ridges and crests like that which characterizes the Atlantic seabed.

The East Pacific Rise may once have been the centre of a great ocean, with the two great halves of an oceanic plate either side. But the eastern half has been almost entirely buried by the rapid westward movement of the American plates that are driving over it and shrinking the Pacific much more rapidly than new oceanic plate can be generated. On the western side of the Pacific, the western half, now known as the Pacific Plate, comes up against the immovable bulk of the Asian, North American, and Australian Plates. As the Pacific Plate moves westward, it is forced down beneath these plates into the Earth's mantle in the world's most dramatic subduction zones.

Here, in the subduction zones, the Earth's surface is deeply gashed and deeply disturbed. The ocean floor plunges down nearly 10,000 m (32,800 ft) below the ocean surface in places, in some of the great line of trenches that mark the point where the Pacific Plate plunges into the interior.

THE RING OF FIRE

The violence of the encounter between the plates also creates a string of volcanoes around the Pacific rim that is known as the Ring of Fire. This has created island chains such as the Japanese islands, the Kurils and Aleutians, and the Marianas. Some of the volcanoes are highly active. The Ring of Fire also sets off earthquakes, and places around the Pacific rim are deeply vulnerable to tremors.

There are other volcanoes in the Pacific, too, such as the chain that begins with the Hawaiian Islands and ends with the Emperor Seamounts, all of which were once islands, until they were carried deeper and deeper into the ocean by the westward movement of the Pacific Plate and drowned. All these islands

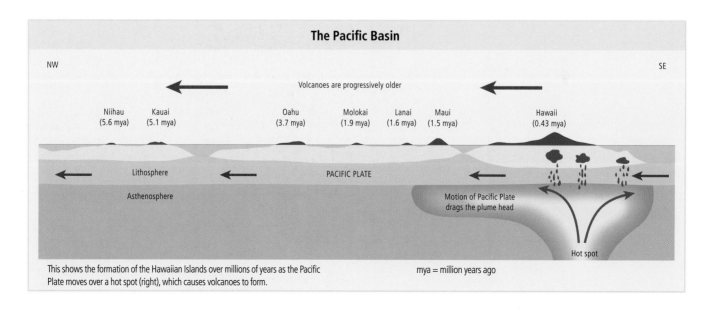

The Pacific Basin

NW | SE

Volcanoes are progressively older

| Niihau (5.6 mya) | Kauai (5.1 mya) | Oahu (3.7 mya) | Molokai (1.9 mya) | Lanai (1.6 mya) | Maui (1.5 mya) | Hawaii (0.43 mya) |

Lithosphere

Asthenosphere

PACIFIC PLATE

Motion of Pacific Plate drags the plume head

Hot spot

This shows the formation of the Hawaiian Islands over millions of years as the Pacific Plate moves over a hot spot (right), which causes volcanoes to form.

mya = million years ago

△ *Brittlestars, like this one crawling over a cushion starfish on a Hawaiian reef, play a key role in reef ecology. They feed mainly on sponges, but also on the algae and urchins that might otherwise smother and devour the coral.*

▷ *Called ilio-holo-i-ka-uaua, the 'dog that runs in rough water', by Hawaiians, the Hawaiian monk seal was almost wiped out in the islands. Thanks to diligent protection, there are now hopes that it can survive.*

and seamounts are actually just a single volcano – a sporadic plume of hot material that keeps punching its way through the Pacific Plate. The plume or 'hot spot' stays in the same place and only forms new volcanoes, apparently in new places, because the Pacific Plate is moving over it.

ISLANDS AND SEAMOUNTS

There are 20,000 to 30,000 islands in the Pacific and even more seamounts hidden beneath the ocean waters. The vast majority are volcanoes, some still active, others long gone quiet. The greatest concentration is the 13,000 or so islands that make up Indonesia and the 7,000 or so in the Philippines. All of these volcanic islands and seamounts act as focuses for marine life in the vast, otherwise largely featureless expanse of the ocean.

Many volcanic islands, for instance, are fringed with coral reefs, and when the ocean bed moves and the volcano is gradually submerged, these may become atolls, rings of coral containing a shallow lagoon. And of course, along Australia's northeast coast is the Great Barrier Reef, the world's biggest reef, more than 2,600 km (1,600 miles) long and home to 400 species of corals, 1,500 kinds of fish, more than 4,000 kinds of molluscs, and 240 kinds of birds, plus dolphins, octopuses, and many other creatures.

The Pacific's seamounts, too, have recently been discovered to be incredibly rich in marine life even at considerable depths. A study of seamounts in the Coral and Tasman seas revealed 850 previously unknown species, while various corals, such as red tree, bubblegum, and bamboo, were found growing 2,700 m (8,860 ft) down on the Kodiak-Bowie seamounts off Alaska.

THE WIDE OCEAN

Between the seamounts and islands, though, stretches the expanse of the open Pacific Ocean at the surface and the unimaginably vast, deep abyssal floor, the deepest and broadest of any in the world by a long way. Marine life is much sparser and less varied here both in the higher layers and deep down, but the sheer scale means there is an absolutely huge quantity of life. The Pacific seabed, for instance, is home to vast numbers of burrowing worms, sea cucumbers, and brittlestars.

◁ *The Hawaiian Islands all formed as the Pacific Plate drifted northwest (top left to bottom right) and was punctured by a series of volcanoes erupting over the same hot spot in the Earth's interior. Hawaii's Mauna Loa (top left) is now above the hot spot.*

THE PACIFIC DEEPS

UNTIL 1977, EVERYONE THOUGHT SUNSHINE was at the basis of all life on the Earth. Without sunlight, there could be no photosynthesis and no plants, and so animals would have nothing to eat. But that year, a remarkable discovery was made in the deep ocean off the Galapagos Islands.

Scientists were looking for signs of volcanic activity called hydrothermal vents along the Pacific's ridge, the East Pacific Rise. Hydrothermal vents are places where mineral-rich waters are superheated underground by hot volcanic rock and erupt on the surface in clouds of steam and smoke. They were already known to exist on land, in places such as North America's Yellowstone National Park, but the scientists believed they existed underwater, too.

BLACK SMOKERS
More than 2,000 m (6,500 ft) down in the heart of the ridge, the scientists found the vents they were looking for, which

were later dubbed 'black smokers' because of the thick plumes of smokelike hot water they belched out. They also found a profusion of life that turned out to be incredibly rich and varied, living here on the dark ocean floor much farther away from sunlight than any animals were supposed to live. This was astonishing. So too was its nature.

Although there were some animals that were recognizably crabs and fish, and even giant clams, though they were rather strangely shaped. Most striking of all were the great clusters of white stalks with bright red tips like surreal lipstick dispensers. Pictures do not do these stalks justice, since they are actually taller than a human and as thick as an arm. They look at first like great thick bamboo stalks. In fact, they are worms, which were given the name *Riftia* because they were found in the rift valley of the ridge. But when they were brought to the surface these tube worms were found to be very peculiar worms indeed, with no mouth and no stomach. So how did they feed?

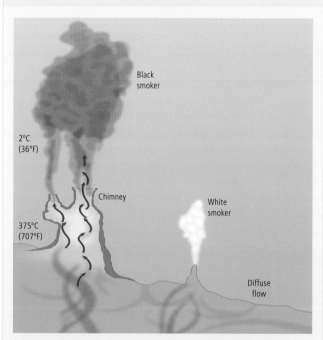

Black Smokers

2°C
(36°F)

375°C
(707°F)

Black
smoker

Chimney

White
smoker

Diffuse
flow

The presence of water makes hydrothermal vents very different from volcanic vents on land. Cold ocean water continually sinks into the crust around the vent. As it is heated under pressure by the Earth's interior, it is loaded with chemicals such as sodium and sulphur. Heat and pressure builds up until it erupts as steamy smoke through the vent. Black smokers form when hot vent water mixes with cold seawater, so that tiny particles of manganese-rich and iron-rich sulphide minerals are precipitated. White smokers form from cooler vent water that precipitates barium and calcium minerals.

◁ *This hydrothermal vent 3,100 m (10,170 ft) down in the Atlantic was photographed by the submersible* Alvin. *Clouds of scalding sulphurous, mineral-rich fluid billow from its chimney – and provide the chemicals to feed the vent community.*

△ *The vent's most spectacular organisms are the clusters of plantlike giant tube worms that survive on a diet of bacteria, which in turn feed on the vent chemicals. The red tube worm in the foreground is* Riftia pachyptila; *behind it is the yellow* Tevnia jerichonana.

It turned out that living inside the tube worms and making up nearly half their weight are huge colonies of bacteria, and the worms get their food from these. The tips are red because they contain haemoglobin, the chemical that makes human blood red, but the tube worms' haemoglobin is special because it absorbs not only oxygen but also absorbs sulphide separately, disposing of it to prevent it from becoming toxic. That way the tube worms can cope with the streams of hydrogen sulphide pouring out of the vents, which would be toxic to most other creatures. The result is that tube worms thrive in this hostile environment, growing faster than any other marine invertebrate – almost 1 m (3 ft) a year.

CHEMICAL FEEDERS

The bacteria in the tube worms cannot only tolerate incredibly high temperatures, formerly thought impossible for life to survive in, they also get their food not from sunlight or other organisms, but by absorbing and changing chemicals. And these are not just any chemicals, but the hydrogen sulphide pouring out of the vents. The organisms have become the basis of a chain of life that depends ultimately not on sunlight but on chemicals made in the Earth – and which can survive forever in pitch-black darkness. The discovery of these chemical-living bacteria fundamentally changed biologists' view of the possibility of life elsewhere in the Universe, which might soon be found in places far from sunlight in extreme conditions once thought inimical to life.

Cold Seeps

In 1984, scientists diving deep in the Gulf of Mexico discovered that it was not just the hot chemistry of black smokers that can feed life, so too can the cold chemistry of oil. Oil-rich rocks at the bottom of the Gulf, the rocks that the oil and gas industry looks for, ooze hydrocarbons into the water. Like the black smokers, these 'cold seeps' are too deep to receive sunlight, yet there were thriving animal communities down here, including small mussels and thin tube worms. It turns out that these mussels and tube worms, like the clams and worms of black smokers, get food from colonies of bacteria living inside them. But these cold-seep bacteria live not on hot hydrogen sulphide but cold methane. Everything happens very slowly here and cold-seep tube worms are thought to take two centuries to reach full-size. The remarkable thing is that they are able to live here at all.

It turned out that other creatures such as the clams have communities of bacteria similar to the tube worms and likewise get their food from this mutual arrangement in which the creature provides a home and the bacteria provide food. And fish such as deep-sea lizardfish and the dumbo octopus feed on the creatures that feed on the bacteria.

Since 1977, new species have been found every few weeks in the Galápagos hydrothermal vent community that stretches all along the East Pacific Rise. Similar vents have been discovered elsewhere in the Pacific, and each has its own species. Vent communities were thought to be unique to the Pacific, but they have now been found in every ocean, including the Atlantic where, instead of tube worms, the vents swarm with shrimp. One particularly groundbreaking discovery was that there were other kinds of microbes at the vents. They are so different in genetic makeup that they have been given their own biological kingdom called the Archaea. The Archaea are thought to be one of the two original branches of life on Earth.

▽ *Deathly white or pink and entirely scaleless, the eelpout or vent fish is one of the few fish to be seen at the vents, surviving by feeding on amphipods and crabs. This fish is uniquely able to tolerate the cocktail of chemicals and warm water.*

CORAL ISLANDS

DOTTED THROUGHOUT THE CENTRAL PACIFIC ARE SOME OF THE WORLD'S MOST REMOTE AND BEAUTIFUL ISLANDS – ISLANDS BUILT ENTIRELY BY LIVING CREATURES – THE CORAL ISLANDS.

The most remarkable of all these animal-made islands are the atolls. Atolls are ring-shaped coral islands enclosing a central lagoon. Although only the top few tens of metres in reefs beyond the shore are living coral, boreholes have confirmed that the bed of coral skeletons goes down thousands of metres in some places before bedrock is reached.

ATOLL BUILDERS

The question of how corals formed these ring-shaped islands – and how coral, which grows only in the surface layers of the ocean could build structures so far down – puzzled Darwin when he saw them on his famous voyage aboard the *Beagle* in the 1830s. Darwin's ingenious theory, which he published in 1842, was that atolls initially formed as fringing reefs encircling islands formed by the tops of volcanoes. As the sea level rose, Darwin suggested, the volcano was gradually drowned, leaving just the reef ring as the growth of corals

▽ *Whenever disease strikes, healthy spiny lobsters move on together, keeping in close touch with their antennae and abandoning their diseased kin to their fate. To repel predators en route, they rasp the base of their antennae noisily.*

kept pace with the rising sea. Scientists believe he was essentially right, but it is not rising sea levels that drowned the volcanic island. Instead it is the movement of tectonic plates that has carried the volcano deeper and deeper.

On most atolls, the solid reefs are built mostly by colonies of coral polyps, but in some places coralline algae has spread over much of the reef. On Rose Atoll, the entire surface is coated with a pink calcareous algae called *Lithothamnium*. The shells of sea creatures can also add to the reef structure. Even the dazzling beaches are built by animals; the sand is mostly the powdered skeletons of corals.

PACIFIC HOT SPOTS

In the nutrient-poor tropical waters, reefs, and atolls in particular, are magnets for marine life in the vastness of the Pacific. Pooled up within an atoll, nutrients can be recycled through the ecosystem again and again, not lost to the open ocean, and countless creatures benefit from this concentration. The biomass of fish and other marine animals around some atolls is remarkable. Rare species such as green and hawksbill sea turtles, spinner dolphins, melon-head whales, pearl oysters,

giant clams, coconut crabs, reef sharks, large groupers, grey humphead wrasses, and bumphead parrotfish all thrive here.

These small dots of land within the vast Pacific, rich with food, are also nesting habitats for millions of seabirds, such as tropicbirds, frigate birds, boobies, and terns and resting places for migrating shorebirds. On the islands themselves, shore pools may be home to numerous small fish, sea urchins, starfish, seaweeds, rock crabs, molluscs, and other creatures. On the beach may live burrowing crabs. Inside the lagoon, especially if it is almost entirely enclosed, there may be a unique range of creatures, not found elsewhere, including species of worms, eels, sea cucumbers, burrowing crabs, and flatfish.

TAKING A TOLL

The richness of life on many atolls, combined with their remoteness, means they have become priceless last refuges for many species of marine life threatened elsewhere. Yet despite their isolation, they have been vulnerable to exploitation in the past, for their resources (guano) and for their military value, and today for their fish and other natural resources. There is a very real danger that even these last refuges may be damaged irreparably if not legally protected, as the waters around the Phoenix islands of Kiribati, the Rose Atoll in Samoa, the northern Marianas, and the American central Pacific atolls have been (see pages 170–171).

THE GUANO ISLANDS

In the 19th century, many of the coral islands were known mostly for bird excrement – and were called the Guano Islands. Although largely uninhabited by humans, seabirds have long been coming to these islands to feed on the fish-rich waters of the surrounding reefs. The dry climate and strong winds ensured the guano that the birds left behind as they perched, did not rot away but dried out, and over thousands of years, built up in white layers often tens of metres thick.

Guano is rich in nitrates and phosphates, and in the 1840s, Liverpool merchant William Myers excavated 2,000 tonnes (2,200 tons) of guano and shipped it to Britain to sell to farmers to use as fertilizer. It proved such a success that the next few decades saw a guano rush to the Pacific islands by British, European, and American businesses. In 1856, the US government passed the Guano Islands Act, which allowed Americans to take possession of any desert island anywhere in the world if it had guano deposits. Dozens of Pacific islands became American possessions and were mined intensively for their guano. By the end of the 19th century, virtually all the guano had been stripped away, but most of the islands were retained by the USA for their military value. The guano island Johnston Island, for instance, was used by the USA for nuclear tests.

▷ *Despite their unglamorous names, slow-moving nudibranches or sea slugs are some of the most beautiful of all sea creatures, coming in a huge variety of stunning colours and patterns.*

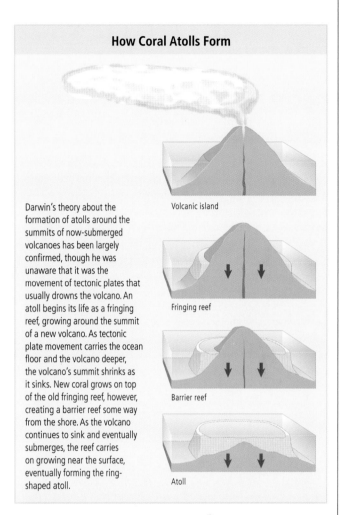

How Coral Atolls Form

Darwin's theory about the formation of atolls around the summits of now-submerged volcanoes has been largely confirmed, though he was unaware that it was the movement of tectonic plates that usually drowns the volcano. An atoll begins its life as a fringing reef, growing around the summit of a new volcano. As tectonic plate movement carries the ocean floor and the volcano deeper, the volcano's summit shrinks as it sinks. New coral grows on top of the old fringing reef, however, creating a barrier reef some way from the shore. As the volcano continues to sink and eventually submerges, the reef carries on growing near the surface, eventually forming the ring-shaped atoll.

Volcanic island

Fringing reef

Barrier reef

Atoll

THE GREAT BARRIER REEF

THE GREAT BARRIER REEF IS ONE OF THE WONDERS OF THE NATURAL WORLD,
AND ONE OF THE MOST IMPORTANT MARINE HABITATS.
BUT HOW CERTAIN IS ITS FUTURE?

Australia's Great Barrier Reef is a reef system made up of almost 3,000 separate reefs and over 900 islands. It stretches more than 2,600 km (1,600 miles) along the northeastern coast of Australia, and encompasses a range of reef types, including fringing and barrier reefs, as well as linking into many different habitats, from mangrove swamps to seagrass meadows.

The living structure of the current reef is about 6,000 to 8,000 years old, and is growing on top of earlier reefs that formed when sea levels were lower. Although some parts of the reef stone below are more than two million years old, the bulk is less than half a million years old, which is relatively young for reefs. But what it lacks in age, it more than makes up for in size – it covers an area of more than 344,000 sq. km (133,000 sq. miles) – and diversity. The CNN news channel dubbed it one of the seven wonders of the natural world.

The reef is a wonderful, sparkling place, full of vivid colours and bristling with an incredible profusion of life. It is built by 350–400 different species of corals and is home to more than 1,500 species of fish, more than 4,000 kinds of molluscs, 30 species of whales and dolphins, numerous sponges and rays, 6 species of sea turtles, 14 species of sea snakes, and 240 kinds of birds. On just a single reef, researchers found 250 kinds of shrimp, and on one small chunk of coral, researchers found 1,441 sea worms. Two particular creatures have attracted a lot of attention – dugongs and saltwater crocodiles. Indeed, the Great Barrier Reef is home to the world's largest populations of both these remarkable, but endangered creatures.

Recognizing its ecological importance, the Australian government have gradually been affording the Great Barrier Reef more and more protection. In 1975, it was made a Marine Park. The Park saw the introduction of a programme to control the impact of the 1.6 million tourists who come to visit the reef every year and to conserve some of the rare species that live here or pass through. But the reef remained highly vulnerable

▽ *The Great Barrier Reef is home to more than 1,500 species of fish. In this reef scene are, among others, sergeant major fish with their distinctive stripes like rank markings, and numerous peach-coloured fairy basslets (also known as royal grammas). Like some other tropical reef fish, fairy basslets can change sex from female to male.*

to fishing and the effects of invasive species such as the crown-of-thorns starfish. So in July 2004, the Great Barrier Reef was made what was then the largest protected sea area in the world, and fishing is now banned entirely in 'no-take' zones that cover more than a third of the reef.

NO TAKERS

It was a groundbreaking piece of legislation, and a study published in spring 2010 showed that it is already having an encouraging measure of success. The study showed that 'no-take' zones can really benefit fish populations. The scientists found, for instance, that coral trout numbers doubled within two years of the ban, and the numbers and size of all key species seems to be up significantly. They also predicted that as fish grew bigger in the no-take zones, they would produce more larvae and so spread the benefits into areas that remain open to fishing. Larger, more mobile species such as grey reef sharks have gained less than residential species, but even they have become more abundant in the protected areas as the food supply of prey fish swells. And it is not just fish that benefit. As the fish populations regain their numbers, so the outbreaks of crown-of-thorns starfish, and other animals that feed on corals have been reduced.

With such promising results, it was therefore that much more distressing when a huge Chinese coal ship, the *Shen Neng 1*, slammed into the reef on 3 April, 2010. The ship should never have been inside the protected area, but the impact not only flattened the reef as the boat scraped along for nearly 3 km (2 miles), crushing the corals and smearing them with toxic paint, it also spilled 3 tonnes (3.3 tons) of fuel oil as the hull was gashed. First assessments suggest that it might take decades for this area of the reef to recover.

Dugong gone?

Known as sea cows for their habit of grazing on seagrasses, dugongs are fascinating sea mammals that were once widespread from the Mediterranean to Japan. The Mediterranean dugong has long since vanished, and it is now increasingly rare throughout its range. Dugong numbers were drastically reduced over the centuries as it was hunted relentlessly for its meat and oil. Hunting dugongs has long been banned, but the numbers are now so low the sea cow is vulnerable to many other threats, including the loss of the seagrass on which it relies for food (see pages 106–107), collisions with and disturbances by boats, and accidental capture by fishing nets that drown them. The Great Barrier Reef has two of the only remaining substantial populations of dugongs, in Moreton Bay and Sharks Bay. Experts are campaigning for the inshore seagrass meadows there to be given the same level of protection as the reef itself. But the future of the dugong is looking uncertain.

▽ *On Australia's southern coast, Kangaroo Island near Adelaide is home to the beautiful leafy sea dragon. These animals were popular targets for collectors to use in traditional medicine, and were badly affected by pollution, but they are now protected by law.*

▽ *One of the largest of all reef fish, the humphead, or Napoleon wrasse, is a key predator of the crown-of-thorns starfish which can ravage coral reefs. Although once badly affected by overfishing, humpheads are now well protected in Australian waters.*

PLASTIC SOUP

IN AUGUST 1997, AMERICAN YACHTSMAN CHARLES MOORE MADE A DISCOVERY THAT CHANGED HIS LIFE. RIGHT OUT IN THE MIDDLE OF THE PACIFIC OCEAN, HIS CATAMARAN *ALGUITA* SAILED INTO WHAT SEEMED LIKE A LANDFILL DUMPED IN THE OCEAN – A MASS OF FLOATING PLASTIC RUBBISH.

Including anything from bath toys to traffic cones, this trash patch was vast – so vast that it took Moore a week to sail through it. Moore was so shocked that he gave up his career and set up the Algalita Marine Research Foundation to monitor what has become known as the Great Pacific Garbage Patch.

It was originally thought that the Garbage Patch was a floating island, but it is more like a soup. One reason it took a while to spot was that much of it sinks out of sight below the surface. In fact, small particles may float in the water up to 1.6 km (1 mile) below the surface. It partly consists of recognizable objects such as plastic bags, containers, and toys, but fragments, pellets, and microscopic grains make up the larger portion.

PLASTIC POLLUTION

The plastic has entered the water in many ways, but it has been swept together by the circulating currents, or gyres, of the North Pacific into two linked areas either side of Hawaii, known as the Western and Eastern Pacific Garbage Patches. Estimates of the size vary. Charles Moore suggests they 'may be twice the size [of the] continental United States' and contain a staggering 90 million tonnes (99 tons) of plastic. About a fifth of the plastic has been jettisoned from ships, but the rest – up to 5.4 million tonnes (6 tons) a year – came from land. According to Project Kaisei, an organization set up to investigate the problem, the plastic is coming from rivers, streams, drains, gutters, and beaches within 1.6 km (1 mile) of the shoreline. On most beaches around the world, some scientists suggest, sand is mixed in with pale particles of plastic, and that you have

to dig quite deep to reach pure, unadulterated sand.

Plastic can do untold damage to wildlife. Seabirds, marine mammals, and larger fish can become entangled in old netting, plastic lines, bags, and boxes with devastating effects. Animals can also ingest plastic. Turtles, for example, choke on plastic bags, mistaking them for edible jellyfish, while albatrosses swoop upon floating fragments to feed their chicks. The stomach of one Laysan albatross chick found dead on a remote Pacific island contained a cigarette lighter, a toy robot, a toothbrush, and a tampon applicator.

POISON PILLS

Many problems also occur farther down the food chain. Plastic may not be biodegradable, but that does not mean that it stays intact. Exposure to light and warmish water means much of it quickly fragments into tiny particles known as mermaid tears, or nurdles. Many fish eat nurdles, mistaking them for fish eggs. And nurdles can break down even further into microscopic particles ingested by plankton. Once in the food chain, it can go all the way up to whales.

Some chemical damage is done by the plastic itself. Certain chemicals that are used in the manufacture of plastic, such as Bisphenol A, are thought to be carcinogenic and can cause other types of damage. Plastic particles in the oceans also absorb all the toxic chemicals to which they are exposed, forming little poison pills that feed such dangerous chemicals as DDT into animals right up the food chain to whales – and the higher up the food chain the toxins go, the more concentrated they become.

▽ *Albatross chicks are unwittingly fed plastic by their parents – as the horrific stomach contents of this dead chick, killed by a diet of plastic toys and toothbrushes, bear witness to all too grimly.*

▽ *Plastic soup consists of larger floating items, such as bottles, and many much smaller components, including the tiny nurdles (inset) from which plastic is made and which it breaks down into in the sea.*

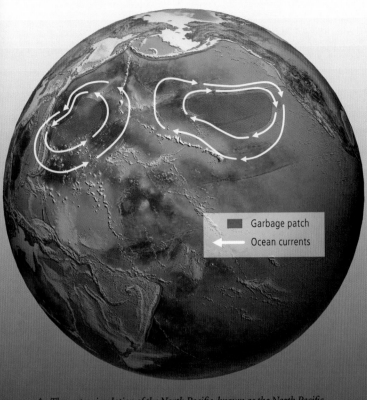

How Animals are Affected

Animal	Effect
Zooplankton, mussels, and barnacles	Very tiny particles are ingested by these smaller creatures
Fish	Bigger pellets, such as nurdles, are mistaken for eggs by many fish
Turtles	Plastic bags are easily mistaken for jellyfish prey by turtles
Seabirds	Smaller plastic items, such as toothbrushes, are fed to many seabird chicks, especially those of albatrosses
Birds, turtles, and marine mammals	Many types of larger animals become entangled in netting
Seabirds and turtles	Bottle caps, pocket combs, cigarette lighters, tampon applicators, cotton-bud shafts, toothbrushes, toys, syringes, and plastic shopping bags are routinely found in the stomachs of dead seabirds and turtles
Whales	These huge creatures feed on tiny plankton that have ingested tiny plastic particles

△ The water circulation of the North Pacific, known as the North Pacific gyres, has swept the oceans' floating plastic rubbish into two vast patches either side of Hawaii.

▽ The potentially fatal muzzle on this poor bottlenose dolphin is all too recognizably a plastic six-pack beer can holder. Dolphins are particularly susceptible to entanglement because of their curiosity.

Ocean Refuges

MORE AND MORE AREAS OF THE OCEAN ARE BEING OFFERED LEGAL PROTECTION
AS 'MARINE PROTECTED AREAS' IN ORDER TO CONSERVE FISH AND
OTHER MARINE WILDLIFE. BUT HOW EFFECTIVE ARE THEY?

National parks and conservation areas have existed to protect wildlife and natural environments on land for over a century. North America's Yellowstone National Park dates back to 1872, and now more than 13 percent of the land in the USA is protected. The idea that areas of the ocean might benefit from protection, too, is much more recent. Australia's Great Barrier Reef was one of the first areas to be given protection, as recently as 1975, the same year that the USA set up its own first marine sanctuary, a tiny reserve around the wreck of the Union warship *Monitor* in the waters off North Carolina.

In 1980, though, the International Union for Conservation of Nature (IUCN) and the World Wildlife Fund began to collaborate to develop a network of Marine Protected Areas (MPAs) across the world to maintain ecosystems, preserve genetic diversity, and ensure the sustainable use of species and ecosystems. The idea has caught on, and by February 2009 there were more than 5,000 MPAs around the world. Most are coastal and quite small, covering less than 1 sq. km (0.4 sq. miles). But in recent years, a few gigantic reserves have been set up, covering vast areas of ocean.

MASSIVE PROTECTION

In 2006, US president George Bush was persuaded to set up a huge reserve to protect the fish off the northwestern Hawaiian Islands. Covering nearly 362,000 sq km (140 sq miles) of open ocean, the Papahanaumokaukea Marine National Monument was then the world's largest marine protected area. Two years later, the tiny island nation of Kiribati established an even bigger reserve, covering 410,000 sq. km (158,000 sq. miles). It was an area of pristine coral reefs and rich fishing the size of California around the Phoenix archipelago of atolls, which is threatened by global warming and overfishing. What made it such a bold move was that it did not just include Phoenix's recognized natural treasures around the eight atolls, but extended far beyond the coast to include large areas of open ocean, including underwater mountains and deep sea habitats.

The idea was catching on, and in January 2009, George Bush created three new marine protected areas covering more than 600,000 sq. km (232 sq. miles) of the Pacific Ocean. The three areas encompass the 2,400-km (1,500-mile)-long Mariana Trench, including underwater active volcanoes and thermal vents; the Rose Atoll in American Samoa; and a string of remote coral islands and reefs in the Central Pacific. Then in April 2010, the UK's Foreign Secretary David Miliband announced the establishment of the world's biggest marine reserve yet, which covered 650,000 sq. km (251 sq. miles) of the Indian Ocean around the Chagos Islands.

▽ *The coral reef-rich waters around the Phoenix Islands is the site of a vast marine reserve set up by the tiny Pacific island nation of Kiribati in 2008. Here, fairy basslet fish* (Gramma loret) *dart among blooms of lettuce coral.*

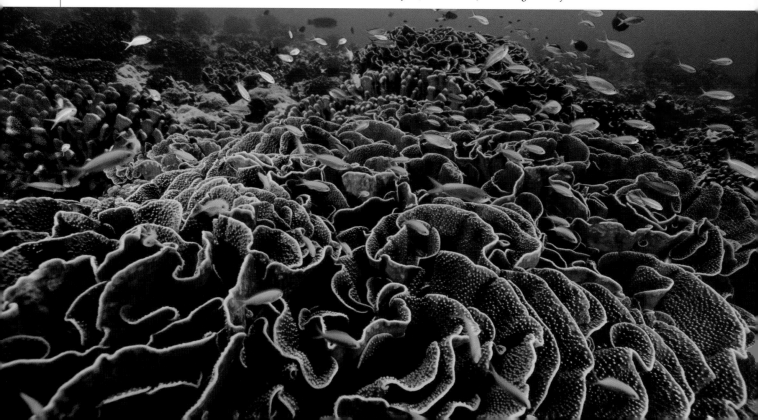

Marine Protected Areas

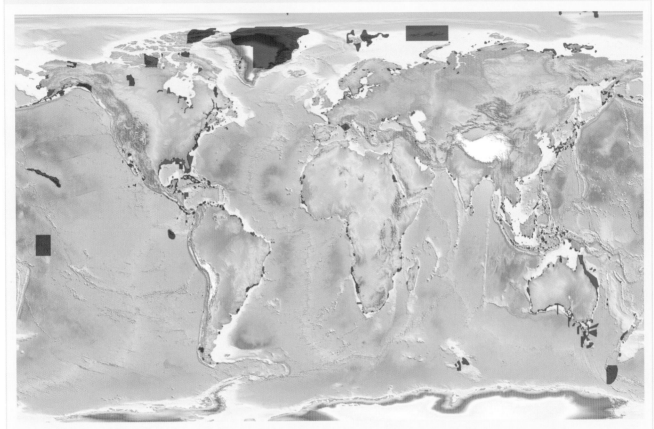

The area of the ocean under some kind of protection has expanded dramatically in the last decade. This map, based on data from the World Database of Protected Areas, shows Marine Protected Areas around the world in 2009. Since then several substantial areas have been added, including the Chagos reserve.

FOCUSING ON FISHING

This last reserve brought the total area of ocean in protected areas up to just under 2 percent. This is progress, but still short of the 10 to 30 percent that the world's nations agreed should be in place by 2012. The idea is that MPAs either reduce or prevent altogether, within the designated area, commercial fishing, seafloor mining, oil exploration, and other uses, and limit indigenous and recreational fishing. There is no certainty of how effective they are yet. According to US anthropologist Richard Pollnac, only a third of a sample of more than 500 reserves were functioning properly.

But studies suggest that if properly monitored and targeted, fishing bans might be very effective. A special issue of the American Proceedings of the National Academy of Sciences (PNAS) in 2010 included studies showing that fishing is responsible for 90 percent of the overall damage to ecosystems in areas such as the South and East China Seas, the Sea of Okhotsk, the Bering Sea, the North Sea, and the Norwegian Sea, as well as in much of the Coral Triangle. The implication was that if fishing is tightly controlled by an MPA, it could do a great deal to rescue the ecosystem. Another study suggested that protecting areas that are heavily fished can have a much more dramatic impact on the overall health of the ocean than protecting less fished areas, even if much bigger. It is clear that there is no chance of meeting the 30 percent target for marine protected areas by 2012, but some scientists wonder if a great deal can be achieved by targeting fishing practices in carefully chosen areas.

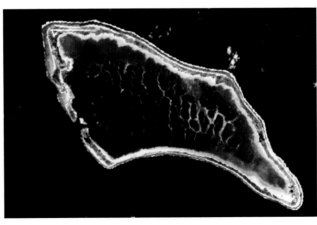

△ *The coral atoll of Canton is the sole inhabited island in the newly created marine reserve of the Phoenix Islands. The island's lagoon is filled with marine life, with 153 different species of fish, including tuna, sharks, stingrays, and eels.*

THE WORLD'S OCEANS AND SEAS
THE INDIAN OCEAN

The Indian Ocean is the youngest of all the three big oceans geologically, and is the third largest, spanning a gigantic triangle between Africa, Southern Asia, and Australia.

The northern half of the Indian Ocean lies entirely within the tropics, and is dotted here and there with the idyllic tropical islands that so appeal to tourists. The Seychelles, the Maldives, and Mauritius all help create an image of a tropical ocean paradise, complete with coral reefs swarming with fish and palm-fringed white beaches where sea turtles crawl ashore to lay their eggs.

But the Indian Ocean is not always so balmy. In the monsoon season, the rains lash down ferociously, and sudden winds whip up freak waves that can overwhelm ships in an instant. The southern half of the ocean merges into the Southern Ocean and the world's stormiest, coldest seas. Indeed in some definitions, the Indian Ocean runs all the way south to the icy continent of Antarctica. According to the International Hydrographic Organization (IHO), however, the southern edge of the Indian Ocean is the 60° South latitude line. Beyond that lies the Southern Ocean.

None of the other oceans has been crossed by explorers and traders for even half as long as the Indian Ocean. The Egyptians may have sailed there when looking for the legendary land of Punt 5,000 years ago, and the Ancient Greek Eudoxus of Cyzicus explored the Indian Ocean in the 2nd century B.C., while his contemporary (and maybe fellow crewman) Hippalus is said to have discovered how to use the monsoon winds to sail to India. Later, the Arab scholar Ibn Battuta became famous for his travels here in the 14th century and in the 15th century the Chinese admiral Zheng-He led great fleets on voyages of discovery across the Indian Ocean. Yet much of the Indian Ocean, and the Indian Ocean seabed – less known than either the Atlantic or the Pacific, remains a mystery.

◁ *The Indian ocean village of Weligama on Sri Lanka is famous for its stilt fishermen. Each fisherman perches on a cross-bar at the top of a pole stuck into the seabed close to the shore, so that the fish they are hunting are unaware of their presence.*

OPENING THE INDIAN OCEAN

COMPARED TO THE ATLANTIC OCEAN, which simply opened up along the Mid-Atlantic Ridge and kept spreading, the formation of the Indian Ocean is a convoluted story. Indeed, a decade ago, scientists were amazed to discover an entire lost continent sunk beneath the waves in the south of the ocean around the Kerguelen Islands. The Kerguelen Plateau first appeared as a result of a massive volcanic eruption 110 million years ago, and by the late Cretaceous was home to conifers and small dinosaurs, only finally sinking under the sea 20 million years ago.

Meanwhile, a very complex process was opening up the rest of the Indian Ocean. It all started some 180 million years ago when the southern continent of Gondwanaland began to break up. Africa, Madagascar, Antarctica, and Australia are all fragments of this breakup. So is India, which was still attached to Africa, not Asia, 70 million years ago. The Indian Ocean today is the net result of the way these fragments have drifted over the Earth since then.

The key to much of this movement is the Indian Ocean's mid-ocean ridge which begins in the Gulf of Aden and runs southwest under the Arabian Sea. This is not a single line, but splits into two branches right in the middle of the ocean at what is called a 'triple junction'. So the Indian Ocean is spreading not in two directions like the Atlantic but three, and it is the spreading of the ocean floor around this junction that has opened up the Indian Ocean over the last 80 million years.

INDIAN PLATE

As the spreading of the southern plate drove Antarctica south, so the huge eastern plate, known as the Indo-Australian plate, carried Australia more than 10,000 km (6,200 miles) away from Africa and, at the same time, carried India northeast.

But while Australia drifted on with no obstacles in its path, about 10 million years ago India ran into the immovable mass of Asia. As India surged relentlessly on, Asia would not budge, but its edge buckled under the strain, throwing up the world's highest mountain range, the Himalayas, in just a few million years. The stress of the impact now seems to be tearing India away from the Indo-Australian plate along a line running northeast–southwest beneath the Indian plate from Burma.

Two other great tracks were left across the Indian Ocean floor by two volcanic hot spots under the crust that kept on erupting as the plate drove north. One formed a line of seamounts that just peak above the blue ocean in places to form thousands of jewel-like emerald-green islands, such as the Maldives, Laccadives, and Chagos. The other forms a ridge that runs straight along the ocean floor from north to south for more than 5,000 km (3,000 miles) along the 90° East meridian, earning it the name the Ninety East Ridge. It is the world's longest straight ridge, yet was only discovered in 1962 because it is entirely submerged.

OFFSHORE

Around much of the Indian Ocean's 66,500 km (41,300 miles) of shores, the continental margin is much narrower than it is in the Pacific and Atlantic. The continental shelf is just 120 km (75 miles) wide on average, and in some places drops off into the abyss of the ocean within a few tens of miles of the shore. Around some islands there is a sheer drop into the abyss

within 300 m (980 ft) of the beach. But there are places where submarine canyons are carved in the continental slope, especially close to the mouths of rivers such as the Zambesi, Indus, and Ganges. Huge loads of sediment are poured into the Indian Ocean by rivers, more than any other ocean. More than half of it comes from India – in particular from the Indus and the Ganges–Brahmaputra, which have spilt vast cones of silt fanning out over the abyssal plains. The Ganges has spewed out a fan that is many kilometres thick and extends under the Bay of Bengal almost as far south as Sri Lanka.

There are fewer deep ocean trenches in the Indian Ocean than any other ocean. The one exception is the long, narrow, volcanically active Java Trench off the coast of Java. It was the sudden movement of the Earth's crust along the portion of this trench near the Andaman and Nicobar islands that caused the earthquake that generated the tsunami that swept around the Indian Ocean and devastated coastal communities in December 2004.

7 The coral reefs off the Seychelles are still blessed by the sight of a hawksbill turtle skimming gracefully through the blue water. But there are no more than a few thousand of these critically endangered animals altogether in the Indian Ocean.

LIFE IN THE INDIAN OCEAN

THE NORTHERN HALF OF THE INDIAN OCEAN lies entirely within the tropics and, while the ocean depths are cold, the surface layers can get as warm as anywhere on the planet. In the east, surface temperatures in the Bay of Bengal reach 28°C (82°F) in summer. Only in the west, along the coast of the Horn of Africa, are there upwellings of cold water that bring the surface temperature down to about 22°C (71°F). The Indian Ocean is also quite salty except in the Bay of Bengal.

All this warmth and saltiness means that the Indian Ocean lacks some of the plankton growth that turns cooler seas murky green, and the Indian Ocean has some of the most sparkling, clear, vivid blue waters on the planet. The contrast can often be seen off the southern cape of South Africa, where the cool green Atlantic waters of the Benguela Current intermingle with the blue Indian Ocean waters of the Agulhas Current. The upwellings of cool water in the northwest of the Indian Ocean, off the Horn of Africa and the Persian Gulf, produce summer plankton blooms that make these areas rich in fish and other

marine life. Elsewhere, though, the clarity and warmth of the water are perfect for corals, and corals are the Indian Ocean's great treasures.

Almost half the continental shorelines in the Indian Ocean are fringed by corals. There are none in the Bay of Bengal and off Pakistan because the massive amounts of freshwater and sediment washing out of the Indus and Ganges rivers prevent corals growing, and the turmoil of the monsoon season hinders their growth in the South of India. But corals are abundant on nearly all the Indian Ocean islands, from the Chagos to the Andaman, and along the coasts of Kenya and Tanzania, Sumatra, and northwestern Australia. The Great Chagos Bank is the world's biggest atoll. All of these coral reefs are home to a host of marine animals including sponges, worms, crabs, molluscs, sea urchins, brittlestars, and colourful fish such as snappers, groupers, and triggerfish.

Migrating between these hot spots there were once numerous whales, sharks, and sea turtles, but all of them

△ *Camouflaged almost invisibly among the coral, the reef stonefish (Synanceia verrucosa) is the world's most deadly fish. The venom in their dorsal spines is enough to cause excruciating pain and kill a human in just a few hours.*

△ *Giant groupers appear so docile that they seem harmless, but they are reef predators, and once a victim comes within range, they lunge quickly to make a kill. They are very big fish, growing up to 2.7 m (9 ft) in length.*

have been the victims of human activity. Whaling had all but wiped out many species of whales by the middle of the last century, and the situation reached a crisis point in the 1970s, when the depletion of whales in Antarctic waters drove Japanese and Soviet whalers north into the Indian Ocean. Populations of some whales such as Oman's humpbacks were thought to have been entirely destroyed. Then in 1979, at the instigation of the Seychelles, the entire Indian Ocean was made a whale sanctuary. Oman's humpbacks survived, but only just – and the creation in 1994 of another whale sanctuary in the Southern Ocean, where many Indian Ocean whales commute in summer (see page 193), seems to have given the Indian Ocean's whales a fighting chance.

All six of the species of sea turtles of the Indian Ocean – green, hawksbill, leatherback, loggerhead, olive Ridley, and flatback – are in some danger. After centuries of hunting for their meat and shells, most sea turtle populations in the Indian Ocean are at such low levels that all of them are vulnerable to other environmental impacts, such as by-catch. However, decades-long protection plans, particularly at beaches in the Indian Ocean where turtles come ashore

△ *Named for their strange bulbous foreheads, bumphead parrotfish play a key part in creating the beautiful coral beaches of the Indian Ocean by grazing on the coral and excreting the skeletal remains as fine grains of sand. However, numbers of bumpheads have been severely reduced by spearfishing.*

to lay their eggs, have achieved some success with hawksbills and Orissa's olive Ridleys.

Many of the Indian Ocean's coastlines are lined with mangrove swamps. Indeed, the Indian Ocean has almost half of all the world's mangroves. The majority of these are in Indonesia, but the biggest swamp in the world is Bangladesh's famous Sundarbans, which is the only mangrove swamp in which tigers live. Many of these swamps though are coming under threat from logging, shrimp farming, and pollution.

Coral Bleaching

In 1998, three months of very warm weather set off by an El Niño event (see page 53) caused the worst coral bleaching episode ever witnessed in the Indian Ocean. As the temperatures stayed warm, 90 percent of all the ocean's corals were affected – they expelled their symbiotic algae guests, ceased to grow, and turned pale. Only Mauritius' corals seem to have escaped, because it was cloudy there at the time. It takes a decade or more for coral to recover from such events, and the worry is that as global warming gathers pace, bleaching events may become too frequent in the Indian Ocean for the corals to recover inbetween. There is some encouragement, however. The reefs in the Chagos Islands recovered astonishingly quickly. It is thought that this is because the water there is so clear that the corals thrive deeper down and in cooler water. Now half of all the healthy corals in the Indian Ocean are in the Chagos Islands, which is why their designation as a Marine Protected Area (MPA) in 2010 was so important. Also encouraging was the discovery in 2010 of a diversity of species of corals housing unusual symbiotic algae that seemed to thrive in warm waters off the Andaman Islands. If new relationships like this develop, the chances of corals surviving mild global warming seem slightly better.

THE RED SEA

THE RED SEA MAY SEEM LIKE JUST A NARROW INLET. In fact, just as the Indian Ocean was born from a triple junction in the Earth's crust that pushed away continents, so the Red Sea is on the cusp of a triple junction that will one day – perhaps not for 100 million years – force Africa and Asia apart to form a great ocean. The junction lies where the Red Sea meets the Gulf of Aden.

THE INFANT OCEAN

The Red Sea is one arm of this incipient ocean. The Gulf of Aden is the second. The third is not even under the water yet, but it surely will be one day. This third arm is the Great Rift Valley in East Africa, and marks the line where Africa is gradually rifting, splitting apart so that one day the Horn of Africa and much of East Africa will form an entirely separate continent.

The split began to form the Red Sea about 3.5–5 million years ago. It is now about 2,000 km (1,200 miles) long and about 2,200 m (7,200 ft) deep at its deepest point. It is also the warmest, saltiest sea in the world. The average salinity there is 40 parts per thousand (ppt), compared to 35 in the tropics in the major oceans. Surface water temperatures hit 28°C (82°F) even in winter, and in summer rise to an average of 34°C (93°F). In the 1950s, the Swedish research vessel *Albatross* also discovered hot, salty deeps in the Red Sea, and there are now known to be more than 20 of these. Although they are clearly connected with volcanic activity, they are not the same as the hydrothermal vents. Yet it seems that these deeps, too, have developed their own range of life forms. In 2002, the research vessel *Meteor* discovered unique forms of bacteria in the Red Sea, and earlier explorations found other animals – bivalves, crabs, shrimp, amphipods, and eel-like fish – not far away.

RED SEA CORALS

The real treasure of the Red Sea, though, is its coral. Most of the reefs are fringing reefs, lining the coast, composed mainly of the branching corals of the genera *Acropora* and *Porites*. But there are not just unique species of corals in the Red Sea, such as the *Erythrastrea flabellata* brain coral; there are unique forms, too,

△ *The venomous spines of the lionfish are one of the perils for reef divers in the Red Sea. Some species of these voracious fish are now established off the Atlantic and Gulf coasts of North America, after being carelessly released from aquaria.*

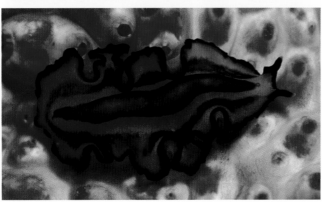

◁ *When pairs of hermaphroditic* Pseudobiceros *flatworms mate, they fight a duel with their penises. The winner is the one that jabs its penis into the other and injects sperm.*

▷ *Also known as anemonefish, Red Sea clownfish find lifelong protection amid the stinging tentacles of their host anemone to which they are immune. In return, they feed on the invertebrates that might attack the anemone.*

that seem to owe something to the special nature of the seabed. There are atoll-like rings. There are wall-like ridges. There are amoeba-shaped corals, and other odd shapes. The high salinity and high temperatures might be too much for some coral species to cope with, but the Red Sea has its own native species that seem to be more heat- and salt-tolerant.

Marine biologists are naturally interested in these heat- and bleaching-resistant corals, because of what they may teach us about how corals might cope with global warming. The Red Sea seems especially abundant in corals that fluoresce. There are fluorescent corals everywhere but, in the Red Sea, divers who go down at night can be treated to a stunningly beautiful light show of glowing corals. No one knows quite why corals fluoresce, but one theory is that fluorescence acts like a sunscreen, as fluorescent pigments absorb ultraviolet light and help protect the zooxanthellae algae on which they rely. Corals that grow in deep water, however, may be reflecting light back on to the algae to give them extra light for turning into nutrients. In shallow-water corals, the fluorescence is above the algae and in deep-water corals it is below.

Anyone who goes diving in the Red Sea, though, cannot fail to be mesmerized by the sheer, astonishing range of colourful reef fish. There are 1,400 different species here altogether, and 10–20 percent of them are unique to the Red Sea, including the stunning lemon and electric blue Red Sea anemone or clownfish, six species of butterflyfish, including the Red Sea bannerfish and the masked butterflyfish, the brilliant orange Red Sea eightline flasher wrasse, and the deadly predator, the Red Sea fusilier. Parrotfish, damselfish, surgeonfish, and rabbitfish are often grazers, feeding on algae, although some damselfish feed on plankton. Triggerfish and puffers tend to be carnivores. Then there are a few deadly poisonous fish including stonefish, scorpionfish, lionfish, and rabbitfish.

PRESERVING THE REEFS

Not surprisingly, given the Red Sea coral's heat tolerance, coral-bleaching is far less common here than elsewhere. Indeed, the Red Sea corals are on the whole surprisingly healthy, except near urban centres such as at Eilat, where there has been careless development and in unregulated dive tourism areas where boat anchors and scuba divers take their toll. A growing number of Marine Protected Areas have been set up to help reduce some of these problems. The best known is the Ras Mohammed National Park established by Egypt in 1983.

THE GIANT CLAM

THE GIANT CLAM IS THE LARGEST LIVING BIVALVE MOLLUSC WITH A SHELL THAT
CAN GROW MORE THAN 1 METRE (1 YARD) ACROSS. BUT ITS HUGE SIZE AND TOUGH
SHELL CANNOT PROTECT IT FROM HUMAN PREDATORS.

△ *Diver Richard Henry is taking part in a programme to preserve giant clams by raising them in safe undersea sea farms in the Cook Islands.*

In 2008, scientists diving in the Red Sea discovered a new species of giant clam to add to the six previously known. It was quite a surprise to find a new species of clam so big and obvious, let alone in the Red Sea, which has been so closely studied. At first, they thought it might be a variation on other known species. But genetic analysis showed that *Tridacna costata*, the ribbed clam, as it was named, is a separate species that uniquely lives in very shallow water and reproduces in a brief burst each spring.

STONE AGE CLAMBAKE

What was all the more surprising about *T. costata* was that fossils seemed to show that it was incredibly abundant in the Red Sea 150,000 years ago. Indeed, it seems that 80 percent of all clams in the Red Sea belonged to this species at that time. Then, suddenly, the population plummeted around 125,000 years ago. This is about the time modern humans appeared in the Red Sea area and some scientists speculate that this is not a coincidence. *T. costata* lives in shallow water, and was considerably bigger

▽ *When they feed, giant clams open their crusty shells to reveal a vividly coloured mantle. This one is on the seafloor off the Marshall Islands in the Pacific.*

than it is now. The scientists suggest that it is highly unlikely that early humans would have ignored such an accessible and completely stationary source of food. If so, *T. costata* may have been the first major species of sea food – maybe even the first major species of wildlife – to be decimated by humans. It is now critically endangered, and the chances of it surviving are small.

Giant clams are still suffering from human predation, and the biggest of them all, *T. gigas* (the true giant clam), is now also an endangered species. *T. gigas* is indeed a giant. Specimens have been measured at more than 1.2 m (4 ft) across and weighing more than 260 kg (570 lb). They grow to their enormous size mostly by consuming the sugars and proteins provided by the billions of algae that live inside them, just as they do inside corals. In exchange, the clams provide the algae a safe home, and open their fluted shells, so that daylight can flood into their mantles where the algae nestle so that the algae can photosynthesize. The multicoloured mantle (no clam has a mantle quite the same colour) has two holes or siphons – one to draw water in so that the clam can feed on plankton from the water, and one to let it out again.

LONG LIVE THE CLAM

The opening and closing of its shell is about as much action as a clam gets. Even that happens quite slowly, despite, almost certainly, false stories about divers getting their legs trapped by a clam. When a clam is just one week old, it looks for a place to settle down, and though it might change its mind over the next

*△ The true giant clam (*Tridacna gigas*) has the world's biggest shells, often 1 m (3 ft) or more across. The feathery orange shape behind is not a plant but an animal, a relative of jellyfish known as the gorgonian sea fan.*

few weeks, once it has chosen a place, it sits there for the rest of its life. And that life can be very long indeed. Scientists believe that some true giant clams are more than 200 years old, and recently scientists found a quahog clam in the Arctic that they calculated as being more than 400 years old, which makes it the longest living animal. That means that clam settled down into its home at about the time Shakespeare was writing *Romeo and Juliet* and before the *Mayflower* sailed to the USA.

Yet though the clam may be protected against the ravages of age, it is not protected against human activity. Like corals, clams may be affected by damage to their helpful algae caused by global warming. But they have been excessively harvested, both for their meat and the aquarium – giant clams have not been seen in Fiji, where they were once abundant, for more than 50 years. Losing giant clams would not only mean losing a fascinating, beautiful creature, but one that plays a key role in the life of the reef. Clams serve as nurseries for a host of fish and invertebrates, such as damsels, gobies, and shrimp, and improve water quality as they filter out planktonic debris.

As natural clam populations dwindle, laboratory- and farm-raised clams are being reintroduced into the wild. Laboratory-raised giant clams recently settled on 50 reefs in the Philippines seem to be thriving as indicated by their mantles changing from pale ochre to vivid electric blues and violets.

THE SOUTHERN OCEAN

Whirling like a great icy river around the frozen wastes of Antarctica, the Southern Ocean is the stormiest and most intimidating of all the oceans.

Until a decade or so ago the Southern Ocean was not recognized as a separate ocean at all; it was simply the southern extension of the three great oceans, the Pacific, Atlantic, and Indian. But in 2000, the International Hydrographic Organization (IHO) decided that these waters could be designated the Southern Ocean and become the fourth largest of the world's five oceans.

Not everyone agrees with the IHO's decision, since the Southern Ocean has no obvious boundaries like the other oceans. But the then director of the IHO, Commodore John Leech, argued that '[Recent oceanographic research has] identified that one of the main drivers of ocean systems is the "Southern Circulation", which sets the Southern Ocean apart as a separate ecosystem.' What he was identifying was the significance of the Antarctic Circumpolar Current (ACC), the great river of cool water that runs around Antarctica, in creating a unique and separate marine realm in the chill waters around the continent.

The problem with this designation is that the natural boundary between the oceans is forever shifting. In theory, it is the Antarctic Convergence, or Antarctic Polar Front, the natural boundary between the mass of cold water that dominates the polar ocean and the warmer water to the north. But this is so hard to define that the IHO hit upon the 60° South latitude line as the northern boundary of the Southern Ocean to coincide with the political boundary of Antarctica set by the UN Antarctic Treaty of 1959. It seems likely to be challenged in the future.

◁ *Antarctica is still the coldest place on Earth, and much of the sea around the continent is permanently ice-covered—but as the world warms, so more and more chunks of the ice shelf are breaking away to form icebergs like this one near South Georgia island.*

SOUTHERN OCEAN WATERS

THE SOUTHERN OCEAN FINALLY CAME INTO BEING some 17–49 million years ago, when Antarctica split from the southern tip of South America, opening up Drake Passage between them and allowing the ocean waters to flow in a continual current right around the world. Antarctica had once been part of the great southern continent of Gondwanaland, attached to Australia, India, and Africa as well as South America.

THE OLD CONNECTION

Indeed, fossils of tropical plants and dinosaurs found on Antarctica show that it was once much farther north, well within the tropics. Fossils of the same species of prehistoric reptile, *Lystrosaurus*, dating from 250 million years ago, have been found in Antarctica, India, and South Africa, showing fairly conclusively that they were once adjoined. But when it split from Gondwanaland, Antarctica drifted farther south until it could go no farther and it sat right at the South Pole, as remote from the other continents as it could be. There, about 35 million years ago it was so cold that the gradual accumulation of snow and ice built up a vast ice sheet thousands of metres thick and containing 90 percent of all the world's fresh water.

THE DIVIDING CURRENT

It was the separation of South America and Antarctica, which allowed ocean waters to flow right around the globe, that was crucial for the significance of the Southern Ocean. The opening of this channel allowed the development of the Antarctic Circumpolar Current (ACC). This great current is what makes the Southern Ocean so important for the planet's climate by linking the great oceans to form a global network that drives heat around the planet.

With no land barriers to act as a drag, the winds in the Southern Ocean are the strongest on Earth – spurring rueful sailors to dub these latitudes the Roaring Forties and the Furious Fifties. These winds whip up huge waves – and drive the ACC in an unimpeded path right around the world, 3,000 m (9,843 ft) deep and 21,000 km (13,000 miles) long. The ACC carries 145 million cu. m (5,120 million cu. ft) of water a second, one hundred times more water than all the world's rivers put

▽ *Huge fin whales, seen here in the Sea of Cortez in Baja California, were once a common sight in the Southern Ocean. But 704,000 were caught there by whalers between 1904 and 1973, and there are now just a few thousand left.*

together. And it is a hard stretch of water to cross. Warm water currents flowing south through all three main oceans are blocked and forced to turn eastward when they meet the ACC.

ALONG THE WATER FRONT

The flow of the ACC is channelled along 'fronts' where waters of different origins stream alongside, notably the Subtropical Front, the Subantarctic Front, the Polar Front, and the Southern Boundary Front. Across each front are invisible but measurable differences in temperature, salinity, oxygen, and nutrients that mark the transition from the warm, relatively salty waters of the oceans in the north to the cool, fresh Antarctic surface waters of the Southern Ocean, which are diluted in salinity by melting ice. Temperature differences across the Sub-Antarctic Front can be as much as 9°C (16°F). The transitions are so biologically distinct that early oceanographers could work out which side of the front they were on by the species of krill there. The Southern Boundary Front is especially important because this is where deep waters well up from the abyss almost to the surface, bringing up nutrients and generating a lot of plankton growth in spring.

Beneath this whole system, though, there are complex flows of deep water. The thin layer of Antarctic surface water, for instance, sinks under the warmer water along the Polar Front and spreads northward deeper down. Under the Antarctic Ice Shelf, particularly in the Weddell and Ross seas, the water is especially cold. It is also much saltier, because salt is left behind as ice forms. The cold and salt make this water very dense. In fact, it is the densest seawater in the world, and sinks en masse over the edge of the Antarctic continental margin and flows far northward deep down in the ocean. As it sinks, this mass of

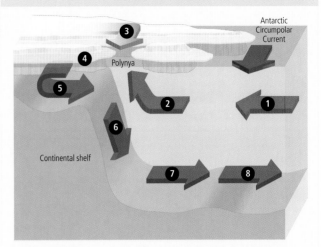

Antarctic Waters

1 Warm water flows from the equator. **2** Warm water rises to the surface, through a gap in the ice called a polynya. **3** Cold, dry air blows off the Antarctic continent, cooling the water. **4** Water freezes forming ice, expelling the salt as it freezes. **5** Water with salt saturation sinks because it is denser than the surrounding water. **6** Saline water flows down over Antarctic continental shelf. **7** Cold water becomes Antarctic bottom water. **8** Water flows towards the equator, and the cycle begins again.

dense water, known as the Antarctic Bottom Water (AABW), carries oxygen with it into the ocean deeps, and becomes the lungs of the abyssal ocean throughout the southern hemisphere. It also carries carbon dioxide, which would otherwise contribute to global warming. In 2007, a return flow of warm water that links the three oceans deep down, known as the Tasman Outflow, was discovered.

Melting Ice

For the last 35 million years, Antarctica has been all but completely covered by a vast sheet of ice, the biggest ice block on Earth. It weighs so much that it presses the whole continent of Antarctica thousands of metres, making it by far the lowest ground in the world. There is more than 30 million cu. km (7 million cu. miles) of ice in this ice sheet, and if melted entirely it would add 60–70 m (197–230 ft) to the water level of the global oceans. Global warming may be melting this great ice cap.

The first indication that something was afoot came in the 1990s when NASA scientists were analyzing radar pictures from satellites of glaciers flowing from the West Antarctic Ice Sheet (WAIS). The WAIS is the part of the ice sheet that covers Antarctica west of the Transarctic Mountains. It is smaller than the East Antarctic Ice Sheet (EAIS), accounting for only a tenth of the volume of Antarctic ice. The bulk of it lies on bedrock that has been depressed far below sea level by the weight. Around the edges, it merges with ice shelves such as the Ross Ice Shelf.

What the NASA scientists noticed from the satellite images was that the 'grounding line' – the point where a glacier flowing into the sea begins to float – on one of the WAIS's glaciers was retreating rapidly. Since then, scientists have found that all of the glaciers in the western Antarctic are retreating. A major review in 2009 showed that the rate of retreat has quadrupled since the 1990s. This matters because, while floating sea ice can be lost from the polar ice caps without any effect on global sea levels, ice that melts from the land-based ice sheets pours into the oceans, raising the water level and causing flooding to low-lying coasts.

OFF THE SHELF

One of the reasons glaciers seem to be retreating faster than ever is the collapse of ice shelves around them. In 2002, the world witnessed the spectacular collapse of the Larsen B Ice Shelf, the middle portion of the three big ice shelves in the Weddell Sea. Before summer 2002, this vast block of floating ice, 220 m

(722 ft) thick and covering 3,250 sq. km (1,255 sq. miles) had been there for more than 12,000 years. But that summer, over a period of just five weeks, the entire ice shelf shattered, releasing thousands of icebergs into the Weddell Sea. Then in April 2009, the Wilkins Ice Shelf followed the Larsen B into oblivion.

In itself, the loss of the ice shelves has no effect on global sea levels, because the ice in them is floating. But the signs are that the ice shelves helped hold up the glaciers that flowed out of the ice sheets. If the ice shelves go, then the glaciers are unblocked and can flow much quicker. This is why the apparently contradictory evidence of a slight decrease in melting on the top of the Antarctic ice sheet is no consolation. The surface may freeze harder, but if quantities of ice flow out from the ice sheet in glaciers and melt, a lot of extra water may end up in the sea.

THE BIG SHEET

Until recently, all the attention was focused on the small WAIS. It seemed as if nothing much was happening to the vast EAIS, a slab of ice 3 km (2 miles) thick completely covering a continent the size of Australia. If the WAIS melted altogether it would raise global sea levels by 5–7 m (16–23 ft). If the EAIS melted it would flood the world by a depth of 60 m (197 ft).

It seemed as if ice lost from the EAIS around the edges was being more than made up for by new freezing and snowfall in the middle. Then in late 2009, gravity measurements by NASA's GRACE satellite showed that ice loss from the edges of the EAIS is accelerating. In the Arctic, the Greenland ice sheet is losing 250 billion tonnes (275 billion tons) of ice a year, adding 0.7 mm (0.02 in) to the global sea level. The WAIS is only losing half that, while it seemed the EAIS was losing very little indeed. These new measurements show that Antarctica could be losing water faster than the Arctic. If so, the pace of sea level rise around the world could accelerate well beyond what is predicted, with worrying consequences for low-lying coastal communities and ecosystems.

Antarctic Mass Variation since 2002

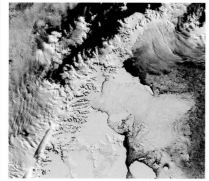

Before its spectacular collapse in 2002, the Larsen B iceshelf had floated rigidly on the Weddell Sea for more than 12,000 years, more than 200 m (655 ft) thick.

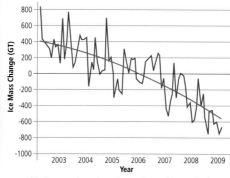

This diagram shows how the continent of Antarctica has been losing 100 cu. km (24 cu. miles) of its ice cover every year since 2002.

In summer 2002, the Larsen B iceshelf softened and collapsed in a matter of months, leaving a great gap like a pulled tooth in the ice around Antarctica.

△ *All recent scientific evidence suggests that all the glaciers in the Antarctic are slowly retreating as global temperatures warm. As land-based Antarctic ice melts into the sea, it may contribute to a significant rise in global sea levels.*

LIFE IN THE ICY OCEAN

THE WATERS OF THE SOUTHERN OCEAN may be stormy and bitterly cold, but the constant churning of the waters means they are astonishingly rich in marine life. The constant overturning of the waters draws up a superabundance of the nutrients that stimulate plankton growth. Indeed, the upward flood of nutrients here is so rich that in summer Antarctic waters are seven times more productive of phytoplankton than nearby sub-Antarctic waters.

This feast of phytoplankton feeds, in turn, on the banquet of shrimplike krill that form the bottom of a food chain that nourishes countless whales, seals, fish, squid, and seabirds. By themselves, krill are so tiny that they would not make much of a meal for a large marine animal, but they gather in such vast, closely packed schools that whales can strain a tonne or more in just a few minutes through their gigantic baleens.

ANTARCTIC MAMMALS

For most whales, only the summer months provide enough food to brave the cold. Once the weather cools and the krill swarms begin to dwindle, they head north to warmer waters to breed. Southern right whales, humpbacks, blues, fins, seis, and minkes are all summer visitors here.

Only the diminutive pygmy right whale stays here all year round, feeding mainly on copepods, not krill. Swimming in a slow, undulating motion, it would be easy to catch, but its small size of less than 6 m (20 ft) and remote habitat have probably helped save it from the whaling business. Killer whales hunt in the Southern Ocean in packs preying on larger fish, seals, penguins, and other seabirds.

There is food for some kinds of seals here all year round, and their thick blubber and fur insulates them from the worst of the cold. Little gatherings of Weddell seals can often be seen on the ice in summer, and in winter they escape from the blizzards in the water, breaking through the ice with their teeth to make holes to come up for air. Crabeater seals live in groups, too, and are seen on the sea ice in vast numbers – they are the most numerous large mammals on Earth in the wild. Despite their name, they feed mainly on krill. Big and aggressive leopard seals, though, are solitary hunters, lurking near the edges of the ice to catch a penguin, or snatch a fur seal if it comes too close. Ross seals are the least common seals. They are hard to see because they live in the middle of the pack ice away from predatory killer whales, surviving on squid caught in the water below. Beyond the ice are fur seals and huge elephant seals.

THE COLD BOTTOM

Unlike mammals, fish cannot cross easily into the icy Antarctic waters, and of nearly 20,000 kinds of fish around the world, only about 100 are ever seen in the Southern Ocean. Most of these live near the seabed and three-quarters of them belong to the Notothenioid family of icefish, with their remarkable ability to survive the cold (see page 116). The few other bottom dwellers include eelpouts (*Zoarcidae*), snailfish (*Liparidae*), rat-tails (*Macrouridae*), and the codlike *Gadidae*. Near to the Antarctic shore, the seabed is inhabited by sessile hydrozoans, corals, sponges, and bryozoans, as well as the foraging, crablike pycnogonids and isopods, the annelid worm *Polychaeta*, echinoids, starfish, and a variety of crustaceans and molluscs.

△ *The Census of Marine Life is revealing a host of new species in the Southern Ocean, including the* Epimeria, *a 25-m (80-ft) long amphipod crustacean found near Elephant Island, Antarctica, in 2010 by the team on the research ship* Polarstern.

Patagonian Toothfish

As overfishing drove trawlers to hunt farther afield for catches, so they began to fish far to the south in the waters off southern Chile and Argentina, and even into the Southern Ocean. Their prime target was the Patagonian toothfish, also known as Chilean sea bass, which unfortunately for it, tastes delicious. So sought after has this fish of the cold seas become that it fetches premium prices in top-end restaurants and is also known as 'white gold'.

This large, remarkable fish lives in deep water around seamounts and islands in the sub-Antarctic, where it forms the prime food of sperm whales, elephant seals, colossal squids, and many other species. Like many deep-living, coldwater fish, though, it grows slowly and lives long and so is vulnerable to overfishing – and that is just what has happened. Although it only became a target in the early 1990s, it was commercially fished out within five years.

Many scientists argue that the quotas put in place since to save it from extinction are too generous. But the real problem has been illegal catches, which may at times have accounted for much of the trade. Since 2004, regular patrols may have reduced the pirate catch dramatically. The National Oceanic and Atmospheric Administration (NOAA) and other organizations argue that it is restaurateurs' and fishmongers' responsibility to make sure they buy fish only from legal sources, but that is not always easy to verify. Many environmental organizations argue that Patagonian toothfish should not be on anyone's dinner menu anyway – not just because of the danger to the toothfish itself, but because of the key role it plays in the Antarctic food chain, and because too many albatrosses and petrels are unfortunate victims of the longline fishing methods used to catch the fish.

The circulation of water means that many of these extraordinary bottom-dwelling species are found far under the floating ice. However, in March 2010, NASA scientists drilling through 180-m (590-ft) thick ice nearly 20 km (12 miles) from open water on the Ross Ice Shelf were astonished to find their cameras catching a glimpse of a pink shrimplike amphipod *Lyssianasid*. In fact, amphipods are quite common under the ice, and when the Larsen B Ice Shelf collapsed in 2002, scientists also found clams and large mats of bacteria in the ocean beneath where the ice had been.

Up on top of the ice, the ferocious cold is braved only by seals and by the penguins. Of the 17 species of penguins, only four actually breed in Antarctica – the adelie, the chinstrap, the emperor, and the gentoo. Most of the others are found on the sub-Antarctic islands such as South Georgia, which, with its deep fjords, massive glaciers, and icebergs is a vital nesting site for millions of other seabirds including fulmars, petrels, cormorants, skuas, gulls, terns, sheathbills, and albatrosses.

Strangely, the Antarctic's penguins are now experiencing something of a population boom. The decimation of baleen whales by whaling in the last century has been good for the penguins because huge amounts of krill once hoovered up by whales has become available for these birds. Penguins breed in large rookeries on ice or bare land, where 180,000 or more birds may be crowded together in an unforgettable, noisy, smelly mass. Some species, though, spend more than 75 percent of their lives at sea, swimming and diving for fish with a grace and agility that counterbalances their awkward waddling on land.

▽ *Because oxygen dissolves better at lower temperatures, the unique Antarctic icefish (seen here with brittle stars and yellow sponges) has no need of red haemoglobin cells in its blood to carry oxygen around its bodies. Its blood is consequently much thinner and requires less energy to pump around the body.*

WHALING BUSINESS

ALMOST THREE DECADES AFTER the first complete ban on commercial whaling, whales are still hunted and killed and many believe it is too late to save some of these magnificent creatures from extinction.

Few environmental causes have as much widespread support as the ban on whales. It has long been acknowledged that catching whales in any number is unsustainable, as the number of whale species and populations in serious danger bears ample witness. Moreover, the more that people learn about whales, the more they are horrified by the idea of slaughtering these beautiful, intelligent creatures.

THE WHALING BAN

As whale numbers plummeted in the middle of the last century, and more and more people protested on humane grounds, the International Whaling Commission (IWC) introduced a total ban on all commercial whaling in 1982, a ban brought into force in 1986. By then, many species, especially blue and humpback whales, were in deep trouble. At that time there were thought to be just 450 blue whales around the world, and there was serious doubt if they could survive.

The blue whale, the largest creature that ever lived, seems to have just about come back from the brink, and there are now maybe 3,000 blue whales altogether. That is a long way short of the 220,000 of the species that there were in pre-whaling days, but it shows the value of the ban.

AVOIDING THE BAN

Not every country goes along with the IWC ban, however. Norway, for instance, officially objected to the ban, and so was exempted. Japan and Iceland accepted the ban, but have exploited a loophole that allows whales to be hunted for 'scientific research'. In fact, more than 25,000 whales have been killed since the ban came into place, and 1,700 whales were killed in 2009 alone (up from 300 in 1990). As other threats begin to make themselves felt on the diminished whale population, such as global warming, by-catch, and toxic waste, the frustration of many countries that some nations are still catching and killing whales has sparked some bitter tensions.

By far the majority of nations agree that no whales should be caught at all. But Japan and Iceland argue that there is a 'sustainable' catch, and that whales are depleting the world's fish stocks. At a key meeting of the IWC in 2006, they successfully argued that a complete moratorium on whaling was unnecessary, and they had the backing of some undeveloped countries, such as the Pacific island nation of Tuvalu who, it is alleged, have been offered development aid in return for their support. Since then, Japan has not only increased its 'scientific quota' (they took more than 1,000 whales in 2009), but also continued to send whaling ships inside the Southern Ocean Whale Sanctuary, making a mockery of the sanctuary's purpose.

THE FIGHT FOR WHALES

Tempers threatened to boil over when in January 2010 a Japanese whaling ship rammed and sank the Sea Shepherd whale conservation group's catamaran *Ady Gil*, which was trying to monitor their activities in the Southern Ocean. Then in April 2010, the IWC proposed a deal with Japan and the other whaling nations. In return for allowing the IWC to close the 'scientific research' loophole, the whaling nations would be allowed to resume commercial whaling under 'strictly enforceable' quotas.

Under the proposal, Japan's limit would fall to 400 Antarctic whales in 2011 (it took a little over 500 in 2009), then fall again in the 2015–2016 season to 200. Iceland, which caught 125 fin whales in 2009, would get a quota of 80 fin whales and 80 minke whales, while Norway would get a 600 minke whale limit. The whaling nations also proposed that the catch should be DNA checked – an important point since DNA tests of whale meat on sale had revealed that more whales had been caught than were officially declared.

Many argued that this deal was an important breakthrough and would finally bring whaling under proper control and save anywhere between 4,000 and 18,000 whales from the hunt. Other whale conservationists were hugely dismayed, pointing

◁ *Despite the international moritorium on whaling, Japanese whaling ships like this, the* Yushin Maru, *continue to hunt whales for 'scientific' purposes, but the whale meat is often fed to Japanese schoolchildren.*

Underestimating Whales

The IWC says there can be no more whaling at all until populations have returned to 54 percent of their historic levels. But just what are their 'historic levels'? In 2003, Stephen Palumbi and Joe Roman of Harvard published a study that suggested those historic levels had been hugely underestimated. They analyzed whales today for their mitochondrial DNA and found that it was tremendously varied for such small numbers of whales. Such variation, Palumbi and Roman argued, could only be explained if there were many, many more whales in the past than official estimates suggest. The IWC suggests that, in the past, there were 40,000 fin whales and 20,000 humpbacks. Since there are now about 10,000 humpbacks, it might not be long before numbers reach the 54 percent benchmark and hunting can resume. Palumbi and Roman estimate that there were almost ten times those numbers of fin whales – 360,000 fins and 240,000 humpbacks. Their theory still provokes fierce controversy.

▷ *Like Japan, Iceland accepts the international ban on whaling, but continues to take a small number of whales each year for the permitted exception of scientific purposes, such as this fin whale hauled ashore at Hvalfjordur.*

out that besides allowing commercial whaling again almost 30 years after it had been banned outright, it only tied in the whaling nations for ten years – after which they would be free to resume whaling without limits. The proposal will probably be rejected, but the battle is still on.

Outsiders are not quite sure why Japan champions whaling so keenly. Whaling became popular in Japan in the years after the war when there was a shortage of protein. But now demand for whale meat in Japan has all but dried up, and much of the whale meat catch is simply frozen and stockpiled, or sold off at rock bottom prices. Moreover, there are now cheaper and more plentiful substitutes for all the other products that once came from whales, such as whale oil. Many people believe that it is a matter of national pride to protect the way of life of the few whaling harbours that survive. The future of whales, meanwhile, is in serious doubt.

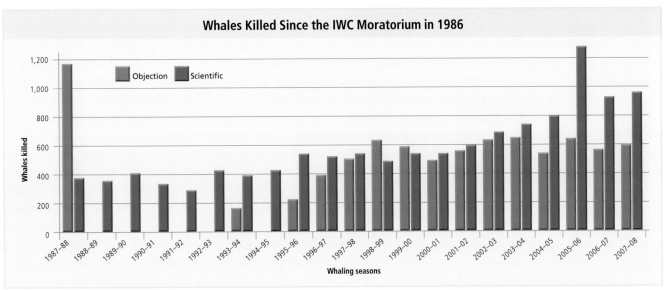

WHALE SANCTUARY

EVER SINCE IT WAS ESTABLISHED IN 1994, THE SOUTHERN OCEAN WHALE
SANCTUARY HAS BEEN A FOCUS OF DISPUTE IN THE WHALING INDUSTRY.

With whale numbers still in decline and whale populations
in the Southern Ocean, in particular, in a parlous state, the
International Whaling Commission (IWC) decided to establish
an area of 50 million sq. km (19 million sq. miles) in the
Southern Ocean to be known as the Southern Ocean Whale
Sanctuary. Within this area, commercial whaling was to be
banned for all time.

It was not a new idea. The IWC had created a whale
sanctuary in Antarctic waters as long ago as 1938, and only
opened it again in 1955 to reduce pressure on surrounding
waters. And in 1979, the IWC had established a sanctuary
covering the entire Indian Ocean. The Southern Ocean
sanctuary was intended to protect whales in their summer
feeding grounds as well as the breeding places in the warmer
Indian Ocean to which they migrated. Since 80 percent of the
world's whales spend some time in the Southern Ocean, it
seemed a valuable measure of protection.

THE BATTLE FOR WHALES

To outsiders, the establishment of a wildlife sanctuary seems
harmless enough. But the Southern Ocean Whale Sanctuary
has been the focus of bitter controversy ever since its creation.
The meeting to create the sanctuary in Puerto Vallata in Mexico
in 1994 was riven with political intrigue as Japan campaigned
vigorously against the idea. In the end, 23 member nations
of the IWC voted for the sanctuary and only Japan voted
against. But the battle did not stop there.

The Japanese have tried to have the sanctuary declared
illegal ever since. The Japanese received some support from
American academics who argued that the sanctuary was not
based on any scientific rationale and was simply a political act.
Meanwhile, the Japanese have continually asserted their rights to
hunt whales in the Southern Ocean. Again and again, using their
'scientific quota' as justification (see page 190), Japanese whaling
ships have headed south into the stormy Antarctic waters to
hunt 935 minke and 10 fin whales each year. Again
and again, they have fought a running battle with whale
conservationists who send out boats to monitor and hamper
their operations. This culminated in the showdown in which
the conservationist boat *Ady Gil* was rammed and sunk by the
whalers in January 2010.

THE SANCTUARY BREACHED

The question of the Southern Ocean Whale Sanctuary, thought to
have been settled back in 1994, came back onto the agenda at the
IWC talks in Morocco in April 2010. The new deal, which would
let Japan, Iceland, and Norway resume commercial whaling with
limited quotas for ten years, may reopen the Southern Ocean.
Much to the outrage of some whale conservationists, Japanese
whaling ships would be legally entitled under the deal to sail
into the whale sanctuary and hunt a certain number of minke

▽ *Thanks to the whaling moratorium, Southern right whales are now not
quite as rare as they had become, and the establishment of the Southern Ocean
Whale Sanctuary may ensure pods like these become a more common sight.*

and fin whales simply for commercial reasons.

The ending of protection for fin whales seems particularly galling to some. Fin whales, the second largest of all the whales, are an endangered species. The Antarctic population is especially threatened, with some estimates suggesting that there may be as few as 2,000 fins in the Southern Ocean, where once 400,000 are thought to have lived. After the IWC meeting at which the deal to allow hunting of fins inside the sanctuary was proposed, New Zealand Foreign Minister Murray McCully fulminated, 'The proposal to include fin whales in the Southern Ocean [in the deal] is inflammatory. New Zealanders will not accept this.' Clearly the battle for the future of whales is not over.

THE WHALE HUNT

Whaling dates back thousands of years, but it was in the 19th century when whale oil was in demand for lamps that the whale hunt began on a massive scale. Herman Melville's great novel *Moby Dick* gave whaling a heroic, if grim, image. But there was nothing heroic in the rising tide of whale slaughter that continued with the coming of factory ships that could dismember and package whales at sea – this escalated the numbers of whales caught to what people realized were unsustainable levels as long ago as the 1930s.

By the 1940s, numbers of the bigger whales, such as blues, were so reduced that the whalers were forced to pursue smaller quarry, first fin and humpback whales in the 1950s and 1960s until they became scarcer, and finally seis and minkes. The focus of whaling shifted, too, from the Antarctic, where whales were already rare, to the North Pacific. With numbers

△ *Dwarf minke whales were only recently identified as a separate species from other minke whales. They are found off the Great Barrier reef, where tourists swim with them, but to survive they rely on their home in the Southern Ocean.*

Most Endangered		
Species	**Population**	**Status**
Northern right whale	500–1,000	endangered (ESA, IUCN)
Southern right whale	3,000	endangered (ESA); vulnerable (IUCN)
Bowhead whale	8,000	endangered (ESA, IUCN)
Blue whale	10,000–14,000	endangered (ESA, IUCN)
Fin whale	120,000–150,000	endangered (ESA); vulnerable (IUCN)
Sei whale	50,000	endangered (ESA)
Humpback whale	10,000+	endangered (ESA, IUCN)
Sperm whale	200,000	endangered (ESA)

of all kinds of whales dwindling at an alarming rate, the first international agreement to limit whaling was introduced in 1946. It prohibited the catching of right and grey whales and limited the take in Antarctica to 15,000 'Blue Whale Units' in which one blue whale equalled two fin, two and a half humpbacks, and six seis. In the 1960s, humpback and blue whales were added to the list. But as numbers continued to plummet and more and more people became outraged by the idea of killing whales, the pressure for an outright ban escalated until in 1982, the IWC banned all commercial whaling, leaving only the loophole for 'scientific' whaling.

THE ARCTIC OCEAN

Almost entirely covered by floating ice for half the year, the Arctic is the least accessible and bleakest of all the oceans of the world.

From late autumn through to late spring, the Arctic Ocean is entirely hidden from view beneath the ice, which stretches with blinding whiteness for thousands of kilometres around the North Pole. Indeed, until the late 19th century, geographers were not entirely sure that there was an ocean under the North Pole.

Unlike the other oceans, which are linked by the Southern Ocean, the Arctic is surrounded by land, connected to the Pacific only via the narrow Bering Strait, and to the Atlantic via the shallow shelf that all but connects Greenland, Iceland, the Faroes, Shetlands, and Norway. Indeed, it is quite possible that 20,000 years ago, early humans walked and canoed all the way from Europe to North America along the edge of the Arctic ice, treating it as icy land, not an ocean. Every winter, land animals such as foxes and hares roam across the Arctic ice just as they would across snowfields on land.

But the solidity of the ice is just an illusion. Even in winter, it is no more than a few metres thick, and beneath is one of the world's most fascinating oceans. Every year it goes through a teasing cycle in which the warmth of summer melts half the ice to reveal the hidden ocean beneath, bathed in daylight that lasts almost 24 hours a day in high summer. Then when winter comes, the ocean vanishes again as a new covering of ice spreads over the water, and the long Arctic nights cloak the scene in almost perpetual darkness.

◁ *Every spring the vast sheet of ice that almost entirely covers the Arctic Ocean rapidly melts, until it is just an island of floating pack ice amid the waters of the world's coldest seas.*

THE ARCTIC BASIN

Because so much of the Arctic Ocean is covered with ice, it has been much harder to explore than the other oceans. Even today, much of the ocean floor cannot be mapped by satellite as the other oceans can, because of the screen of ice. It has only been in the last few decades that the Arctic has begun to yield some of its secrets, as scientific explorations have drilled through the ice to experiment with sonar and seabed bores, and submersibles have ventured far under the ice.

What they have discovered leaves some mystery as to just how the Arctic Ocean formed. It seems that this happened about 55 million years ago, as Eurasia began to separate from North America. But it also seems there are far more fragments, and hard-to-explain ridges and seafloor variations, than there are in some of the larger oceans. The central ridge from which the Arctic Ocean floor is spreading links up with the Mid-Atlantic Ridge north of Iceland, but suddenly shifts far to the west between Greenland and Svalbard along the 'Spitsbergen Fracture Zone' to begin a new ridge, known as the Nansen or Gakkel Ridge. The Nansen Ridge stretches in almost a straight line for 1,800 km (1,118 miles) between north Greenland and the Laptev Sea on the north coast of Russia.

▽ *Walruses like to haul themselves onto floating ice packs to bask and breed, but they are being forced ashore more and more as Arctic ice melts.*

△ *Bowhead whales are the first whales to return to the Arctic in spring, following 'leads', natural channels in the ice, to reach their summer feeding grounds.*

THE WORLD'S SLOWEST SPREADER

No ocean ridge on Earth spreads more slowly than the Nansen, which moves less than 1 cm (0.4 in) a year – compared to 20 cm (8 in) for the East Pacific Rise. Until recently, it was thought that it was so sluggish there would be no volcanic activity there at all. But since 2001, a series of explorations with ice-breaking ships and remote operated vehicles (ROVs) has shown there is plenty going on, including as rich a collection of hydrothermal vents as the Atlantic Ocean.

All the same, the ridge does not seem to have spread the ocean floor that far. The continental slope of the Eurasian continent is just a few hundred kilometres away to the south. Although the Arctic looks quite large from the air, its basin is actually quite small, since more than a third of it is continental shallows. To the north of Eurasia, the continental shelf, underlying the East Siberian, Laptev, and Barents seas, stretches 500 to 1,800 km (310 to 1,118 miles) beyond the coast. Islands such as Svalbard and Franz Josef Land, though far from the mainland, are actually part of the continent of Eurasia, just as the countless large islands to the north of Canada, including Ellesmere and Baffin, are part of the North American continent.

RIDGES AND BASINS

Even the abyssal depths of the Arctic are broken up into numerous submarine ridges and deep basins that disrupt deep-water circulation. Parallel to the Nansen Ridge are two other submarine mountain ranges, each as high as the Alps, gripping the ocean floor like bony fingers – the Lomonosov and the Mendeleyev Ridges. In between these ridges lie deep basins. The North Pole is situated in between the Nansen and Lomonosov Ridge, which is why the basin between them is known as the Pole Plain. Adventurers reaching the North Pole are standing on floating ice just a few metres thick above an abyssal ocean more than 4,300 m (14,100 ft) deep!

It seems that, as Eurasia and North America split apart, the break-up was less than clean, and numerous fragments of each have been left as underwater ridges and plateaus on the ocean floor between them. The Lomonosov is one. So is the Jan Mayen Ridge north of Iceland and the Chukchi Plateau that stretches into the Arctic Ocean basin beyond the Chukchi Sea. Other ridges, though, are simply spreading ridges that seem to have long since gone to sleep, such as the Aegir Ridge in the Norway Basin. To the west of the Aegir is a small continent beneath the sea, once connected to Greenland and known as the Jan Mayen microcontinent. This extends some 500 km (310 miles) beneath the sea to the northeast of Iceland.

ARCTIC ICE

THE ARCTIC IS ONE OF THE COLDEST places on Earth. In summer, the sun peeks over the top of the world here, and sets only shortly before sunrise. Even so, it stays so low in the sky that the weather is cool at best. By the time autumn arrives, the sun barely creeps above the horizon for more than a few hours. By midwinter, it does not rise at all. It is twilight or completely dark 24 hours a day and the temperatures plummet at times to –70°C (–94°F).

The low angle of the sun means that some slopes remain forever in deep, chilly shadow. Even on sunny slopes, the white covering of snow reflects heat away so effectively that a bitter cold descends as soon as the sun dips below the horizon. The coldness of the air above the ice means it can hold little moisture, and in some places, the Arctic gets less rain than

▽ *These scientists are exploring the Beaufort Gyre, the remarkable circulating accumulation of freshwater in the Arctic Ocean created by the melting of sea ice. Some scientists believe this will play a vital role in future climate change.*

a tropical desert. Only in the autumn, when clouds move in off the sea, does moisture fall, usually in the form of snow. When the cold air drains out over the warm sea, though, moisture evaporates readily from the surface to form the steam fogs that are so common in the Arctic.

THE ANNUAL ICEFEST

It is in autumn, too, that the sea ice in the Arctic begins to expand again, after a summer of melting back. Typically in late summer, when the ice is at its minimum, it covers just less than half the Arctic Ocean. In winter, it grows to cover 80 percent of the ocean surface. The Arctic surface water is very low in salt and freezes quite readily. As soon as the weather cools enough, millions of tiny ice crystals begin to form in the water, creating a slushy mix at the surface called 'frazil ice'. As the temperature drops further, the frazil ice thickens, creating a layer of slushy ice called 'grease ice' because it gives the ocean a slick, oily look. Sometimes, the frazil congeals into lumps called 'shuga' because they look a little like sugar. Within the ice are bubbles of extra-salty water left behind as the ocean water froze.

GETTING FRAZILLED

The colder the weather gets, the more chunks of frazil that may freeze together into plates called pancakes. The dense salt bubbles sink slowly through the slush, making it easier for the top layers of water to freeze. Soon the surface freezes in places into sheets of ice so thin that they flex with every slight ripple. At first these sheets, known as 'nilas', are as thin and clear as a window, but as the temperature drops, they turn first grey, then white as the ice grows steadily thicker. Eventually the sheets are so thick that they will no longer flex with the waves. Instead, they break up into myriad tiny cakes of ice, jostling this way and that on the cold ocean surface.

As the temperature drops further, the pancakes thicken and fuse together into giant rafts of ice, known as pack ice. Pack ice is so thick that waves barely move them. Only the biggest swells will snap them and break them into chunks known as ice floes, which turn the surface into a maze of spiky chunks in places.

By mid-September, pack ice is beginning to form along the northern coasts of Canada and Russia, and spreads out from Greenland and the North Pole, where there is ice all through the summer. By mid-October, there is a solid ledge right around the Arctic, extending far beyond the summer ice from the North Pole. As winter progresses, the ice sheets thicken and link up to form a continuous raft of pack ice covering a vast area of the Arctic Ocean. As snow falls on the ice and freezes, the pack ice may grow to 2m (6.5 ft) or so thick by May – but never much thicker, because the ice and snow insulates the ocean water from the cold air so that it never grows cold enough to freeze any further.

THE MIGHTY THAW

As the winter ends and spring arrives, the ice begins to thaw, with shallow pools appearing on the surface. Rising temperatures make some pools melt right through the ice and form cracks. The cracks widen into channels or 'leads' that separate the pack ice into floes. Many floes melt into smaller and smaller pieces and eventually melt away altogether.

Annual ice, the pack ice that forms in winter but melts in summer, usually reaches its maximum in early May then melts away until mid-September when it begins to re-form. Multi-year ice, the ice that stays frozen through the summer year after year may melt a little at the surface in summer. The meltwater drains through the ice. Because it is freshwater, it then sits floating on top of the denser salt of the ocean beneath. When the winter comes, this freshwater will freeze quickly on to the bottom of the ice, allowing it to grow a little thicker than the annual ice – maybe up to 8 m (26 ft). But the summer melt ensures it never grows much thicker. The Arctic ice may look as solid as land in winter, but this is just an illusion; a few metres down there is nothing but deep ocean.

▽ *By July each year, much of the pack ice that extends far across the Arctic Ocean in winter is melting away, with cracks in the ice growing steadily bigger. The hills in the distance here are the island of Svalbard, Norway.*

Fast and Loose

Pack ice that is frozen fast to the land is known as fast ice. But the huge slab of ice that covers most of the Arctic Ocean is known as drift ice because it is not fixed, but slowly drifts – something polar adventurers have to bear in mind when crossing the ice. It was the great Norwegian explorer Fridtjof Nansen (1861–1930) who first demonstrated this in the 1890s. Norwegian meteorologist Henrik Mohn (1835–1916) had speculated that when articles from a ship wrecked north of Siberia turned up a few years later in Greenland, they must have drifted with the ice.

Nansen's idea was to allow his polar expedition ship *Fram* to get locked in the ice and then use the drift to take it to the North Pole. Because the drift was east–west, it actually took the *Fram* towards Greenland, from where Nansen tried to walk to the Pole. He failed in his attempt, but had proved the movement of the ice. It is now known that there are two main ice movements in the Arctic – the Transpolar Drift, which moves from east to west across northern Russia, and the Beaufort Gyre which makes a giant clockwise loop through the Beaufort Sea north of Canada, taking four years to complete a circuit.

▽ *As the coming of winter brings ever colder weather, the early slush of frazil ice begins to freeze together into thin discs or polygons known as pancake ice that are up to 3 m (10 ft) thick. The pancakes float freely, but have raised rims that are formed when pieces float into each other and slush splash freezes on the edges.*

ARCTIC LIFE

COVERED WITH ICE FOR MUCH OF THE YEAR, plunged into almost total darkness throughout the winter, and experiencing some of the coldest seas in the world, the Arctic is not the world's most hospitable habitat. Indeed, it was once thought that the Arctic was all but bereft of life, except for a few very hardy survivors around the edge. But as marine biologists have finally found ways to explore and study this wintry realm, they have realized that it is actually teeming with life – even in the gloomy waters far under the ice.

Not only are there the uncrowned kings of the Arctic, polar bears, but also a complex food chain supporting these apex predators, including plankton, crustaceans, fish, birds, walruses, seals, and whales. The key to this abundance, as always, is a supply of food, and at the heart of this food supply are the phytoplankton that draw their energy from the Arctic summer sunlight.

THE ICE BLOOMS

Every spring, as the long dark night of the Arctic winter draws to a close and the Sun finally climbs into the sky, light begins to filter through the ice to the water below. Like mould on a damp ceiling, algae responds by growing on the underside of the ice. Woods Hole oceanographer Carin Ashjian describes the way 'one green, stringlike form, *Melosira*, grows long, hanging under the ice like Spanish moss. It eventually detaches from the under-ice surface and sinks to the seafloor where it is consumed by the animals living there.'

▽ *Male narwhals are easily identified by their long, single tusk, which can grow up to 3 m (10 ft) long. This is thought to be sexual display, like a lion's mane or a peacock's tail feathers. Here, narwhals group in an icebreak off Baffin Island, Nunavut.*

And there are a huge number of animals living on the Arctic seafloor, all depending on the stream of organic material that falls down from the ice. The Arctic has a seafloor society as rich as any ocean in the world, except perhaps the Southern Ocean. Of the 5,000 or so species of marine invertebrates that live in the Arctic, 90 percent are on the seafloor. On the continental shelves, there are crustaceans such as amphipods and sand fleas, polychaetes such as bristle worms, and many bivalve molluscs, often burrowed deep in the sediment. On top of the sediment there are brittlestars everywhere in huge numbers, while the Barents Sea is heavily populated with sea urchins and the Laptev Sea north of Russia with sea cucumbers.

THE MOVING FEAST

Near the surface, however, as days grow longer and light and warmth increase, the snow that covered the sea ice in winter begins to melt. Once the snow melts, light begins to stream through the ice and stimulate the growth of huge amounts of phytoplankton, especially along the ice edge. As the ice begins to break up, a bloom of phytoplankton spreads into a wide 20–80 km (12–50 miles) belt around the edge of the ice.

With the warmer weather, the ice edge retreats northward and the phytoplankton moves with it, followed by huge swarms of shrimplike copepods and other zooplankton that feed on the phytoplankton, and a host of fish that feed on the zooplankton, such as Arctic cod and capelin. The fish in turn attract fish-eaters, including bigger fish such as Arctic char, Greenland halibut, and Atlantic salmon, and mammals such as ringed, bearded, harp, and hooded seals, as well as cetaceans such as belugas, bowheads, and narwhals. Myriads of seabirds, such

△ *Ringed seals are truly at home in the Arctic Ocean like no other mammal, because they can make breathing holes to pop up through the ice. This one is basking on fast-ice in Lilliehook Fjord, Spitsbergen, Norway.*

▷ *One of the most remarkable discoveries in recent years was the blooming of green algae in spring on the underside of sea ice, providing a feast for krill, which in turn attract a summer cornucopiea of wildlife to the Arctic Ocean.*

as fulmars and terns, join in, too. And so the feasting moves northward with the ice edge throughout the summer.

SEAL WATCH

For seals, the ice edge makes a perfect platform for resting between meals and for mating and raising pups. The drawback is that on the ice they are vulnerable to attack by polar bears and Arctic foxes. Polar bears occasionally prey on walruses that bask on the ice edge and dive to the seabed to feed on crustaceans, which is why they prefer the shallows over the continental shelf. But a big walrus is more than a match for a polar bear.

Most seals can go no farther than the ice edge. But ringed seals can dive far under the ice, since they can make breathing holes in the ice. So unlike other seals, they can live throughout the Arctic Ocean. But it is their breathing holes that make them the favourite prey of polar bears, which sit and wait by the holes for the seal to pop its head up for a breather. Ringed seals are also prey to wolves and wolverines that hunt out on the ice in winter, and killer whales that lurk beneath it.

Life on the Ice

Scientists once thought that ice was a killer and that no organisms could survive in solid ice. In fact, the Arctic sea ice is full of life. Even if much of it is too small to see with the naked eye, a microscope reveals numerous tiny organisms. Bacteria, archaea, algae, protists, flatworms, and even small crustaceans are all able not just to live within the ice but are able to thrive. Some remain active in the ice even down to temperatures of −20°C (−4°F).

Nearer the bottom of the ice, a variety of other microbes live within the web of brine channels, the drains of extra salty water created as the ice freezes. And the underside of the ice is thickly carpeted with minute organisms, many of whom find valuable refuges from predators amid the ice's nooks and crannies. Algae, small crustaceans, and tiny fish live here in abundance, and in places, huge growths of pinnate diatoms turn the underside of the ice golden brown.

SHRINKING ICE

SINCE THE ICE CAP FIRST BEGAN TO FORM year after year in the Arctic some three million years ago, it has never been thick. Even though there are a few places where pressure from the surrounding ice creates deep 'keels' extending some 30 m (100 ft) down into the ocean, over much of the Arctic the ice is just a few metres thick, and melts easily in summer. Only the multi-year ice lasts for long. But now it all seems to be melting away.

MELTDOWN

Scientists have been watching the Arctic ice closely since 1979, and noticed the extent of the summer ice slowly shrinking each year up until 2000. Every year, the sea froze over as usual, but each summer, a little bit more would melt away. For a while, it was not that much – just 1 percent a year. But since 2000, melting has accelerated.

In summer 2007, the ice hit a dramatic record low. When a satellite scanned the Arctic on 16 September that year, it measured just 4.13 million sq. km (1.6 million sq. miles) of sea ice – more than a fifth less ice than the previous record low in 2005. That meant an area of ice the size of California and Texas combined had been lost in just two years. Overall, the ice was a massive third down on the 6.74 million sq. km (2.6 million sq. mile) average for 1979 to 2000. The following year, the summer was cool and a little less ice melted. Then in summer 2009, even less ice melted. But 2007, 2008, and 2009 were still the three smallest ice years on record by some way. The situation in winter was little better, with the maximum ice extent hitting record and near record lows in March 2006 and 2007, with just 14.5 million sq. km (6 million sq. miles) of ice.

THIN ICE

It is not just the extent of the ice that is diminishing. Now it seems to be getting thinner, too. For the first five winters of this century, the Arctic sea ice seemed to be getting slowly thinner year by year. On average, the ice was about 2.5 m (8.2 ft) thick. Then, after the record summer melt of 2007, it suddenly began to thin alarmingly. In the winter of 2007–2008 it lost nearly 0.45 m (1.5 ft) in the western Arctic, slimming to barely 2 m (6.5 ft) thick. What was most noticeable was that for the first time a lot of older ice was being lost.

It is still not clear whether this is a long-term change, or just a short-term variation. In 2007, scientists discovered a reversal in the circulation of the Arctic Ocean that may be triggered by the Arctic Oscillation. The Arctic Oscillation is a natural shift in the pattern of atmospheric circulation that takes place every decade or so, bringing either high pressure or low pressure to the polar region. Since the 1970s, it seems to have been stuck in its 'positive' phase, when pressure over the North Pole is low, and this brings warmer weather to North America and northern Eurasia.

Shrinking Ice

1981–2000

2009

For three years continually, from 2007 to 2009, there was less ice in the Arctic during the summer than ever before – and even less in winter. What is most telling, as these maps show, is the extent of the old, long-lasting ice that has shrunk dramatically over the last decade. The red on the map shows how, between 1981 and 2000, the median area of old ice was almost twice as big as Greenland (far left). In 2009, it was barely a quarter of that size (near left).

First year ice (< 1 year old)

Second year ice (1–2 years old)

Older ice (> 2 years old)

▽ *This female polar bear is hunting for seals on sea ice, off the coast of Norway. In summer, most polar bears drift across the Arctic on rafts of ice, finding mates, hunting for ringed and bearded seals, and fattening themselves up for winter. But as the world warms, these rafts are shrinking and the gaps between the ice are becoming too great for the polar bears to cross. The polar bears' habitat is literally melting away.*

GETTING WARMER?

Of course, other scientists believe that the main culprit for the ice melt is global warming. Average annual temperatures on Ellesmere Island have warmed by 2°C (3.6°F) over the past 50 years and winter temperatures have risen by nearly 5°C (9°F). The effect is that less ice is returning in winter to compensate for the loss of ice in the summer melt. Moreover, as the sea ice retreats, the shelves of fast ice around the edge become more vulnerable to rolling swells coming off the open water, which shake off pieces that then melt easily. In the past, the ice tended to damp down any movement of the ocean, but in recent years scientists have noticed increasing turbulence along the continental shelves in the summer, and this may accelerate melting.

The effect of all these changes on wildlife in the Arctic is hard to predict. There are some signs that the melting of the sea ice may allow nutrient-rich water to rise to the surface over wider areas. If so, it could stimulate explosions of plankton growth and provide a feast for Arctic animals that feed on them, but this is far from certain. Phytoplankton growth seems also to be stimulated by the longer growing season. This bloom may, incidentally, help absorb some of the carbon dioxide that is causing global warming.

The loss of sea ice also has the potential to accelerate global warming trends and to change climate patterns. A small temperature increase at the poles may lead to still greater warming over time, making the poles the most sensitive regions to climate change on Earth.

Yet many sea mammals, such as walruses and seals, are dependent on the ice edge. If the ice edge moved too far away from the shore, walruses, which rely on access to shallow water, may be in trouble. Polar bears meanwhile depend on roaming far and wide. If the distances between ice floes and islands become too great, they may be left stranded, as many polar bears were on Wrangel Island in the warm summer of 1990, leaving them to rely on scavenging walrus carcasses in order to survive.

DIRTY ICE

IN THE SUNSHINE, WHEN THE SKY IS LIQUID BLUE and the snow and ice are a dazzling white, the Arctic Ocean seems a place of unsullied natural purity – but is it?

It is hard to imagine a natural wilderness so pristine and so remote from the dirt and the mess of the urban world as the Arctic. Yet even here, the grime of modern living has lain its filthy fingers on it, and because the Arctic ecosystem is so fragile and finely balanced, the effects of even a little pollution could be significant.

ARCTIC HAZE

Every spring, a persistent brown haze appears more and more often in the once stunningly clear Arctic skies above the Canadian side of the Arctic Ocean. As two Utah meteorologists, Tim Garrett and Lisa Versalla, showed, this haze, now known as Arctic haze, first appeared in the 1800s. Arctic explorer Nordenskjold described in 1870 not only the haze but a fine dust, grey in colour (and when wet, black or dark brown), distributed over the inland ice in a layer that he estimated at 0.1–1 mm (0.003–0.039 in) in depth. Nordenskjold found the dust was a metallic soot, which

▽ *The Arctic has until recently been one of the few entirely unpolluted environments in the world, as pure as the white snow that covers it for much of the year, but its oil wealth is proving too much of a lure for big oil companies.*

he assumed came from cosmic sources, but is more likely to have been industrial pollution. Recent ice cores show that the Arctic air was polluted with soot from coal fires at the beginning of the 20th century, but by the 1970s the main culprit was burning oil.

Although Arctic haze sullies the purity of the Arctic sky, it is not yet clear if it does much damage to the environment. In spring, air bearing the fine particles travels north into the Arctic at the edge of the zone of advancing sunlight. Once it reaches the Arctic Ocean, it seems to be deposited, with the carbon in it darkening the snow slightly and hastening melting, the sulphates adding acidity to the ocean waters, and toxic metals settling on the ice and in the sea. But the levels at present seem low enough to make no measurable difference.

TOXIC CHEMICALS

It is the accumulation of other less visible pollutants that is more of a worry. There are disturbing accumulations of toxic compounds, particularly organochlorines such as dioxins and PCBs (polychlorinated biphenyls), and some heavy metals, in snow, water, and some organisms in the North American Arctic, Greenland, and Svalbard. Arctic organisms seem much more sensitive to pollution than organisms elsewhere. Many animals, adapted to storing biological energy to cope with the cold, may

readily accumulate organic pollutants and toxic metals, with a potentially poisonous effect on animals higher up the food chain – including humans. Organochlorines tend to build up in the fatty tissues and marrow that many Arctic animals use for insulation and to help them through hibernation. Toxic metals, such as mercury and cadmium, are found at high levels in the bodies of seals in some parts of the Arctic, while polar bears and whales all tend to show at least traces of chemicals from modern herbicides and pesticides. People who live in the Arctic also tend to consume significant quantities of toxic chemicals if they eat 'local meat' from the wild.

ARCTIC GOLD RUSH

At the moment, there are no signs of really significant damage, but the Arctic has in recent years become the target of a potential 'gold rush' as the five countries around the ocean – Russia, Canada, the USA, Greenland (Denmark), Norway – explore ways of opening up the region's oil, gas, and mineral resources. The Arctic contains 13 percent of the world's oil reserves and 30 percent of its gas reserves. The melting of the ice is accelerating the issue by making it all the more accessible.

Each of the countries is eager to stake its claim. Ownership depends on proving that the area is part of the country's continental shelf. In April 2009, the United Nations confirmed Norway's bid to extend its territory far into the Arctic Ocean. Russia is currently conducting research to prove its claim, and Canada and Denmark are expected to put forward claims soon. President Barack Obama may ratify a bid from the USA.

Drilling is already under way at several offshore oil platforms,

△ *Although the white beluga whale is now protected from hunting, numbers have not recovered, mainly because of the increased human activity in the Arctic, which brings pollution, noise, and the dangers of extra shipping.*

▽ *A tenth of the world's population of the critically endangered Kittlitz's murrelet was lost during the* Exxon Valdez *oil spill in Alaska in 1989. Now it is threatened by retreating glaciers, boat disturbance, and increasing oil spills.*

and in May 2009, Russia began constructing the world's first nuclear power plant on an offshore platform. Shipping is steadily increasing in the Arctic, too, not just with increased exploration, but also as the melting of the sea ice opens the possibility of 'short-cut' routes north of Russia between Japan and Europe, and north of Canada between New York and Japan (the Northwest Passage). The heat is clearly on in the Arctic and it remains to be seen how its unique and fragile ecosystem copes.

THE SEAS OF EUROPE

Europe is surrounded by seas, none of them large or very deep, but they are hugely rich ecologically and culturally.

The largest of Europe's seas is the Mediterranean. As so evident in its name, which comes from the Latin for 'middle of the land', it is almost entirely surrounded by land. Its southern coast is formed by Africa; its northern coast by Europe; and the east by Anatolia and the Levant. Only the narrow Strait of Gibraltar in the west and the even narrower Bosphorus in the east stop it from being completely landlocked.

Around its shores, many of the great ancient civilizations were built – from the Minoans and Phoenicians to the Greeks and the Romans – and today it has one of the busiest, most populated coastlines in the world. It can be a place of stunning beauty, and its sparkling blue seas, pleasant climate, and myriad islands have inspired poets and pleasure seekers for thousands of years. Yet its very popularity has put its rich marine ecosystem under threat.

Surrounded by some of the world's largest cities and industrial centres, Europe's northern seas, the North and the Baltic, are likewise under immense pressure. Overfishing, pollution, shipping, and many other activities have taken their toll on the ecosystem and despite its remarkable resilience, it is perhaps reaching crisis point.

◁ *The azure blue, island-dotted waters of the Mediterranean – here in Mirabello Bay on Crete – have long been a magnet for tourists with their stunning scenery and often wonderful weather. But the very success of the tourist industry is damaging the marine wildlife that helps make them so special.*

207

THE MEDITERRANEAN

GEOLOGISTS ONCE THOUGHT THAT THE Mediterranean was a tiny remnant of the Tethys Sea, the great ocean that once separated the world's northern and southern continents. In fact, the Black Sea is the only remnant of the Tethys in Europe. The Mediterranean has a far briefer but more complex history. Essentially, the Mediterranean is a deep basin between the converging tectonic plates of Europe, Anatolia, and Africa, and the eastern, central, and western Mediterranean have different geological histories, which is why today, the east is earthquake prone, the centre is dotted with active volcanoes, and the west is relatively quiet.

FILLING THE MED

The modern Mediterranean, though, dates from 5.3 million years ago. About 5.6 million years ago, the Mediterranean basin was completely cut off from the Atlantic, and a warm, dry climate slowly evaporated most of the water leaving just a few very salty dregs in the lower parts of the basin, in what is called the Messinian Salinity Crisis. Then, 5.3 million years ago, the strip of land separating the Atlantic and the Mediterranean basin was suddenly breached through a 200 km (124 mile) wide channel across the Strait of Gibraltar. In a cataclysmic flood,

called the Zanclean flood, water gushed through the breach at a rate that would totally dwarf the Amazon, with a velocity of some 300 km (186 miles) an hour. It filled the basin like a bath, adding 10 m (33 ft) to the water level every day and filling the entire Mediterranean in less than two years.

Because 90 percent of the Mediterranean's water came in from the Atlantic in this way, most of the marine life in the Mediterranean today was originally from the North Atlantic. It has adapted to the warmer, saltier environment of the Mediterranean in the five million years since, but the balance of species reflects their cool Atlantic heritage. The Alboran Sea between Gibraltar and Africa is a transition zone with a mix of Atlantic and Mediterranean species. It is also home to the Mediterranean's last population of harbour porpoises and is a key feeding ground for loggerhead turtles.

DOUBLE LOOPS

Today, there is a constant influx of surface water from the Atlantic through the Strait of Gibraltar to make up for all the water that evaporates from the warm surface of the Mediterranean. This inflow sets a counterclockwise circulation of fresher surface water through the western Mediterranean, streaming along the north coast of Africa, then looping back past Sardinia, France, and Spain. The Atlantic flow also streams on farther through the Strait of Sicily to set in motion a similar counterclockwise circulation in the eastern Mediterranean. As it goes farther east, though, evaporation from the surface makes it increasingly salty and cooler, until eventually it starts to sink and flows back out west into the Atlantic underneath the incoming flow, 150 years or so after it arrived.

MEDITERRANEAN LIFE

The Atlantic water that keeps the Mediterranean topped up is highly oxygenated, which keeps the Mediterranean well aerated, but it is poor in nutrients. So the Mediterranean's phytoplankton blooms are concentrated in the Adriatic Sea, where there are local upwellings, and close to coasts and estuaries where rivers wash in nutrients. It is this limited plankton growth that keeps the Mediterranean so vividly blue in the summer. In summer, the calm, warm weather allows the surface waters to heat up with a minimum of mixing with lower layers, reducing the availability of nutrients in the surface layers. In autumn and winter, however, stormier weather stirs up water from the lower depths and helps stimulate plankton blooms in the autumn, and so provides feeding opportunities for larger organisms, from shrimp to seals.

▷ *Sadly, the high level of human activity around the Mediterranean means that it comes in for a good deal of abuse, as this rubbish floating in the harbour at Tripoli, Libya, bears witness all too clearly.*

◁ *Wild seabass has come increasingly under threat from fishing boats prevented by regulation from catching depleted cod and other fish stocks. But seabass were one of the first fish to be farmed commercially and production around the Mediterranean is rising rapidly. This farm is off the coast of the island of Corsica.*

△ *Greater flamingoes get their pink colour from the carotene pigments in their diet of shrimps and blue-green algae, which turn pink in the flamingoes' bodies.*

If the limited plankton growth means the Mediterranean's marine life is not that large in mass, it more than makes up for it in sheer diversity, with 10,000–12,000 species recorded, which is unusual for a temperate sea. There are 19 species of cetaceans in the Mediterranean alone, including fin whales, sperm whales, pilot whales, striped dolphins, Risso's dolphins, bottlenose dolphins, and common dolphins. There are also endangered monk seals, green and loggerhead turtles, devil rays, and Maltese skates, mako, sandbar, porbeagle, and angel sharks and more than 900 other species of fish, including blue-fin tuna and swordfish. One particularly important plant species is the seagrass *Posidonia oceanica*, which grows on shallow coastal seabeds. The seagrasses act as nurseries for many of the Mediterranean's key species, but like seagrasses in many places (see pages 106–107), they are in decline.

SUEZ CANAL INVASION

THE MEDITERRANEAN HAS ALWAYS BEEN A COSMOPOLITAN PLACE, AND IT SEEMS THAT THIS EXTENDS TO ITS MARINE LIFE, WHICH IS EXPERIENCING A BOOM IN ALIEN SPECIES.

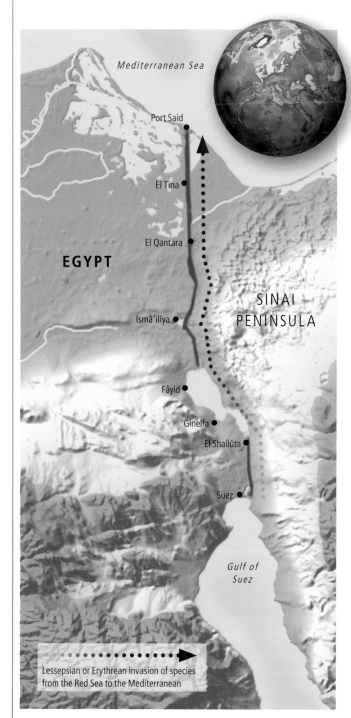

Many of the Mediterranean's original inhabitants were, of course, aliens, flocking in from the Atlantic to find a new home in the Mediterranean as the Atlantic waters poured into the almost dry basins and filled them up. But in the five million years since, these immigrants have adapted to the Mediterranean way of life and have become natives.

SHIPPING IN

Now though, there is a new wave of immigrants. One of the most notorious is the tropical green algae *Caulerpa taxifolia*, which escaped from aquariums in the 1980s and has now spread across vast areas of the Mediterranean seabed. Dubbed the 'killer algae', it has brought devastation by overgrowing native seagrasses and weeds in dense mats that not only inhibit the growth of young fish, but are also very unpleasant for swimmers and boaters.

Shipping in the Mediterranean has increased dramatically in the last few decades. In 2001, 33,000 vessels entered the Mediterranean, and the figure may well be double that now. Ballast water is a major problem (see page 78). The American blue crab, *Callinectes sapidus*, spread around the Mediterranean in this way as long ago as the 1940s. More recently, the comb jellyfish arrived. This notorious American invader wreaked havoc in the Black Sea in the 1990s, and it now seems to be spreading through the Mediterranean. In 2009, comb jellyfish were spotted off the coast of Israel. The much greater range of species in the Mediterranean means it will probably cause less

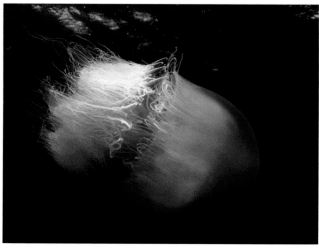

△ *The opening of the 164-km (100–mile) long Suez Canal in 1869 (now 193 km /120 miles/ in length) provided a route for invasive species from the Red Sea to enter the Mediterranean Sea, both in the water and via ships' ballasts.*

△ *One of the most notorious arrivals through the Suez Canal has been the large jellyfish* Rhopilema nomadica, *which can give swimmers a nasty sting that looks like a bad burn.*

damage there, but such invasions are clearly a problem.

In fact, the coast of the Levant has been the site of another jellyfish invasion for the last few decades. Every summer since the mid-1980s, swarms of the jellyfish *Rhopilema nomadica* have turned up in the Mediterranean. The swarms are so big that they can stretch 100 km (60 miles) along the coast, upsetting swimmers who are worried by their stings, clogging up fishing nets, and blocking up the intake pipes of ships' cooling systems.

LESSEPSIAN INVASION

The source of this jellyfish plague is the Suez Canal. The jellyfish are from the Red Sea, but made it through the canal along with the ships. The reason this happens is that the Red Sea is slightly higher than the Mediterranean, so the canal serves as a tidal channel through which water flows from the Red Sea into the Mediterranean, carrying all manner of organisms with it. Because the flow is one way, Red Sea organisms invade the Mediterranean but not the other way around. This invasion from the Red Sea, and from the Indian Ocean beyond, is called Erythrean invasion, or Lessepsian invasion after Ferdinand de Lesseps, the French engineer who designed the canal.

The Suez Canal opened in 1869, but the invasion did not start straightaway. Two very salty lakes, known as the Bitter Lakes, formed in the middle of the canal route in formerly dry valleys, and these lakes proved too salty for organisms to cross. But after a few decades, the constant flow of water from the Red Sea into the lakes reduced their salinity and made it possible for organisms to make the journey. Since then, more than 300 species have made the journey and some 80 percent of the 'foreign' fish, decapods, crustaceans, and molluscs arrived this way.

▽ *Many places around the eastern Mediterranean are plagued in summer by swarms of the invading* Rhopilema nomadica *jellyfish, which not only looks unpleasant on tourist beaches, but reduces fish stocks by feeding on fish larvae.*

△ *The American blue crab probably arrived in the Mediterranean by boat, and now competes with native crabs and feeds on fish caught in fishing nets.*

Adapted to warm, salty seas, these Erythrean invaders often do very well in the warm, salty Mediterranean in competition with the locals who came originally from the cooler fresher Atlantic. They have begun to do especially well in the Eastern Mediterranean since the 1960s when the construction of the Aswan High Dam on the Nile reduced the flow of nutrient-rich fresh water into the sea, and made it more like the Red Sea. One Red Sea invader, the bivalve mollusc *Brachidontes pharaonis*, has all but replaced the native mollusc *Mytilaster minimus* in many places. Another invader, the pearl oyster, has spread across the Mediterranean on boats and maybe even on the backs of sea turtles.

Not all the invaders are bad news. The Erythrean penaeid prawns are now highly prized by fishing fleets in the Eastern Mediterranean, and now account for a large proportion of the catch of small Israeli coastal trawlers.

Just how the natives will cope with all these invaders remains to be seen. Marine biologists have expressed concern about the Egyptian government's intention to widen and deepen the Suez Canal. Even a small increase in the depth may let in invaders that find the waters too shallow at present.

THE MEDITERRANEAN UNDER PRESSURE

THE MEDITERRANEAN IS IN SOME WAYS A MICROCOSM OF THE MULTIPLE PROBLEMS FACING
THE WORLD'S OCEANS, WITH THREATS RANGING FROM TOURISM TO SEWAGE DISPOSAL.

More than 130 million people live all year-round along the Mediterranean's 26,000 km (16,000 miles) of shoreline, and every summer the population doubles as holidaymakers flock in to take advantage of the pleasant weather, blue seas, and beautiful scenery. But this very popularity is putting the Mediterranean's marine ecosystems under increasing pressure.

THE TOURIST TOLL

Tourism has become the Mediterranean's biggest industry. A third of all the world's international tourists come here, whether to enjoy the cultural delights of cities like Barcelona or simply to lie on its beaches. Tourists have become a vital source of income not just for the big city centres but also for small villages once dying on their feet. The Adriatic coast of Croatia, for instance, has been revitalized by the scores of visitors who flock to its beautiful archipelago and historic ports. But the success of the Mediterranean's tourist industry has had a devastating effect on its wildlife. All along the coast, the construction of hotels and related developments, breakwaters, marinas, beach esplanades, and the paraphernalia of the tourist trade have obliterated many natural habitats.

The swell of tourist numbers is so vast that even apparently harmless activities such as walking on the beach, sunbathing, swimming, and boating, can have a huge impact on local wildlife, driving marine green turtles from their beach nesting sites, for instance, or squeezing the life out of countless tiny burrowing creatures – with effects that ripple throughout the food chain.

PRAYING FOR THE MONK

The Mediterranean monk seal has been a particular victim. It is now one of the world's most endangered marine mammals with fewer than 500 individuals left. Much of the damage was done long ago in the days of the Roman Empire, when the seals fell easy prey to hunters because of their trusting nature. But the tourism boom has turned a small population into a tiny number that have little chance of survival.

Countless beaches where the monk seals once congregated are now occupied by sun-seekers, and the seals have been driven to seek refuge in inaccessible caves – where youngsters often fall victim to the pounding of the waves. The colonies once seen on beaches from the Black Sea to the Balearics are

gone and there are now just two small populations, one in the northeastern Mediterranean and the other in the northeastern Atlantic, off the coast of northwestern Africa – so widely separated that the chances of any interaction are minimal. The monk seal has been a protected species for decades, but it is the habitat loss that is crucial and only a handful of their breeding sites has been offered protection.

DIRTY MED
The monk seal has suffered from the Mediterranean's high levels of pollution, too. The Mediterranean is especially sensitive to pollution build-up because the inflow and outflow of water is so limited that it takes a century for all the water to be replenished once. Some 650 million tonnes (715 million tons) of sewage, 129,000 tonnes (142,000 tons) of mineral oil, 60,000 tonnes (66,000 tons) of mercury, 3,800 tonnes (4,200 tons) of lead, and 36,000 tonnes (40,000 tons) of phosphates are dumped into the Mediterranean each year. Untreated sewage and runoff farm fertilizer are especial problems because of the eutrophication and plankton blooms they trigger, and dead zones are becoming increasingly common. The people living along the Mediterranean coast produce 3.8 billion cu. m (134 billion cu. ft) of waste water each year, and 80 percent of sewage inflow is untreated.

Shipping is another major source of pollution. Although occupying only 0.7 percent of the global ocean surface, the Mediterranean Sea suffers 17 percent of the world's marine oil pollution. Every year, there are ten accidental spills from the 100,000 tankers that annually glide through the Mediterranean carrying 370 million tonnes (408 million tons) of oil, a fifth of the world total. But maybe 100,000–150,000 tonnes (110,000–165,000 tons) of crude oil (600,000 tonnes/660,000 tons

◁ *The blue seas, wonderful scenery, and mild weather have made resorts like Monte Carlo a magnet for tourism, but coastal development and the sheer number of visitors are having a serious impact on the sea's ecology.*

▷ *As a slow-moving, slow-reproducing seabed dweller, the angel shark has proved vulnerable to bottom trawling. It is now very rare in the Mediterranean, and the species is critically endangered. Despite protection in marine reserves, angel sharks have not been seen around the Balearic islands since the 1990s.*

△ *Hunted since Roman times, the Mediterranean monk seal is now one of the rarest marine mammals, and with fewer than 500 left scattered across the Mediterranean, its chances of survival seem slim.*

according to the World Wildlife Fund) are deliberately leaked into the sea each year from the 220,000 ships that cross the Mediterranean, a third of the world's entire merchant shipping fleet. To these threats are added overfishing, industrial and urban development, and global warming.

ACTION PLANS
As long ago as 1975, the 21 nations around the Mediterranean Sea set up a Mediterranean Action Plan (MAP), the first Regional Seas agreement reached under the United Nations Environment Programme (UNEP). The MAP aims to control coastal development, reduce pollution, and protect biodiversity in the Mediterranean and it has various Strategic Action Programs (SAPs) to achieve just that. Even now, the goals seem modest. An anti-pollution programme aimed to half the industrial biological oxygen demand (BOD) – an indirect measure of the organic pollution that causes eutrophication (see page 18) – but cut the generation of hazardous wastes by just 20 percent by using cleaner technology. The Mediterranean's ecosystems are in grave danger and it remains to be seen if these measures are enough to make a real difference.

THE NORTH SEA

Few of the world's seas have come under such environmental pressure as the Baltic and North seas. Both seas are surrounded by cities, ports, and industry and some of the most intensively farmed land in the world.

They are conduits for shipping, places for recreation, drains for sewage, dumps for waste and toxic chemicals, and sources of fish for food on an immense scale. And the North Sea, too, is, of course, a major oil and gas field. It is in some ways surprising that the environmental situation is not worse than it is – but it is certainly bad.

THE SCHOOLS OF HERRING

One of the key issues in the North Sea is fishing. In the past, the North Sea was a fantastically rich source of fish. Fish such as cod, haddock, whiting, plaice, sole, mackerel, herrings, sprats, sturgeons, shads, rays, and skates, and shellfish such as oysters, mussels, and whelks, were once so abundant that the North Sea supported the world's richest fishing industry. For centuries, the fishing villages that lined the North Sea coast, from Lowestoft and Hull on the British side to Ålesund on the Norwegian side, were boom towns, and fishermen's tales of huge hauls were the stuff of legend and song. Even today, this little sea supplies 5 percent of all the world's fish. But the catch today is far below what it was a century ago.

Sturgeon, shad, rays, skates, and mackerel have seen especially dramatic declines, but so have all fish species. Oysters vanished as long ago as the 1930s – they were victims of steam trawlers, which dragged their heavy nets over the rich mosaic of invertebrate life on the North Sea floor, destroying oysters,

corals, and seafan beds alike. It is estimated that 99 percent of fish mass has now been removed from the North Sea. All fish catches have declined dramatically since the 1970s, with the haddock catch plummeting from 1 million tonnes (1.1 million tons) in 1970 to fewer than 100,000 tonnes (110,000 tons) now.

▽ *Pair trawling means towing a large net along the seabed between two boats like this pair fishing for haddock. It is an efficient way of scooping up fish, but the quantities have proven too much for the North Sea's haddock population.*

△ *The vast reserves of oil and natural gas under the North Sea have proven a financial bonanza for the UK, but the continual exploitation of the marine environment puts pressure on the North Sea's vulnerable ecosystems.*

QUOTA BATTLES

The North Sea is now the focus of a constant battle between the fishing industry, regulatory authorities, and scientists, as they try to balance the conflicting demands of business, livelihoods, politics, and marine life. On the whole, it has been marine life that has been the loser, despite the European Union's Common Fisheries Policy and the imposition of quotas limiting the catch of most commercial fish. Mackerel fishing was banned completely in the 1970s, and herring, cod, and plaice fishing may soon be banned completely, too. But many experts fear that it may be too late.

The numbers of cod are now so low that there have been calls every year since 2001 for a total ban on cod fishing in the North Sea. Yet although quotas have been steadily reduced, cod can still be legally caught – it seems that the lessons of Newfoundland's Grand Banks (see pages 156–157) have not been learned. In the horse-trading of quotas, any faint signs of stock improvement in some species, such as herring, are traded off with raised quotas to smooth over the quota reductions in other species. Of course, the quotas are bitterly contested by fishing crews who see their livelihood vanishing, and many North Sea fishing villages now face a bleak future.

COD GONE

Some experts believe that cod and other fish will soon disappear from the North Sea altogether because overfishing is combined with another threat – global warming. The North Sea has warmed by more than 1°C (1.8°F) over the last 40 years. It does not sound much, but it has been enough to reduce numbers of the tiny shrimplike copepod by more than 60 percent. In spring, young cod rely on a tiny species of copepod for their food, and without copepods the cod simply cannot grow to maturity. And in a classic example of the effects on one species reverberating through the ecosystem, a reduction in adult cod has led to a proliferation of the seafloor crabs and shrimp on which they feed. Crab larvae are voracious predators and as their numbers exploded, they have been decimating the North Sea's bivalves and the young of cod, plaice, and sole. The consolation is that what may be the North Sea's loss could be the gain of cooler seas farther north, such as the Barents, as copepod and cod find them more to their liking.

◁ *Some fishermen blame grey seals for the decline in North Sea cod stocks, but overfishing is the real culprit. Meanwhile, the seals have become prone to phocine distemper virus (PDV), which attacks the animals' respiratory systems.*

THE BALTIC SEA

In February 2010, Finnish president Tarja Halonen hosted an ambitious one-day 'action summit' in Helsinki to rescue the Baltic from imminent disaster, with not only the leaders of the nine nations surrounding the Baltic but also European Union representatives and 1,500 other delegates from everything from major businesses to environmental activists.

Halonen said she called the summit because someone had to and because it was perverse to have 'some of the richest and most environmentally conscious countries on Earth on the shores of one of the world's most polluted seas.'

The Baltic is indeed in a state of crisis. This sea, half frozen over during winter, is in some ways a gigantic estuary for the 250 rivers that flow into it, including the Oder and the Neva. The rivers make the sea much less salty than other seas, which is why it freezes over so readily. Salty water does flow in from the North Sea, bringing oxygen, which is vital for the Baltic's marine life, but it is the inflow of fresh water that dominates. That is why the Baltic has many of its own local species, such as the Baltic Sea herring, and why the seabed swarms with the shrimplike *Monoporeia affinis*, which was originally a freshwater shrimp.

THE FLOOD OF FILTH

Unfortunately, the rivers are also laden with pollutants, which have been steadily building up. Each year, some 738,000 tonnes (814,000 tons) of nitrates and more than 36,000 tonnes (40,000 tons) of phosphates flood into the sea from farming runoff, human sewage, and airborne pollution. Phosphate levels in particular are escalating in the Baltic and beginning to trigger the algal blooms that have already turned the Black Sea into a dead zone through eutrophication – the suffocation of marine life through oxygen depletion. One of the unique problems of the Baltic is that besides the massive runoff of chemicals from Polish farms and sewage from Russian cities, it has tens of thousands of isolated holiday homes on the Swedish coast flushing untreated human waste directly into the sea.

It is not just the river-borne pollutants that are so damaging to the Baltic. It has long been a dumping ground for industrial and chemical waste. Indeed, half a century ago, many people thought it was a safe place to dispose of things. Huge quantities of chemical weapons were dumped in the sea after World War II, and industry has been following suit ever since. In 2006, 23,000 barrels of mercury from an unknown source were found on the seafloor off Sweden. There are fears that the construction of the

△ *In June 2010, the beaches of the popular German tourist island of Rügen were suddenly covered in a slurry of black paraffin. The source, originally thought to have been a Norwegian tanker, has not been identified.*

giant Nord Stream underwater pipeline from Russia to Germany could stir up some of the toxic chemicals and World War II weapons that have settled on the seafloor.

FISH THREATS

The Baltic was once a rich source of fish for the people living around it, sustaining the lives of millions of people through the centuries. Cod, herring, hake, plaice, flounder, sea trout, and turbot are all key elements of the cuisine of Baltic countries such as Poland, famous for its pickled herrings. But the Baltic is a small, comparatively shallow sea, and the impact of industrial scale fishing has been too much for its limited resources to bear. Fish catches are declining rapidly and European Union regulators and scientists are constantly negotiating about what level of fishing is allowable if fishing is to survive there at all.

If all this was not enough, the Baltic is now beginning to face a new threat. Early in 2008, the dreaded American comb jellyfish, *Mnemiopsis leidyi*, was spotted in the Baltic. This is the jellyfish that multiplied explosively in the Black Sea and devoured many native species of small fish (see pages 224–225). There are grounds for concern that the Baltic, with its severely weakened ecosystem, may suffer the same fate.

Conferences such as the Helsinki summit in 2010 show there is an awareness at all levels that there is a problem, and targets are set for everything from reduction of farm runoff to setting fishing quotas. But is it all too little too late?

◁ *The Baltic is much less salty than other seas because of the constant influx of fresh water from rivers. So, unlike the nearby North Sea, it partially freezes over in winter, as here near Helsinki.*

The Nord Stream Pipeline

- Key pipeline construction sites
- Pipeline

Vyborg
Kotka
Hanko
Slite
Karlskrona
Mukran
Lubmin, near Greifswald

When construction of the Nord Stream gas pipeline finally began in April 2010, it represented a victory for economic and political interests and a defeat for conservationists. The pipeline, which will carry gas under the Baltic from Vyborg in Russia to Greifswald in Germany, will be the longest undersea pipeline in the world at 1,222 km (760 miles) in length. Conservation bodies campaigned hard against it, worried that it would stir up toxic chemicals and abandoned World War II weapons on the sea floor and concerned about its impact on bird and marine life. Swedish groups, for instance, argued that the pipeline's route was too close to the marine reserve near Gotland. But the combined pressures of Russian desire to sell its gas, and western European countries to receive it through a pipe free of any political obstacles such as the troubles in the Caucasus and Middle East, and eastern Europe, eventually outweighed any objections. The pipeline will go on stream in 2012.

LAMENT FOR THE BLUEFIN

SOME EXPERTS BELIEVE THAT IT IS NOW ONLY A MATTER OF TIME BEFORE THE BLUEFIN TUNA IS FISHED FROM THE OCEANS ENTIRELY.

The bluefin tuna is often described as the king of fish. For those who have only seen tuna chopped up into little cans, or even served in large, juicy brown steaks, it is hard to appreciate why. But the bluefin truly is a magnificent fish, shimmering blue on top and silvery white below. It can grow up to 4.5 m (15 ft) in length and weigh more than 600 kg (1,322 lb). It can swim at up to 70 km/h (40 mph) and dive down more than 1.6 km (1 mile) into the ocean deeps. It is one of the ocean's great travellers, able to swim at high speed across thousands of kilometres of ocean as it migrates to find better feeding and spawning grounds. The Atlantic bluefin is, unusually for a fish, warm-blooded, enabling it to cope equally well with the chilly waters off Iceland and the tropical warmth of the Caribbean.

And, of course, bluefin tuna tastes delicious. Its rich, buttery flesh makes it the prize ingredient in sushi, especially in Japan, which takes 80 percent of the world's bluefin catch. The combination of flavour and size makes the bluefin an incredibly sought-after catch. The sums of money involved are extraordinary. In February 2010, a single large bluefin fetched a price of 16.3 million yen, about $166,000 – not far short of $1,000 for 1 kg (2.2 lb). Within hours of it being sold, it had been sliced into slivers and served up as sushi in restaurants across Tokyo, no doubt at a healthy profit. It is hardly surprising that the fishing (and the restaurant) industry has resisted calls to stop catching such a valuable, sought-after fish, and that illegal catches go on even when bans are in place.

DIFFERENT TUNA

There is some confusion about tuna, because there are various different species and various different populations of the different species. There are actually seven main commercially caught species, divided into 23 populations, and not all are under the same threat. Altogether, some 4.2 million tonnes (4.6 million tons) of tuna are caught each year. Nearly 60 percent of that is skipjack tuna for canning. Yellowfin makes up 24 percent, big eye 10 percent, albacore 5.4 percent, and bluefin just 1.5 percent. Skipjack tuna is reasonably abundant and even the overfished Indian Ocean yellowfin, eastern Pacific big eye, and the North Atlantic albacore are not in serious danger. So there is no need to avoid canned tuna. It is just the highly prized bluefin which is in real trouble.

A proper scientific study of the Pacific population is still under way, but all the other populations of bluefin – notably

▽ *This aerial view of Atlantic waters off the coast of Canada shows hundreds of skipjack tuna being herded into a net ready for capture. Skipjack, fortunately, remain abundant.*

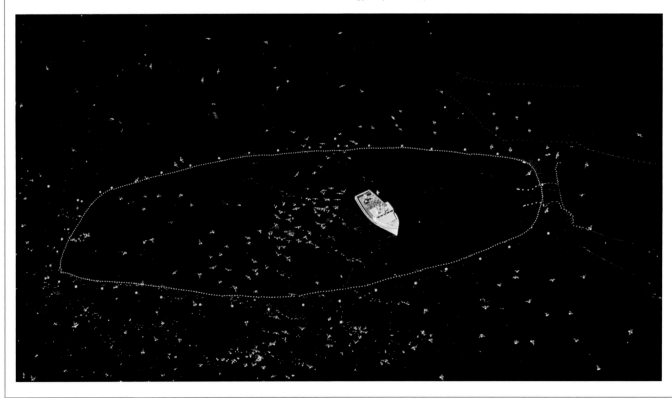

the Atlantic and Mediterranean stocks – are down by 88 percent from their levels in 1975. Moreover, the size of tuna caught is well down on what it used to be. Sushi and the worldwide explosion in sushi restaurants, along with a taste for pan-fried tuna, is to blame for the rocketing price of bluefin and the threat to its survival. Three-quarters of all the bluefin caught goes to Japan, but the Japanese rightly bridle at the suggestion that it is all their fault, since much of the increase has been taken by classy restaurants outside Japan, and the Western sushi bars and supermarkets.

SAVING THE BLUEFIN?

In 2007, the International Commission for the Conservation of Atlantic Tunas (ICCAT) recommended limiting the global catch of bluefin to a global quota of just 15,000 tonnes (16,500 tons). Then under pressure, they raised the quota to 30,000 tonnes (33,000 tons) before dropping it to 22,500 tonnes (25,000 tons) – still more than three times as much as scientists believed is sustainable. In November 2009, they reduced the quota to 13,500 tonnes (15,000 tons). But the high prices fetched by tunas are too much of a temptation, and some 60,000 tonnes (66,000 tons) are still caught annually.

Conservationists argued that the only way to stop the tuna catch was to stop the trade rather than limit the catch. In March 2010, a proposal to ban trade in Atlantic bluefin was the top item at the meeting of the Convention on International Trade in Endangered Species (CITES), in Doha in Qatar. So perilous is the plight of the bluefin tuna becoming that many experts saw the proposal as the last chance to save the bluefin. With the backing of the UK and the USA, it was thought the urgency would see the proposal go through. But to the

△ *Tuna can fetch enormous prices at the auctions at Tukiji market in Tokyo, the world's largest fishmarket, which operates from 5.20 a.m. every day. Bidding is fierce, and a single bluefin can sell for over $100,000.*

consternation of many, the Japanese delegation won the case for rejecting the proposal by arguing that the ICCAT quotas were quite enough. Veteran conservationist George Monbiot was incensed, writing in the *Guardian* newspaper, 'Idiots. Morons. Blockheads. Numbskulls. Nothing quite captures the mind-withering stupidity of what has just happened in Doha… The insistence that the fishing can continue without consequences betrays Olympic-class denial, a flat refusal to look reality in the face.'

The problem is that for the commercial interests involved it makes sense to fish the bluefin out of existence. The rarer it becomes, the higher the price it will fetch, legally or illegally. And when it does vanish, those commercial interests will move on to other prey, leaving us to lament the passing of one of the world's most beautiful and delicious fish – another victim of human greed and thoughtlessness.

The Wrong Tuna

Skipjack tuna make up the bulk of the world's tuna catch. If you buy canned tuna, it's most likely to be skipjack. Skipjack are so abundant that they are not in any immediate danger of being fished out – though if present levels are sustained there may be problems in the future. The problem is that skipjack tuna are usually caught with purse seine nets – and bluefin can easily be caught up accidentally. In theory, the bluefin should be thrown back, but of course not all are – and even when they are their chances of survival are slim. This is why some experts argue the only acceptable way to fish for tuna is with pole and line (rod and line) and some supermarkets now insist that their tuna is caught this way.

THE SEAS OF EURASIA

In the heart of Eurasia are three remarkable seas – the Black Sea, the Sea of Azov, and the Caspian Sea – and three potential ecological disasters.

None of the world's seas are as isolated from the great oceans as these three seas. The Black Sea is connected to the Mediterranean, itself virtually landlocked, only through the narrow strait of the Bosphorus. The Sea of Azov, the world's shallowest sea, is linked to the Black Sea only through the even narrower Kerch Strait. The Caspian Sea is entirely cut off from the world's oceans, and is the largest landlocked body of water in the world.

Geologists dispute their origins but they were once probably all part of the once gigantic Tethys Sea, which separated the world's great northern and southern continents. Now, however, they are entirely isolated, and their isolation gives each a unique character – and unique problems.

Every day, vast quantities of water flow into these seas through the great rivers that drain into them – the Danube, the Dnieper, the Dneister, the Volga, and many others. And with the rivers comes pollutants from a vast area of land around. There may be other rivers in the world that are as polluted as these, but once the water flows into these landlocked seas, there is no escape for the contaminants, no saving dilution by the vastness of the world's oceans.

In the 1990s, the Black Sea was the scene of environmental catastrophe, as marine life all but collapsed entirely creating the first recognized dead zone. It was a stark and salutary warning to the world that even the sea is not so big that it can absorb anything humans can throw at it without harm. There are some signs of recovery there now, but it is luck rather than any concerted conservation action that has brought this small comfort.

◁ *The Caspian Sea, once a jewel in the Eurasian crown, and home to a unique range of marine wildlife, has suffered from oil exploitation on its shores, and the continuous influx of polluted water from rivers such as the Volga.*

THE BLACK SEA

THE BLACK SEA WAS ONCE A RICH FISHING GROUND, an abundant source of fish for everyone from the Ancient Greeks to the modern Soviet Union. Sturgeon and their eggs were so plentiful in the estuaries of Black Sea rivers that they were once the food of the poor.

Huge schools of anchovies migrated each year around the northeastern shores, followed by bonito, mackerel, tuna, and dolphins, which preyed on them and provided a wonderful catch for Black Sea fishermen. Anchovies, known in Russia as *hamsa*, moved in such vast numbers every spring through the Kerch Strait into the Sea of Azov to spawn that fishermen only had to stand in the water to fill their nets again and again.

The anchovies, in turn, depended on lush seagrass meadows and vast kelp forests that grew on the seabed on the northwestern shelves. Countless tiny animals sheltered in the seagrass – amphipods, isopods, shrimp, molluscs, and crabs, as well as the larvae of numerous large fish. Masses of fish, including Black Sea turbot, whiting, rays, and, of course, anchovies, feasted on this seabed banquet. Farther out from the shore were rich oyster beds and carpets of mussels. Farther out still grew vast forests of *Phyllophora* seaweed, the largest forests of red algae in the world. The seaweed forests were not only home to 170 species of animals, from sponges to crabs, but were one of the main sources of oxygen in the oxygen-poor Black Sea, cut off from the main ocean currents.

THE DEAD SEA

However, in the 1990s, the seagrass meadows and kelp forests,

▽ *In November 2007, stormy seas and gale-force winds smashed a Russian oil tanker in half in the narrow Kerch Straits and spilled 1,800 tonnes (2,000 tons) of oil and 6,350 tonnes (7,000 tons) of sulphur into the constricted waters, an essential route for migrating anchovy.*

as well as the oyster and mussel beds, all but vanished, victims of disastrous pollution. Huge amounts of fertilizer and animal manure drained into the Danube and other rivers from the vast farms of Eastern Europe and Russia. As all these nutrients washed out into the Black Sea, they triggered massive algal blooms. So vast were these blooms that the sea stank of rotten eggs. The stench was hydrogen sulphide gas given off by bacteria multiplying to feed on all the decaying matter produced by the algal bloom.

The masses of algae also cast the seabed into deep gloom, blocking out up to 95 percent of the sunlight on which the seagrass and kelp rely for energy. Almost all the kelp forests and

◁ *Anchovies are one of the Black Sea's chief riches, but the shoals were decimated in the 1990s when eutrophication killed seagrass meadows and kelp forests.*

▽ *There are now signs that the Black Sea's vast undersea forests of* Phyllophora *seaweed, which has been devastated by eutrophication, may be recovering.*

the seagrass meadows died within a few years. In the 1950s, there were 10,000 sq. km (3,860 sq. miles) of kelp forests. By 1992, there were just 50 sq. km (19.3 sq. miles), making a loss of 99.5 percent. With the kelp and seagrass went all the many animals that relied on them – all the amphipods, the shrimp, the crabs, and the fish. And as these animals went, so the commercial fish, already reduced by overfishing, dwindled almost to nothing, ruining the livelihoods of millions of Black Sea fishermen. A huge area of the Black Sea became a dead zone.

THE SECOND WAVE

With the Black Sea ecosystem already weak, another, and even more devastating, attack occurred as the invasive comb jellyfish *Mnemiopsis leidyi* multiplied to an astonishing degree and mopped up any survivors (see pages 224–225). It was not just the wildlife and fishermen that suffered. Tourism plummeted, too, put off by the smelly sea, and the fact that it was necessary to shower after swimming to avoid the risk of disease. Many people around the Black Sea stared poverty in the face. In 1998, British born oceanographer Laurence Mee declared sadly, 'The Black Sea is really facing an environmental catastrophe. It is very unusual for scientists to use the word catastrophe. The word is not used lightly.'

Mee orchestrated a campaign to get all the Black Sea countries to come together in a last-ditch effort to save the Black Sea. The Black Sea Environment Program, funded by the United Nations, the European Union, and the World Bank, as well as the Black Sea countries, was a pioneering example of multinational cooperation. But in the end, the reason the

Black Sea is now showing real signs of recovery is down to two remarkable strokes of luck.

FORTUNE'S FAVOURS

The first piece of luck was the political upheaval of the early 1990s. As the communist regimes of countries along the Danube and the Dnieper collapsed, so too did the farm programmes that supplied farmers with fertilizers and created gigantic manure-producing animal farms. Although it brought hardship to farmers who could not afford to fertilize their crops, the nutrient influx into the Black Sea plummeted. The dead zone shrank, and seabed communities began to show small signs of recovery. By 2002, limited bivalve communities could be seen on the gravel of the seabed. By 2006, seaweeds were beginning to grow well.

The second stroke of luck was the arrival of a second comb jellyfish invader in 1997, *Beroe ovata*, which instead of preying on fish fry and zooplankton ate the notorious comb jellyfish *M. leidyi*. Anchovy numbers are now partially recovered, and Black Sea turbot, bonito, and even mackerel are being caught again. But it could all prove to be a false dawn. Scientists warn that recovery will not continue unless fishing is severely curtailed to avoid the knock-on effect through the food chain that impairs the seabed communities. Moreover, the coast is seeing a construction boom as tourism returns. And the massive oil reserves of central Asia and the demand for oil in the West have turned the Black Sea into a major conduit for oil supply. In November 2007, a major oil spill in the Kerch Strait devastated local bird life in what was described as the worst ecological disaster in Russia since Chernobyl in 1986.

THE TRANSPARENT INVADER

THE WARTY COMB JELLY *MNEMIOPSIS LEIDYI* IS ACTUALLY QUITE A
BEAUTIFUL CREATURE – A GLISTENING, UNDULATING OVAL BELL THAT
WAFTS THROUGH THE WATER WITH BALLETIC GRACE.
YET IT IS THE BLACK SEA ECOSYSTEM'S WORST NIGHTMARE.

Comb jellyfish are similar to jellyfish but are not actually related. They do not have the stinging cells that true jellyfish have but have special sticky cells that they wrap around their prey. *M. leidyi* is a native of the estuaries of the eastern coasts of the Americas where it has sufficient local predators to keep it in check. But in 1982, Soviet scientists spotted this American native in the Black Sea. It is assumed that the comb jellyfish got there in the ballast water of ships.

Tolerant of a wide range of conditions, *M. leidyi* had no trouble adapting to the Black Sea and was soon tucking into the feast it found there in the vast numbers of zooplankton that were feeding on the algal bloom. There was nothing to stop it since the mackerel that might have preyed on it had been fished to extinction there in the 1970s, and the anchovies that might have competed with it for food were already in serious decline. Worse still, the comb jellyfish fed on the eggs and larvae of the anchovies and other fish.

▽ *Changing conditions in the ocean seem to be encouraging massive swarms of jellyfish all around the world. In Japan, the problem is plagues of the giant Nomura's jellyfish, which can grow up to 2 m (6 ft) across.*

GLUTTONOUS GELATINOUS

M. leidyi is renowned for being a voracious feeder, able to eat up to ten times its own weight in food every day. And when food is available it can multiply with astonishing speed. Not long after it arrived, it went through one of the most incredible population explosions scientists had ever witnessed. By 1989, there were thought to be more than a billion tonnes of comb jellyfish in the Black Sea, more than ten times the entire world catch of fish, and in many areas, the sea became a seething mass of jelly.

This vast jelly swarm devoured pretty much all the life that was left in the Black Sea after overfishing and the algal bloom disasters. Zooplankton, fish, crab, and mollusc larvae all went into the jellyfishes' expandable bellies. The anchovy catch was cut from 700,000 to 100,000 a year, and the Black Sea ecosystem, already in a parlous state, collapsed. Colin Woodard, in *Ocean's End*, describes some of the effects, 'Dolphin and porpoise numbers dropped by 90 to 95 percent. The monk seal was condemned to extinction when its last breeding refuge was blown up to make way for a Bulgarian hotel. Giant sturgeons became endangered. Oyster populations fell by 95 percent; crabs and mussels by 70 percent.'

AN UNLIKELY SAVIOUR

For ten years, the jellyfish devastation went on. But just as scientists were beginning to despair, imagining the jellyfish spreading through the world's seas, and devouring all the life in them, an unlikely saviour appeared. In 1997, another comb jellyfish invader suddenly appeared in the Black Sea. No one knows how it got there, but like *M. leidyi*, it probably hitched a ride in a ship's ballast water. But this new comb jellyfish, *Beroe ovata*, fed not on zooplankton and fish larvae but on other comb jellyfish – mostly *M. leidyi*. *B. ovata* multiplied rapidly as it fed on its abundant rival jellyfish. *M. leidyi* numbers crashed – and with their main food source gone, so *B. ovata* numbers crashed, too.

It seemed a miraculous chance solution to a seemingly insoluble problem. But the story is not over yet. In 1999, even as *B. ovata* was beginning to save the day in the Black Sea, scuba divers observed the *M. leidyi* jellyfish in the Caspian Sea. The following year, the notorious comb jellyfish began to grow massively in the Caspian, too, and over the next few years, it devastated the Caspian's fisheries. At the moment, scientists are desperately trying to acclimatize *B. ovata* to the much fresher waters of the Caspian to try to solve the problem. And now, *M. leidyi* has made it to the Baltic, which may be too cold for *B. ovata*. It has also been seen in the Mediterranean.

JELLY WORLD

It is not just *M. leidyi* that has been swarming through the world's oceans. Some years before *M. leidyi* arrived in the Black Sea, the moon jellyfish had exploded in numbers there, and were simply displaced by *M. leidyi*. It seems that comb jellyfish and jellyfish swarms are becoming more and more

common. Japanese waters have seen swarms of the giant jellyfish *Nemopilema nomurai*, which grows up to 2 m (6.5 ft) across and can weigh more than 250 kg (550 lb). The waters off Alaska have witnessed swarms of the pink-orange jellyfish *Chrysaora melanaster*. Since many jellyfish feed on the young of fish, these population explosions could have a significant effect on fish numbers. It is not entirely clear why these explosions are happening. It may be to do with changing water temperatures and currents, but scientists are keeping a close eye on them.

▽ *The shores of Alaska have begun to witness frequent swarms of the Pacific sea nettle,* Chrysaora melanaster, *which feed on young fish, and so can have a dramatic effect on the local ecology.*

THE CASPIAN SEA

FOR SOME PEOPLE, THE CASPIAN SEA IS NOT A SEA, but is the world's biggest lake, containing more water than all the Great Lakes put together, and more than 40 percent of all the world's lake water. But it is called a sea not only because of its vast size – it is a sea because it contains salt water.

The Caspian is salty not just because the inflow of fresh water from rivers such as the mighty Volga is matched by the evaporation from the surface, but because it was once part of a much greater sea and was filled with ocean water.

THE LOST SEA

About 20 million years ago, the Caspian Sea, along with the Black Sea and the Sea of Azov, were all part of an ocean that geologists call the Paratethys Sea, which was linked to the Atlantic as well as another large sea called the Tethys. Tectonic upheavals eventually lifted most of the Paratethys' seafloor above the ocean waters forming the mountains of southeastern Europe and the Alps. The Caspian, the Black Sea, and the Sea of Azov were the surviving remnants of this once vast sea. The Black Sea and the Sea of Azov have since become connected to the Mediterranean and to the world's oceans via the Bosphorus. But about 5.5 million years ago, the Caspian Sea became entirely cut off. Since then, at times, the Caspian has almost completely dried out, especially in the shallow northern half, and the sea

level fluctuates. But it is refilled by rivers in the north, such as the Volga, which is why in its northern half, the Caspian is almost fresh water. Only in the southern half near to Iran is it fairly salty. On average, the refilling with freshwater means the Caspian is about a third as salty as the rest of the world's seas.

△ *The Volga River pours huge amounts of fresh water, more than any other river in Europe, into the Caspian Sea, which has a marked effect on the plants and animals that live there.*

226

◁ Fishermen catch sturgeon and beluga (white sturgeon) in the mouth of the Ural River, one of the main spawning grounds for fish in the Caspian Sea. Demand for sturgeon roe has pushed these fish almost to extinction.

▽ The Caspian Sea produces 90 percent of the world's black caviar, as wild sturgeon is known. But exploitation beyond legal limits, plus pollution from sewage washed into the sea, continues to threaten the sturgeon.

CASPIAN SPECIES

This low salinity is a major factor in the range of wildlife in the Caspian. It is too salty for most freshwater species and not salty enough for most marine species. So the Caspian does not have a wide number of species but many of those that it does have are unique to the Caspian. The Caspian has its own seal, for instance – the Caspian seal, which is the world's smallest seal, and one of only three that live in lakes.

There are also fish such as the Caspian roach, the Caspian salmon (which is really a kind of trout), the Caspian bream, and the Caspian white fish or kutum, as well as birds such as the Caspian gull and the Caspian tern. Interestingly, the Caspian and Black Sea each have, for instance, their own range of sturgeons. But the Volga–Don ship canal now links the two seas, and this has led to some mixing of the races – with the result that there are fears that the Black Sea and Caspian sturgeons may lose some of their biodiversity. Some organisms have arrived in the Caspian relatively recently. Barnacles, crabs, and clams, for example, have been transported by ships, while grey mullets have been deliberately introduced by humans.

The isolation of the Caspian has enabled it to develop its own unique wildlife, but pollutants have no escape. The result is that the Caspian is one of the world's most polluted seas. Much of the pollution comes from spillages during the extraction, processing, and transport of oil and gas from the huge deposits under the seabed. Another major polluter is the Volga River, which washes in vast amounts of agricultural runoff from Russian land as well as domestic and industrial waste products. The Caspian Sea's unique ecology is also damaged by uranium-contaminated coolant from nuclear power plants on the coast.

SEALS AND STURGEONS

The pollution comes on top of a long history of overfishing and hunting in this region. Numbers of the Caspian seal, for instance, are down from maybe three to four million a century ago to just a few hundred thousands now. The main culprit was hunting, but pollution is now damaging the female seal's ability to reproduce.

It is the fate of the sturgeon, though, that has caught most attention. High demand for sturgeon roe, used to make the highly prized delicacy, caviar, has helped decimate stocks in the Caspian. Unfortunately, despite bans, illegal fishing has gone on at maybe 10 to 15 times over the official limit. Pollution has also had its effect on the reproduction of the fish, while the damming and control of rivers has damaged access to spawning grounds. The result is that the numbers of beluga sturgeon, the most highly prized of all for its black caviar, have dropped rapidly in the past few decades. Twenty-seven species of sturgeons are now listed by the International Union for Conservation of Nature (IUCN) as endangered, but it is the beluga that is most in trouble. By 2007, the legal limit for caviar that can be taken from Caspian beluga had been reduced to 3,700 kg (8,160 lb). Nonetheless, by March 2010, the beluga's situation had become so grave that the IUCN listed it as 'critically endangered' – its highest risk category. The one consolation is that they can produce millions of eggs, so if they are given decent protection, there is just a chance that they might recover.

THE WORLD'S OCEANS AND SEAS
THE SOUTH CHINA SEA

With the ports of Singapore at one end and Hong Kong-Macau at the other, the South China Sea is one of the most heavily shipped seas in the world.

Thousands of ships pass through the South China Sea every day, and more than half the world's tonnage of shipping passes through the great gateways to the sea, the straits of Malacca, Lombok, and Sunda. A quarter of the world's oil (15 million barrels) slips daily into the South China Sea through the narrow neck of the Strait of Malacca alone.

But the nations surrounding the South China Sea have realized that there is much more to this sea than just a conduit. Vast amounts of oil and gas lie as yet untapped under the sea, especially around the hundreds of small, mostly uninhabited, islets known as the Spratlys. China and Taiwan both claim much of the ocean as their own, which of course, Vietnam, the Philippines, Malaysia, Indonesia, and Thailand strongly dispute. There have only been a few minor armed conflicts so far but there are frequent bristling encounters between naval vessels of the competing nations. The Association of Southeast Asian Nations (ASEAN) has negotiated rules for developing the ocean's resources jointly, and China, too, has agreed to plans to share the benefits, without renouncing its claims to sovereignty.

As these vigorous international disputes go on, protection of the South China Sea's rich wildlife has not always been high on the list of priorities. Many people who live around the shores are poor, and the seemingly abundant marine life living among the sea's wealth of coral reefs – from sea turtles for food to tropical fish for the aquarium trade – are just too tempting. It remains to be seen whether the competing nations can agree on a workable plan for protecting the wildlife while allowing people to make a living before it is too late.

◁ *This picture shows the bustling container port of Kowloon in Hong Kong with some of the huge volume of shipping that is taking a real toll on the marine wildlife of the South China Sea.*

THE SEA OF ISLANDS

THE SOUTH CHINA SEA IS ONE OF THE MOST biologically diverse marine ecosystems in the world. There are coral reefs in abundance, vast seagrass meadows, richly sedimented shallows, and mangrove swamps of wonderful variety. Indeed, nearly a third of the world's coral reefs are found in the region.

The wonderful reefs of this sea are also among the most diverse on the planet. There are more than 2,000 different species of fish on the coral reefs around the Philippines alone. Green and hawksbill turtles, sharks of numerous kinds, and myriad seabirds make this an astonishingly rich place for marine life.

GROWING PAINS

But the sea is also caught in the middle of some of the world's fastest developing regions. The population of the South China Sea countries is growing rapidly, at 5 to 10 percent a year. Maybe half a billion people live not far from the ocean's shore, and that number is set to rise dramatically over the next few years, with cities like Guangzhou set to become the world's biggest urban centre. As these countries develop, their energy consumption is rising even faster than their population. This is bound to place increasing pressure not only on the South China Sea's already busy sea lanes, but on the gas and oil resources lying, as yet, barely developed beneath its bed.

The gateway to the South China Sea through the Strait of Malacca carries more oil than any seaway in the world but the Strait of Hormuz. More than 15 million barrels of oil are shipped through the Strait of Malacca every day, and in a year, nearly 20,000 oil tankers glide over and past its abundant seagrass beds and coral reefs, its mangrove swamps, and coastal wetlands.

Even more general cargo vessels make the transit. Oil spills are inevitable, not just from collisions and groundings but also from deliberate dumping. As oil exploration gets under way, too, oil spills are becoming more and more of a hazard, and it is not always easy to pinpoint the blame when spills do happen. Early in 2007, 800 km (497 miles) of Vietnam's coast were blackened by huge quantities of oil coming ashore from a mystery source, devastating tourist beaches, lobster farms, and nature reserves alike. Huge efforts failed to identify the source.

OVERFISHING

The most current and immediate threat to the South China Sea's marine life, though, is overfishing and over-exploitation of its

natural resources. Around the edges, huge swathes of mangrove swamps have been cleared to make way for the world's largest shrimp farms (see pages 108–109) and maybe three-quarters of the mangrove swamps on the South China Sea's coast have been swept away in the last few decades. The remaining mangroves and their tangle of roots and shrubs are still home to many unique species, but their future is certainly threatened.

Fish is the main source of animal protein in the region, and as the population grows, pressure on the sea's fish increases. Much of the fishing is still done in traditional ways, with small boats and nets. But industrial fishing fleets are becoming more and more common, and there is no doubt that the South China Sea has begun to reach its limits of sustainability.

CORAL DAMAGE

Coral reefs have been particularly vulnerable to exploitation. Two-thirds of the corals have been severely degraded or destroyed. Damaging illegal fishing methods, such as dynamite and cyanide fishing, are partly to blame. With dynamite fishing, bottles filled with explosives made from potassium nitrate from fertilizer are dropped on the reef and exploded. The blast ruptures the swim bladders of small fish so that they float to the surface, where the fishermen collect them. The reefs are reduced to rubble and countless other 'useless' animals are caught in the blast.

Cyanide fishing involves squirting cyanide into the water to stun and capture valuable fish for the aquarium trade, or fish such as the Napoleon wrasse or groupers for 'live fish' restaurants. The fish that are harvested often die very quickly, while the corals and other creatures left behind are poisoned and soon die.

At the beginning of the millennium, the seven nations that border the sea – Cambodia, China, Malaysia, Indonesia, Thailand, Vietnam, and the Philippines – agreed to a United Nations Environment Programme to tackle the problems,

and the South China Sea has been designated one of the International Union for Conservation of Nature's 64 Large Marine Ecosystems. The Chinese navy is becoming increasingly assertive in preventing overfishing and illegal fishing, with regular patrols policing the reefs around the Spratlys in particular. But of course, because this is part of China's territorial claims to the sea and resources, these patrols do not meet with approval from other nations. It remains to be seen whether the South China Sea nations can act together to preserve the sea's marine life or if it gets caught in the crossfire between them.

△ The extraordinary pink colour of the rare Chinese white dolphin that lives in the waters around Hong Kong is not a pigment but blood vessels near the surface of its skin that help the dolphin keep cool.

▽ The eroded limestone islands of Ha Long Bay in Vietnam form one of the most distinctive and beautiful seascapes in the world, but its very beauty has attracted the kind of pressure of tourist activity that threatens its marine life.

THE CORAL TRIANGLE

SOMETIMES CALLED THE AMAZON OF THE OCEAN, THE CORAL TRIANGLE
IS A ROUGHLY TRIANGULAR AREA OF OCEAN AND ISLANDS BETWEEN
SOUTHEAST ASIA AND AUSTRALIA.

Covering some 6.8 million sq. km (2.6 million sq. miles), the
Coral Triangle includes 18,500 islands and six countries – the
Philippines, Indonesia, Malaysia, Timor-Leste, Papua New
Guinea, and the Solomon Islands. This triangle has been
identified by marine biologists as one of the world's most
remarkable ecological hot spots, with a biodiversity unrivalled
by any other area of ocean.

BIO HOT SPOT
Although the Coral Triangle occupies barely 2 percent of
the world's oceans, it is home to half the world's coral reefs,
three-quarters of all reef species, 40 percent of the world's reef
fish species, and five out of seven of the world's sea turtles.
More than 605 different species of corals are found there,
out of the world's 796, and 2,228 of the world's 6,000 reef
fish – 235 of those species are unique to the Coral Triangle.
Such is the diversity of reef species in the Coral Triangle that
some scientists believe this is where corals first evolved before
radiating through the world's oceans.

There is one remarkable place within the Coral Triangle that
has the most astonishing cornucopia on Earth. When divers
explored the seas around the Raja Ampat (Four Kings) islands
to the northwest of the Bird's Head Peninsula in New Guinea,
in 2001, they found that they are blessed with the highest
recorded biodiversity of any habitat. An incredible 537 different

The Coral Triangle

Centred on the island of Papua New Guinea, the Coral Triangle is an area of ocean
half the size of the USA. It is filled with a completely unique variety of coral reef
wildlife, with over 40 percent of the world's coral reef fish living there.

coral species live in this small area alone, along with more
than 1,000 kinds of reef fish and nearly 700 kinds of molluscs.

▽ *The stunningly beautiful coral reefs of Indonesia's Komodo National
Park have come under severe threat from destructive fishing practices
such as dynamite fishing and cyanide fishing.*

△ *Although not receiving the same attention as marine animals and fish, tropical molluscs such as this Pfeffer's flamboyant cuttlefish are among the most colourful of all marine creatures – but this cuttlefish is deadly poisonous.*

MULTICOLOUR MAGIC

Some of the triangle's most special creatures are the technicolored sea slugs called nudibranches. There are more than 1,400 species of these small creatures in the Coral Triangle. Many of them are astonishingly vividly coloured, such as the stunning *Chromodoris annae*, which looks like a navy blue and gold velvet cushion. Their colour probably warns predators away. Nudibranches move far too slowly to escape by speed, so instead, they are poisonous, or at least foul tasting and their colour acts as a warning.

Another strikingly coloured inhabitant of these waters is Pfeffer's flamboyant cuttlefish, which lives up to its name. Just like the nudibranches, the colours warn that it is highly toxic. Indeed, a sting from its tentacles is as deadly as one from the notorious blue-ringed octopus, one of the world's most venomous animals.

Other remarkable inhabitants of the Coral Triangle include the mantis shrimp. Related to neither shrimp nor praying mantids, this strange creature resembles both and boasts some of the most powerful claws in nature, earning it the name 'thumbsplitter' among divers because of the damage it can do to fingers. Some larger species can smash the glass of an aquarium with a single strike of their claw.

TRIANGULAR THREATS

The richness of the Coral Triangle's marine life is due to its special combination of light, warm water, and nutrient-rich waters, due to the mixing of currents from the Indian and Pacific oceans. The seasonal inflow of these nutrients, and water warmed by the tropical sunshine, produces an abundance of phytoplankton and zooplankton. Plankton in turn provides a feast for fish and their larvae as well as the corals.

Such abundance has provided the people of the region with a rich catch of fish, and the Coral Triangle is one of the world's hot spots for skipjack tuna as well as reef fish. Two-thirds of the reefs are overfished, though, and, like the neighbouring South China Sea, it has found its reefs become victim to damaging

△ *Live fish restaurants make a wonderfully exotic eating experience, but they can encourage the cyanide fishing that brings devastation to the reefs. Cyanide fishing is illegal in most Indo-Pacific countries, but still goes on.*

practices such as dynamite fishing and cyanide fishing.

Perhaps the greatest threat to the Coral Triangle in the future, though, is global warming. Because the waters are already warm, it may need only a slight warming to wreak havoc. Sea temperatures here are currently rising at about 0.1°C (0.18°F) every decade, and are projected to rise between 1 and 4°C (1.8 and 7.2°F) towards the end of this century. It is thought that a rise of 2°C (3.6°F) will wipe out all the corals from the region.

PLAN OF ACTION

Because of its immense importance ecologically, the Coral Triangle has become the focus of attention among conservationists, and the nations within the triangle have joined with international bodies to put plans in place to conserve wildlife in the triangle.

In May 2009, the six national governments launched a Regional Plan of Action at the first ever World Ocean Conference, organized by Indonesia's President Susilo Bambang Yudhoyono. It is a commitment to protect marine resources for the wellbeing of the region's citizens and future generations. It is a combination of conservation measures that take into account local people's need to make a living. Although it is just signatures on paper at the moment, it may provide a blueprint for other conservation agreements.

OCEAN FUTURE – THE SEA ETHIC

THE PURPOSE OF THIS BOOK has been both to celebrate the richness and diversity of life in the oceans, and to draw attention to the escalating threats facing marine ecosystems from human activity. In many ways, it has been an uncomfortable, even depressing, story. During the course of this journey, we have had to recount numerous tales of creatures on the brink of extinction, growing dead zones, the catastrophic effects of pollution, and much more. At every turn, we seem to encounter yet another tragedy, actual or potential, as dolphins choke in fishing nets by the thousand, and multi-coloured living coral reefs turn into ghostly skeletons.

Yet the situation, while dire, is far from hopeless. This book is not alone in drawing attention to the problems, and over the last few decades, an increasing number of marine biologists and conservationists have campaigned vigorously to stop the damage and have met with successes. Many supermarkets, for instance, are now keenly aware that it makes a difference to their sales when they promote their fish as being from 'sustainable sources'. International organizations frequently meet to negotiate fishing limits, and numerous species are now protected by law. Although there is a constant battle between the different interests, some measure of protection is now in place for most species recognized as being in critical danger of extinction. For some species, these measures are likely to be too little too late. But for others they have brought real hope. The moratorium on whaling, for instance, while still a source of intense conflict, has succeeded in bringing back some species from the brink.

There are signs, too, that natural ecosystems can prove remarkably resilient if only they are given a little breathing space

▽ *As the numbers of Marine Protected Areas in the oceans increase around the world, so too do the numbers of endangered species that are brought back from the brink of extinction.*

and a chance to recover. In the 1990s, things looked hopeless in the Black Sea as pollution fed into it through rivers created a Dead Zone so stultifying that it seemed if the sea might soon be as lifeless as the seas of the Moon. Yet today, with the reduction of pollution in the last decade, the marine life of the Black Sea, while not exactly healthy, has shown real signs of recovery.

One of the crucial lessons that is being learned is that it is not enough to protect individual species; their homes and habitats must be conserved, too. Hidden beneath the waves, ocean habitats have not been on the public radar in the way that tropical rainforests and other terrestrial ecosystems have. But they are just as vital to the creatures that live there. That is why they have become issues of critical importance to conservation efforts, local and national governments, and international marine conservation groups. The number of Marine Protected Areas and Marine Reserves around the world is growing year by year, turning more and more places in the oceans into refuges for endangered species.

But while there are signs of progress, the problems are immense, and it is not enough to leave it to the experts and the specialist conservationists. The reason the oceans are under threat is the way we all live. Fish are only overfished because too many of us expect to eat fish cheaply and often. Seabirds are only choked by plastic because too many of us use a lot of plastic – and then throw it away carelessly. Seas are only polluted with oil because too many of us drive cars that burn too much oil.

Some conservationists talk about developing a 'sea ethic'. We may need to learn how to adjust our lifestyles to cherish life in the ocean just as we cherish the life of our friends and families. The oceans are as much our home as any part of this planet; they are wonderful, colourful, life-filled places that deserve and need our care. As Jacques Cousteau put it so memorably, when it comes to the oceans, 'we are all in the same boat'.

ENDANGERED MARINE SPECIES

THE INTERNATIONAL UNION FOR THE CONSERVATION OF NATURE AND NATURAL RESOURCES (IUCN) is the world's main authority on the conservation status of species, and it publishes a continuously updated red list of threatened species. There are 620 animal species or species populations on this list, but this just shows the animals that are known to be in trouble. There are likely to be many, many more to which the risk is unknown. The list here is based on the latest red list, published in 2008.

THREATS

It is not always easy to be sure why a species or population is in decline. So the threats listed in this table are not the only problems facing these animals but simply some of the main threats that have so far been identified.

- Over-exploitation which includes hunting and fishing

- By-catch which includes animals that are caught accidentally when people are hunting or fishing for other species; trawling, with its big nets, is responsible for a lot of by-catch

- Climate change

- Disease

- Pollution

- Habitat damage; this includes a wide range of problems from coastal development to the introduction of rogue species

- Predation; this includes predation by invasive species, or species that have increased dramatically in population

Conservation Status: The Risk Categories

The degree of danger to a taxon – the species or the regional population of a species – is categorized on a scale from Least Concern to Critically Endangered, and beyond that to Extinction. Threatened taxons are taxons that fall into one of the three top categories of danger: Critically Endangered, Endangered, and Vulnerable.

Extinct (EX)	A taxon is Extinct when there is no reasonable doubt that the last individual has died.
Extinct In The Wild (W)	A taxon is Extinct in the Wild when it is known only to survive in cultivation, in captivity, or as a naturalized population (or populations) well outside the past range.
Critically Endangered (CR)	A taxon is Critically Endangered when it meets certain criteria that show it to be at very high risk of imminent Extinction in the Wild.
Endangered (EN)	A taxon is Endangered when it meets certain criteria that show it to be at high risk of Extinction in the Wild.
Vulnerable (VU)	A taxon is Vulnerable when when it meets certain criteria that show it may soon be at risk of Extinction in the Wild.
Near Threatened (NT)	A taxon is Near Threatened when it meets certain criteria that show it may become threatened with Extinction in the future.
Least Concern (LC)	A taxon is of Least Concern when it meets certain criteria that show it is widespread and not likely to be threatened with Extinction in the future.

Different Versions

Over the years, different sets of criteria have been put forward for defining each of the risk categories and taxon. These are known as versions. So the listing of a taxon and the risk to it in the table is given according to a particular version. Population: This shows whether numbers are increasing, decreasing, or stable at present.

Scientific Name	Common Name	Status	Pop.	Threats
Acanthastrea bowerbanki		VU	–	⬛➕🔷
A. brevis		VU	–	⬛➕🔷
A. faviaformis		VU	–	⬛➕
A. hemprichii		VU	–	⬛➕
A. ishigakiensis		VU	–	⬛➕
A. regularis		VU	–	⬛➕
Acipenser brevirostrum	Shortnose Sturgeon	VU	B	⬛
A. nudiventris	Fringebarbel Sturgeon	EN	–	⬛➕⬛⬛
A. oxyrinchus ssp. desotoi	Gulf Sturgeon	VU	B	⬛⬛⬛⬛⬛
A. sinensis	Chinese Sturgeon	EN	–	⬛⬛⬛⬛
Acropora abrolhosensis		VU	B	⬛⬛
A. aculeus		VU	B	⬛⬛
A. acuminata		VU	B	⬛⬛⬛
A. anthocercis		VU	B	⬛⬛⬛
A. aspera		VU	B	⬛⬛⬛
A. awi		VU	B	⬛⬛➕⬛
A. batunai		VU	B	⬛⬛➕⬛
A. caroliniana		VU	B	⬛⬛➕⬛
A. cervicornis	Staghorn Coral	CR	•	⬛➕
A. dendrum		VU	B	⬛⬛➕⬛
A. derawanensis		VU	B	⬛⬛➕⬛

Scientific Name	Common Name	Status	Pop.	Threats
A. desalwii		VU	B	⬛⬛➕⬛
A. donei		VU	B	⬛⬛➕⬛
A. echinata		VU	B	⬛⬛➕⬛
A. elegans		VU	B	⬛⬛➕⬛
A. globiceps		VU	B	⬛⬛➕⬛
A. hemprichii		VU	B	⬛⬛➕⬛
A. hoeksemai		VU	B	⬛⬛➕⬛
A. horrida		VU	B	⬛⬛➕⬛
A. indonesia		VU	B	⬛⬛➕⬛
A. jacquelineae		VU	B	⬛⬛➕⬛
A. kimbeensis		VU	B	⬛⬛➕⬛
A. kirstyae		VU	B	⬛⬛➕⬛
A. kosurini		VU	B	⬛⬛➕⬛
A. listeri		VU	B	⬛⬛➕⬛
A. loisetteae		VU	B	⬛⬛➕⬛
A. lokani		VU	B	⬛⬛➕⬛
A. lovelli		VU	B	⬛⬛➕⬛
A. microclados		VU	B	⬛⬛➕⬛
A. multiacuta		VU	B	⬛⬛➕⬛
A. palmata	Elkhorn Coral	CR	•	⬛➕
A. palmerae		VU	B	⬛⬛➕⬛

Scientific Name	Common Name	Status	Pop.	Threats
A. paniculata		VU	B	
A. papillare		VU	B	
A. pharaonis		VU	B	
A. plumosa		VU	B	
A. polystoma		VU	B	
A. retusa		VU	B	
A. roseni		EN	B	
A. rudis		EN	B	
A. russelli		VU	B	
A. simplex		VU	B	
A. solitaryensis		VU	B	
A. speciosa		VU	B	
A. spicifera		VU	B	
A. striata		VU	B	
A. suharsonoi		EN	B	
A. tenella		VU	B	
A. turaki		VU	B	
A. vaughani		VU	B	
A. verweyi		VU	B	
A. walindii		VU	B	
A. willisae		VU	B	
Aetobatus flagellum	Longheaded Eagle Ray	EN	B	
Aetomylaeus maculatus	Mottled Eagle Ray	EN	B	
Aetomylaeus nichofii	Banded Eagle Ray	VU	B	
Aetomylaeus vespertilio	Reticulate Eagle Ray	EN	B	
Agaricia lamarcki	Lamarck's Sheet Coral	VU	B	
Alopias pelagicus	Pelagic Thresher Shark	VU	B	
A. superciliosus	Bigeye Thresher Shark	VU	B	
A. vulpinus	Common Thresher Shark	VU	B	
Alveopora allingi		VU	–	
A. daedalea		VU	–	
A. excelsa		EN	–	
A. fenestrata		VU	–	
A. gigas		VU	–	
A. japonica		VU	–	
A. marionensis		VU	–	
A. minuta		EN	–	
A. verrilliana		VU	–	
Amblyraja radiata	Thorny Skate	VU	B	
Amblyrhynchus cristatus	Galapagos Marine Iguana	VU	–	
A. cristatus ssp. albemarlensis	Galapagos Marine Iguana	VU	–	
A. cristatus ssp. cristatus	Galapagos Marine Iguana	VU	•	
A. cristatus ssp. hassi	Galapagos Marine Iguana	VU	•	
A. cristatus ssp. mertensi	Galapagos Marine Iguana	EN	–	
A. cristatus ssp. nanus	Galapagos Marine Iguana	EN	B	
A. cristatus ssp. venustissimus	Galapagos Marine Iguana	VU	•	
Anacropora matthai		VU	B	
A. puertogalerae		VU	B	
A. reticulata		VU	B	
A. spinosa		EN	B	
Anomastraea irregularis		VU	B	
Anoxypristis cuspidata	Knifetooth Sawfish	CE	B	
Antrisocopia prehensilis		CE	–	
Aptychotrema timorensis	Spotted Shovelnose Ray	VU	–	
Arctocephalus galapagoensis	Galapagos Fur Seal	EN	B	
Argyrosomus hololepidotus	Madagascar Meagre	EN	–	
Astreopora cucullata		VU	B	
A. incrustans		VU	B	
A. moretonensis		VU	B	
Atelomycterus baliensis	Bali Catshark	VU	–	
Atlantoraja cyclophora	Spotback Skate	EN	B	
A. cyclophora	Eyespot Skate	VU	B	
A. platana	La Plata Skate	VU	B	

Scientific Name	Common Name	Status	Pop.	Threats
Aulohalaelurus kanakorum	New Caledonia Catshark	VU	–	
Australogyra zelli		VU	B	
Bahaba taipingensis	Chinese Bahaba	CR	B	
Balaena mysticetus (Bering-Chukchi-Beaufort S sub)	Bowhead Whale			
B. mysticetus (Okhotsk S sub)	Bowhead Whale	EN	–	
B. mysticetus (Svalbard-Barents S (Spitsbergen) sub)	Bowhead Whale	CR	–	
Balaenoptera borealis	Sei Whale	EN	–	
B. musculus	Blue Whale	EN	A	
B. musculus ssp. intermedia	Antarctic Blue Whale	CR	A	
B. musculus ssp. musculus (N Pacific stock)	Blue Whale	–		
B. physalus	Fin Whale	EN	–	
Barabattoia laddi		VU	B	
Bathyraja griseocauda	Graytail Skate	EN	B	
Benthobatis kreffti	Brazilian Blind Electric Ray	VU	–	
B. yangi	Taiwanese Blind Electric Ray	VU	–	
Bolbometopon muricatum	Green Humphead Parrotfish	VU	B	
Callorhinus ursinus	Northern Fur Seal	VU	B	
Cantharellus noumeae		EN	–	
Carcharhinus brachyurus (E Asia sub)	Bronze Whaler	VU	B	
C. brevipinna (NW Atlantic sub)	Spinner Shark	VU	–	
C. hemiodon	Pondicherry Shark	CR	–	
C. limbatus (NW Atlantic sub)	Blacktip Shark	VU	–	
C. longimanus	Oceanic Whitetip Shark	VU	B	
C. obscurus	Dusky Shark	VU	B	
C. obscurus (NW Atlantic and Gulf of Mexico sub)	Dusky Shark	VU	B	
C. plumbeus	Sandbar Shark	VU	B	
C. plumbeus (NW Atlantic sub)	Sandbar Shark	VU	–	
C. signatus	Night Shark	VU	B	
Carcharias taurus (E coast of Australia sub)	Spotted Ragged-tooth Shark	CR	B	
C. taurus (SW Atlantic sub)	Spotted Ragged-tooth Shark	CR	B	
Catalaphyllia jardinei		VU	–	
Caulastrea connata		VU	B	
C. curvata		VU	B	
C. echinulata		VU	B	
Centrophorus granulosus	Gulper Shark	VU	B	
C. harrissoni	Harrison's Deepsea Dogfish	CR	B	
C. lusitanicus	Lowfin Gulper Shark	VU	–	
C. moluccensis (Australian sub)	Smallfin Gulper Shark	EN	B	
C. squamosus	Nilson's Deepsea Dogfish	VU	B	
C. uyato (Australian sub)	Little Gulper Shark	CR	B	
Cephalorhynchus hectori	Hector's Dolphin	EN	B	
Cephalorhynchus hectori ssp. maui	North Island Hector's Dolphin	CR	B	
Chaenogaleus macrostoma	Hooktooth Shark	VU	–	
Cheilinus undulatus	Undulate Wrasse	EN	B	
Chelonia mydas	Green Turtle	EN	B	
Coscinaraea hahazimaensis		VU	–	
Cromileptes altivelis	Hump-back Rock-cod	VU	B	
Ctenella chagius		EN	B	
Cyphastrea agassizi		VU	B	
C. hexasepta		VU	B	
C. ocellina		VU	B	
Cystophora cristata	Hooded Seal	VU	B	
Dasyatis colarensis	Colares Stingray	VU	–	
D. fluviorum	Estuary Stingaree	VU	B	
D. margarita		EN	B	
Delphinapterus leucas (Cook Inlet sub)	Beluga Whale	CR	–	
Delphinus delphis (Mediterranean sub)	Short-beaked Common Dolphin	EN	B	
Dendrogyra cylindrus	Pillar Coral	VU	•	
Dermochelys coriacea	Leatherback Sea Turtle	CR	B	
Dichocoenia stokesii	Elliptical Star Coral	VU	B	

Scientific Name	Common Name	Status	Pop.	Threats
Diomedea amsterdamensis	Amsterdam Albatross	CR	B	▣✦
D. antipodensis	Antipodean Albatross	VU	B	▣
D. dabbenena	Tristan Albatross	CR	B	▣
D. epomophora	Southern Royal Albatross	VU	•	▣
D. exulans	Wandering Albatross	VU	B	▣
D. sanfordi	Northern Royal Albatross	EN	B	▣
Diplobatis colombiensis	Colombian Electric Ray	VU	–	▣
D. guamachensis	Brownband Numbfish	VU	–	▣
D. ommata	Ocellated Electric Ray	VU	–	▣
D. pictus	Variegated Electric Ray	VU	–	
Dipturus australis	Sydney Skate	VU	–	▣
D. batis	Flapper Skate	CR	B	▣
D. crosnieri	Madagascar Skate	VU	–	▣
D. laevis	Barndoor Skate	EN	•	▣
D. mennii	South Brazilian Skate	VU	–	▣
D. trachydermus	Roughskin Skate	VU	B	▣
D. whitleyi	Melbourne Skate	VU	–	▣
Discopyge tschudii (SW Atlantic sub)	Apron Ray	VU	B	▣
Dugong dugon	Dugong	VU	–	▣✦▣
Echinophyllia costata		VU	–	▣
Echinopora ashmorensis		VU	B	▣
Echinopora robusta		VU	B	▣
Electrolux addisoni	Ornate Sleeper Ray	CR	–	▣
Epinephelus akaara	Hong Kong Grouper	EN	B	▣
E. albomarginatus	White-edged Rockcod	VU	B	▣
E. bruneus	Longtooth Grouper	VU	B	▣
E. cifuentesi (Galápagos I sub)	Olive Grouper	VU	B	▣
E. drummondhayi	Strawberry Grouper	CR	–	▣
E. flavolimbatus	Yellowfinned Grouper	VU	B	▣
E. gabriellae	Multispotted Grouper	VU	B	▣
E. itajara	Goliath Grouper	CR	–	▣
E. lanceolatus	Queensland Groper	VU	B	▣
E. marginatus	Dusky Grouper	EN	B	▣
E. nigritus	Warsaw Grouper	CR	–	▣
E. niveatus	Spotted Grouper	VU	B	▣
E. striatus	Nassau Grouper	EN	B	▣
Eretmochelys imbricata	Hawksbill Turtle	CR	B	▣
Eschrichtius robustus (W sub)	Gray Whal	CR	A	▣▣▣
Eubalaena australis (Chile-Peru sub)	Southern Right Whale	CR	–	▣▣▣
E. glacialis	North Atlantic Right Whale	EN	–	▣▣
E. japonica	North Pacific Right Whale	EN	–	▣▣
E. japonica (NE Pacific sub)	North Pacific Right Whale	CR	B	▣▣
Eudyptes chrysolophus	Macaroni Penguin	VU	B	▣▣
E. pachyrhynchus	Fiordland Penguin	VU	B	▣
E. robustus	Snares Penguin	VU	•	▣▣
E. schlegeli	Royal Penguin	VU	•	▣▣
E. sclateri	Erect-crested Penguin	EN	B	▣
Eumetopias jubatus	Steller Sea Lion	EN	B	▣▣
Euphyllia ancora		VU	–	▣▣▣
E. cristata		VU	•	▣▣▣
E. paraancora		VU	–	▣▣▣
E. paradivisa		VU	–	▣▣▣
E. paraglabrescens		VU	–	▣▣▣
Favia rosaria		VU	B	▣▣
Favites spinosa		VU	B	▣
Fregata andrewsi	Christmas Frigatebird	CR	B	▣
F. aquila	Ascension Frigatebird	VU	–	▣
Fungia curvata		VU	–	▣
F. seychellensis		VU	–	▣
F. taiwanensis		VU	–	▣
Galaxea acrhelia		VU	–	▣
G. astreata		VU	–	▣
G. cryptoramosa		VU	–	▣

Scientific Name	Common Name	Status	Pop.	Threats
Galeorhinus galeus	Liver-oil Shark	VU	B	▣
Galeus mincaronei	Southern Sawtail Catshark	VU	B	▣
Glyphis gangeticus	Ganges Shark	CR	B	▣▣
Glyphis siamensis	Irrawaddy River Shark	CR	–	▣▣
Goniastrea deformis		VU	B	▣
G. ramosa		VU	B	▣
Goniopora albiconus		VU	–	▣▣▣
G. burgosi		VU	–	▣▣▣
G. cellulosa		VU	–	▣▣▣
G. planulata		VU	–	▣▣▣
G. polyformis		VU	–	▣▣▣
Gurgesiella dorsalifera	Onefin Skate	VU	B	▣
Gymnura altavela		VU	B	▣▣
G. zonura	Zonetail Butterfly Ray	VU	B	▣▣
Haliotis cracherodii	Black Abalone	CR	B	▣▣▣
H. kamtschatkana	Northern Abalone	EN	•	▣
Halomitra clavator		VU	–	▣
Haploblepharus fuscus	Brown Shyshark	VU	–	▣▣
H. kistnasamyi		CR	–	▣
Heliofungia actiniformis		VU	–	▣▣▣
Heliopora coerulea	Blue Coral	VU	B	▣▣▣
Hemigaleus microstoma	Sickle Fin Weasel Shark	VU	B	▣▣
Hemipristis elongatus	Snaggletooth Shark	VU	B	▣▣
Hemiscyllium hallstromi	Papuan Epaulette Shark	VU	–	▣▣
H. strahani	Hooded Carpet Shark	VU	–	▣▣
Heteronarce garmani	Natal Electric Ray	VU	–	▣▣
Himantura gerrardi	Whitespotted Whipray	VU	–	
H. hortlei	Hortle's Whipray	VU	B	▣
H. lobistoma	Tubemouth Whipray	VU	B	▣
H. pastinacoides	Round Whipray	VU	B	▣
H. uarnacoides	Bleeker's Whipray	VU	B	▣
H. uarnak	Reticulate Whipray	VU	B	▣
H. undulata	Bleeker's Variegated Whipray	VU	B	▣
Hippocampus barbouri	Barbour's Seahorse	VU	B	▣▣▣
H. comes	Tiger Tail Seahorse	VU	B	▣▣▣
H. erectus	Northern Seahorse	VU	B	▣▣▣
H. ingens	Pacific Seahorse	VU	B	▣▣▣
H. kuda	Estuary Seahorse	VU	B	▣▣▣
H. spinosissimus	Hedgehog Seahorse	VU	B	▣▣▣
H. trimaculatus	Low-crowned Seahorse	VU	B	▣▣▣
Holohalaelurus favus	Honeycomb Izak	EN	B	▣
H. punctatus	Whitespotted Izak	EN	B	▣
Horastrea indica		VU	–	▣▣
Hucho perryi	Sakhalin Taimen	CR	B	▣▣▣
Hydnophora bonsai		EN	–	▣▣
Isogomphodon oxyrhynchus	Daggernose Shark	CR	B	▣▣
Isopora brueggemanni		VU	–	▣▣
I. crateriformis		VU	B	▣▣
I. cuneata		VU	B	▣▣
I. togianensis		EN	B	▣▣
Isurus oxyrinchus	Shortfin Mako	VU	B	
I. oxyrinchus (Atlantic sub)	Shortfin Mako	VU	B	▣▣
I. oxyrinchus (Indo-W Pacific sub)	Shortfin Mako	VU	B	▣▣
I. paucus	Shortfin Mako	VU	B	▣▣
Lamiopsis temmincki	Broadfin Shark	EN	B	▣▣
Lamna nasus	Porbeagle	VU	B	▣▣
L. nasus (Mediterranean sub)	Porbeagle	CR	B	▣▣
L. nasus (NE Atlantic sub)		CR	B	▣▣
L. nasus (NW Atlantic sub)	Porbeagle	EN	B	▣▣
Latimeria chalumnae	Coelacanth	CR	–	▣▣
Lepidochelys olivacea	Olive Ridley Sea Turtle	VU	B	▣▣▣
Leptastrea aequalis		VU	B	▣▣
Leptoria irregularis		VU	B	▣▣

Scientific Name	Common Name	Status	Pop.	Threats
Leptoseris incrustans		VU	–	
L. yabei		VU	–	▢✚
Leucoraja circularis		VU	B	▢▧
L. melitensis	Maltese Skate or Ray	CR	B	▢▧
L. ocellata	Winter Skate	EN	B	▢▧
Lithophyllon ranjithi		EN	–	▢✚
Lobophyllia dentatus		VU	–	▢✚
L. diminuta		VU	–	▢✚
L. flabelliformis		VU	–	▢✚
L. serratus		EN	–	▢✚
Malacoraja senta	Smooth Skate	EN	B	▧
Megadyptes antipodes	Yellow-eyed Penguin	EN	B	▢✚
Megaptera novaeangliae (Arabian S sub)	Humpback Whale	EN	–	▢▧
M. novaeangliae (Oceania sub)	Humpback Whale	EN	–	▢▧
Millepora boschmai		CR	–	▢✚
M. foveolata		VU	B	▢✚
M. latifolia		VU	B	▢✚
M. striata		EN	B	▢✚
M. tuberosa		EN	B	▢✚
Mobula mobular	Giant Devil Ray	EN	B	▧
M. rochebrunei	Lesser Guinean Devil Ray	VU	–	▧
Monachus monachus	Mediterranean Monk Seal	CR	B	▢▧▢✚
M. schauinslandi	Hawaiian Monk Seal	CR	B	▢▧
Montastraea annularis	Boulder Star Coral	EN	B	▢✚
M. faveolata		EN	B	▢✚
M. franksi		VU	B	▢✚
M. multipunctata		VU	B	▢✚
M. salebrosa		VU	B	▢✚
M. serageldini		VU	B	▢✚
Montipora altasepta		VU	B	▨▢✚
M. angulata		VU	B	▨▢✚
M. australiensis		VU	B	▨▢✚
M. cactus		VU	B	▨▢✚
M. calcarea		VU	B	▨▢✚
M. caliculata		VU	B	▨▢✚
M. capricornis		VU	B	▨▢✚
M. cebuensis		VU	B	
M. cocosensis		VU	B	
M. corbettensis		VU	B	▨▢✚
M. crassituberculata		VU	B	▨▢✚
M. delicatula		VU	B	▨▢✚
M. dilatata		EN	B	▨▢✚
M. flabellata		VU	B	▨▢✚
M. florida		VU	B	▨▢✚
M. friabilis		VU	B	▨▢✚
M. gaimardi		VU	B	▨▢✚
M. hodgsoni		VU	B	▨▢✚
M. lobulata		VU	B	▨▢✚
M. mactanensis		VU	B	▨▢✚
M. malampaya		VU	B	▨▢✚
M. meandrina		VU	B	▨▢✚
M. orientalis		VU	B	▨▢✚
M. patula		VU	B	▨▢✚
M. samarensis		VU	B	▨▢✚
M. setosa		EN	B	▨▢✚
M. stilosa		VU	B	▨▢✚
M. turtlensis		VU	B	▨▢✚
M. verruculosus		VU	B	▨▢✚
M. vietnamensis		VU	B	▨▢✚
Morus capensis	Cape Gannet	VU	B	▢
Moseleya latistellata		VU	B	▢✚
Mustelus fasciatus	Striped Smooth-hound	CR	B	▧
M. mustelus	Common Smoothhound	VU	B	▧
M. schmitti	Narrownose Smoothhound	EN	B	▧
M. whitneyi	Humpback Smoothhound	VU	B	▧
Mycedium steeni		VU	–	▢✚
Mycetophyllia ferox	Rough Cactus Coral	VU	–	▢✚
Mycteroperca fusca	Island Grouper	EN	B	▢
M. interstitialis	Yellowmouth Grouper	VU	B	▢
M. jordani	Gulf Grouper	EN	B	▢
M. olfax	Colorado Grouper	VU	–	▢
M. rosacea	Leopard Grouper	VU	B	▢
Myliobatis hamlyni	Purple Eagle Ray	EN	B	▧
Narcine bancroftii	Caribbean Electric Ray	CR	–	▧
N. brevilabiata	Shortlip Electric Ray	VU	–	▧
Narke japonica		VU	–	▧
Nebrius ferrugineus	Tawny Nurse Shark	VU	B	
Negaprion acutidens	Sharptooth Lemon Shark	VU	B	▢
N. acutidens (Southeast Asia sub)	Sharptooth Lemon Shark	EN	B	▢
Nemenzophyllia turbida		VU	–	▢✚✚
Neophoca cinerea	Australian Sea Lion	EN	B	▧
Neophocaena phocaenoides	Finless Porpoise	VU	B	▧▢
Nesofregetta fuliginosa	White-throated Storm-petrel	VU	B	▨
Oceanodroma homochroa	Ashy Storm-petrel	EN	B	▨▨
O. macrodactyla	Guadalupe Storm-petrel	CR	–	▨▢
Oculina varicosa	Large Ivory Coral	VU	–	▢✚✚
Odontaspis ferox	Small-tooth Sand Tiger Shark	VU	B	▢▢
O. ferox (Australian sub)	Small-tooth Sand Tiger Shark	VU	B	▢▢
Okamejei pita	Pita Skate	CR	–	▢▨▢
Oncorhynchus nerka (Alaska coastal downwelling, E Gulf of Alaska)	Sockeye Salmon	VU	B	▢▢
O. nerka (Columbia R: Payette R)	Sockeye Salmon	EX		▢▢
O. nerka (Columbia R: Redfish Lk)	Sockeye Salmon	CR	B	▢▢
O. nerka (Columbia R: Suttle Lk/Deschutes R)	Sockeye Salmon	EX		▢▢
O. nerka (Columbia R: Upper, Headwater/Arrow, Whatsan Lk)	Sockeye Salmon	EX		▢▢
O. nerka (Columbia R: Wallowa Lk)	Sockeye Salmon	EX		▢▢
O. nerka (Fraser R, Bowron)	Sockeye Salmon	EN	B	▢▢
O. nerka (Fraser R, lower: Cultus Lk, Chilliwack R)	Sockeye Salmon	EN	B	▢▢
O. nerka (Fraser R, lower: Widgeon Slough)	Sockeye Salmon	VU	A	▢▢
O. nerka (Fraser R, middle: Gates Ck)	Sockeye Salmon	CR	B	▢▢
O. nerka (Fraser R, middle: Stuart to Nahatlatch R)	Sockeye Salmon	EN	B	▢▢
O. nerka (Hecate Str-Q.C. Sound: Atnarko R)	Sockeye Salmon	EN	B	▢▢
O. nerka (Hecate Str-Q.C. Sound: Lowe Lk/Granville Ch)	Sockeye Salmon	EN	B	▢▢
O. nerka (Hecate Str-Q.C. Sound: Queen Charlotte Sound)	Sockeye Salmon	EN	B	▢▢
O. nerka (Kamchatka R)	Sockeye Salmon	EN	B	▢▢
O. nerka (Nass-Skeena Estuary: Hugh Smith Lk/Boca de Quadra)	Sockeye Salmon	EN	B	▢▢
O. nerka (Nass-Skeena Estuary: N of Nass)	Sockeye Salmon	EN	B	▢▢
O. nerka (Puget Sounds-Georgia Basin: Village Bay Ck, Sakinaw)	Sockeye Salmon	CR	B	▢▢
O. nerka (Skeena R, Lower: Kitsukalum, Lakelse, Gitnadoix R)	Sockeye Salmon	VU	B	▢▢
O. nerka (Skeena R, Middle: Nanika Lk/Morice R)	Sockeye Salmon	CR	B	▢▢
O. nerka (Skeena R, Upper)	Sockeye Salmon	EN	B	▢▢
Orcaella brevirostris	Irrawaddy Dolphin	VU	B	▧▢
O. brevirostris (Malampaya Sound sub)	Irrawaddy Dolphin	CR	B	▧▢
Oxynotus centrina	Angular Rough Shark	VU	–	▧
Pachyseris involuta		VU	–	▢✚
P. rugosa		VU	–	▢✚
Papasula abbotti	Abbott's Booby	EN	B	▢

Scientific Name	Common Name	Status	Pop.	Threats
Parapinnixa affinis	Californian Bay Pea Crab	EN	–	
Parasimplastrea sheppardi		EN	B	▢▢
Pastinachus solocirostris	Roughnose Stingray	EN	–	▢▢▢
Pavona bipartita		VU	–	▢▢
P. cactus		VU	–	▢▢
P. danai		VU	–	▢▢
P. decussata	Cactus Coral	VU	–	▢▢
P. diffluens		VU	–	▢▢
P. venosa		VU	–	▢▢
Pectinia africanus		VU	–	▢▢▢
P. alcicornis		VU	–	▢▢
P. lactuca	Lettuce Coral	VU	–	▢▢
P. maxima		EN	–	▢▢
Pelecanoides garnotii	Peruvian Diving-petrel	EN	B	▢
Phalacrocorax campbelli	Campbell Island Shag	VU	–	▢
P. carunculatus	New Zealand King Shag	VU	•	▢
P. chalconotu	Stewart Island Shag	VU	–	▢
P. colensoi	Auckland Islands Shag	VU	•	▢
P. featherstoni	Pitt Island Shag	EN	B	▢
P. harrisi	Flightless Cormorant	EN	–	▢
P. neglectus	Bank Cormorant	EN	B	▢
P. nigrogularis	Socotra Cormorant	VU	B	▢
P. onslowi	Chatham Islands Shag	CR	B	▢
P. ranfurlyi	Bounty Islands Shag	VU	•	
Phocarctos hookeri	New Zealand Sea Lion	VU	B	▢▢▢
Phocoena phocoena (Baltic Sea sub)	Harbor Porpoise	CR	B	
P. phocoena ssp. relicta	Black Sea Harbor Porpoise	EN	–	▢▢
P. sinus	Vaquita	CR	B	▢▢
Phoebastria albatrus	Short-tailed Albatross	VU	A	▢▢
P. immutabilis	Laysan Albatross	VU	B	▢▢
P. irrorata	Waved Albatross	CR	B	▢▢
P. nigripes	Black-footed Albatross	EN	B	▢▢
Phoebetria fusca	Sooty Albatross	EN	B	▢▢
Physeter macrocephalus	Sperm Whale	VU	–	▢▢▢
Physogyra lichtensteini		VU	–	▢▢▢
Platygyra yaeyamaensis		VU	B	▢▢
Platyrhina sinensis	Fanray	VU	–	▢▢
Plectropomus areolatus	Squaretail Leopardgrouper	VU	B	▢
P. laevis	Blacksaddled Coral Grouper	VU	B	▢
Plerogyra discus		VU	–	▢▢▢
Pocillopora ankeli		VU	–	▢▢
P. danae		VU	–	▢▢
P. elegans		VU	–	▢▢
P. fungiformis		EN	–	
P. indiania		VU	–	▢▢
P. inflata		VU	–	▢▢
Polycyathus isabela		VU	–	
Polyprion americanus (Brazilian sub)	Wreckfish	CR	B	▢
Pontoporia blainvillei	Franciscana or La Plata Dolphin	VU	B	▢▢
P. blainvillei (Rio Grande do Sul/Uruguay sub)	Franciscana or La Plata Dolphin	VU	B	▢▢
Porites aranetai		VU	–	▢▢▢
P. attenuata		VU	–	▢▢▢
P. cocosensis		VU	–	▢▢▢
P. cumulatus		VU	–	▢▢▢
P. desilveri		EN	–	▢▢▢
P. eridani		EN	–	▢▢▢
P. horizontalata		VU	–	▢▢▢
P. napopora		VU	–	▢▢▢
P. nigrescens		VU	–	▢▢▢
P. okinawensis		VU	–	▢▢▢
P. ornata		EN	–	▢▢▢
P. pukoensis		CR	–	▢▢▢
P. rugosa		VU	–	▢▢▢

Scientific Name	Common Name	Status	Pop.	Threats
P. sillimaniana		VU	–	▢▢▢
P. sverdrupi		VU	–	▢▢▢
P. tuberculosa		VU	–	▢▢▢
Poritipora paliformis		VU	–	▢▢
Pristis clavata	Queensland Sawfish	CR	B	▢▢
P. microdon	Leichhardt's Sawfish	CR	B	▢▢
P. pectinata	Wide Sawfish	CR	B	▢▢
P. perotteti	Largetooth Sawfish	CR	B	▢▢
P. zijsron	Narrowsnout Sawfish	CR	B	▢▢
Procellaria aequinoctialis	White-chinned Petrel	VU	B	▢
P. conspicillata	Spectacled Petrel	VU	A	▢
P. parkinsoni	Parkinson's Petrel	VU	•	▢
Procellaria westlandica	Westland Petrel	VU	•	▢
Psammocora stellata		VU	–	▢
Pseudobulweria aterrima	Mascarene Petrel	CR	B	▢
P. becki	Beck's Petrel	CR	B	▢
Pseudoginglymostoma brevicaudatum	Shorttail Nurse Shark	VU	–	▢▢
Pterapogon kauderni	Banggai Cardinalfish	EN	B	▢▢
Pterodroma alba	Phoenix Petrel	EN	B	▢
P. arminjoniana	Trindade Petrel	VU	•	▢
P. atrata	Henderson Petrel	EN	B	▢
P. axillaris	Chatham Petrel	EN	B	▢
P. baraui	Barau's Petrel	EN	B	▢
P. cahow	Bermuda Petrel	EN	A	▢
P. cervicalis	White-necked Petrel	VU	A	▢
P. cookii	Cook's Petrel	VU	A	▢
P. defilippiana	De Filippi's Petrel	VU	–	▢
P. externa	Juan Fernandez Petrel	VU	–	▢
P. hasitata	Black-capped Petrel	EN	B	▢
P. incerta	Atlantic Petrel	EN	B	▢
P. leucoptera	Gould's Petrel	VU	B	▢
P. longirostris	Stejneger's Petrel	VU	–	▢
P. magentae	Magenta Petrel	CR	B	▢
P. phaeopygia	Galapagos Petrel	CR	B	▢
P. pycrofti	Pycroft's Petrel	VU	A	▢
P. sandwichensis	Hawaiian Petrel	VU	B	▢
P. solandri	Providence Petrel	VU	A	▢
Puffinus auricularis	Townsend's Shearwater	CR	B	▢
P. bulleri	Buller's Shearwater	VU	A	▢
P. creatopus	Pink-footed Shearwater	VU	–	▢
P. heinrothi	Heinroth's Shearwater	VU	–	▢
P. huttoni	Hutton's Shearwater	EN	B	▢
P. mauretanicus	Balearic Shearwater	CR	B	▢▢
P. newelli	Newell's Shearwater	EN	B	▢
Raja pulchra	Mottled Skate	VU	B	▢▢
R. undulata	Undulate Ray	EN	B	▢
Rhina ancylostoma	Bowmouth Guitarfish	VU	B	▢▢▢
Rhinobatos albomaculatus	White-spotted Guitarfish	VU	B	▢▢▢
R. cemiculus	Blackchin Guitarfish	EN	B	▢▢▢
R. formosensis	Taiwan Guitarfish	VU	–	▢▢▢
R. granulatus	Sharpnose Guitarfish	VU	B	▢▢▢
R. horkelii	Brazilian Guitarfish	EN	B	▢▢▢
R. irvinei	Spineback Guitarfish	VU	B	▢▢▢
R. jimbaranensis		VU	B	▢▢▢
R. obtusus	Widenose Guitarfish	VU	B	▢▢▢
R. penggali		VU	B	▢▢▢
R. rhinobatos	Common Guitarfish	EN	B	▢▢▢
R. thouin	Clubnose Guitarfish	VU	–	▢▢▢
R. typus	Common Shovelnose Ray	VU	B	▢▢
Rhinoptera brasiliensis	Brazilian Cownose Ray	EN	B	▢
R. javanica	Javanese Cownose Ray	VU	–	▢
Rhinoraja albomaculata	Whitedotted Skate	VU	–	▢▢
Rhizopsammia wellingtoni	Wellington's Solitary Coral	CR	B	▢

Scientific Name	Common Name	Status	Pop.	Threats
Rhynchobatus australiae	White-spotted Guitarfish	VU	B	
R. djiddensis	Whitespotted Wedgefish	VU	B	
R. laevis	Smoothnose Wedgefish	VU	–	
R. luebberti	Lubbert's Guitarfish	EN	B	
R. sp. nov. A	Roughnose Wedgefish	VU	B	
R. sp. nov. B	Broadnose Wedgefish	VU	B	
Rioraja agassizi	Rio Skate	VU	–	
Rostroraja alba	Bottlenose Skate	EN	B	
Schroederichthys saurisqualus	Lizard Catshark	VU	–	
Semicossyphus pulcher	California Sheephead	VU	B	
Seriatopora aculeata		VU	–	
S. dendritica		VU	–	
Siderastrea glynni		CR	•	
Sousa chinensis (E Taiwan Str sub)	Indo-pacific Humpback Dolphin	CR	B	
S. teuszii	Atlantic Humpbacked Dolphin	VU	B	
Spheniscus demersus	African Penguin	VU	B	
S. humboldti	Humboldt Penguin	VU	B	
S. mendiculus	Galapagos Penguin	EN	B	
Sphyrna lewini	Scalloped Hammerhead	EN	–	
S. lewini (E Central and SE Pacific sub)	Scalloped Hammerhead	EN	B	
S. lewini (E Central Atlantic sub)	Scalloped Hammerhead	VU	B	
S. lewini (NW and W Central Atlantic sub)	Scalloped Hammerhead	EN	B	
S. lewini (SW Atlantic sub)	Scalloped Hammerhead	VU	B	
S. lewini (W Indian Ocean sub)	Scalloped Hammerhead	EN	B	
S. mokarran	Great Hammerhead Shark	EN	B	
S. tudes	Smalleye Hammerhead Shark	VU	B	
Squalus acanthias	Piked Dogfish	VU	B	
S. acanthias (Black Sea sub)	Piked Dogfish	VU	B	
S. acanthias (Mediterranean sub)	Piked Dogfish	EN	B	
S. acanthias (NE Atlantic sub)	Piked Dogfish	CR	B	
S. acanthias (NE Pacific sub)	Piked Dogfish	VU	B	
S. acanthias (NW Atlantic sub)	Piked Dogfish	EN	B	
S. acanthias (NW Pacific sub)	Piked Dogfish	EN	B	
S. acanthias (South America sub)	Piked Dogfish	VU	B	
S. montalbani	Philippines Spurdog	VU	B	
Squatina aculeata	Sawback Angel Shark	CR	B	
S. albipunctata	Eastern Angel Shark	VU	B	
S. argentina	Argentine Angel Shark	EN	B	
S. formosa	Taiwan Angel Shark	EN	–	
S. guggenheim	Spiny Angel Shark	EN	B	
S. guggenheim (Brazilian sub)	Angular Angel Shark	EN	B	
S. japonica	Japanese Angel Shark	VU	–	
S. nebulosa	Clouded Angel Shark	VU	–	
S. occulta	Smoothback Angel Shark	EN	B	

Scientific Name	Common Name	Status	Pop.	Threats
S. oculata	Smoothback Angel Shark	CR	B	
S. squatina	Angel Shark	CR	B	
S. tergocellatoides	Ocellated Angel Shark	VU	–	
Stegostoma fasciatum	Leopard Shark	VU	B	
Stenella longirostris ssp. orientalis	Eastern Spinner Dolphin	VU	A	
Stereolepis gigas	Black Sea Bass	CR	–	
Stylocoeniella cocosensis		VU	–	
Stylophora madagascarensis		EN	–	
Symphyllia hassi		VU	–	
Sympterygia acuta	Bignose Fanskate	VU	B	
Taeniura meyeni	Black-blotched Stingray	VU	–	
Temera hardwickii		VU	–	
Thalassarche carteri	Indian Yellow-nosed Albatross	EN	B	
T. chlororhynchos	Atlantic Yellow-nosed Albatross	EN	B	
T. chrysostoma	Gray-headed Albatross	VU	B	
T. eremita	Chatham Albatross	CR	–	
T. impavida	Campbell Albatross	VU	A	
T. melanophrys	Black-browed Albatross	EN	B	
T. salvini	Salvin's Albatross	VU	–	
Triakis acutipinna	Sharpfin Houndshark	EN	B	
T. maculata	Spotted Houndshark	VU	B	
Trichechus manatus	West Indian Manatee	VU	B	
T. manatus ssp. manatus	Antillean Manatee	EN	B	
T. senegalensis	West African Manatee	VU	–	
Trygonorrhina melaleuca	Magpie Fiddler Ray	EN	–	
Tubastraea floreana	Floreana Coral	CR	B	
Turbinaria bifrons		VU	–	
T. heronensis		VU	–	
T. mesenterina		VU	–	
T. patula		VU	–	
T. peltata		VU	–	
T. reniformis		VU	–	
T. stellulata		VU	–	
Tursiops truncatus ssp. ponticus	Black Sea Bottlenose Dolphin	EN	–	
Urolophus bucculentus	Sandyback Stingaree	VU	B	
U. orarius	Coastal Stingaree	EN	–	
U. sufflavus	Yellowback Stingaree	VU	B	
U. viridis	Greenback Stingaree	VU	B	
Urotrygon reticulata	Reticulate Round Stingray	VU	–	
U. simulatrix	Fake Round Ray	VU	–	
Ursus maritimus	Polar Bear	VU	B	
Zapteryx brevirostris	Shortnose Guitarfish	VU	B	
Zearaja chilensis	Yellownose Skate	VU	B	

FURTHER RESOURCES

BOOKS AND MAGAZINES

50 Ways to Save the Ocean by David Helvarg, foreword Philippe Cousteau (Inner Ocean, 2006)

Defying Ocean's End: An Agenda for Action by Graeme Kelleher, Linda K. Glover, and Sylvia A. Earle (Island Press, 2004)

Encyclopedia of Underwater Life edited by Andrew Campbell and John Dawes (Oxford University Press, 2004)

Mapping the Deep: The Extraordinary Story of Ocean Science by Robert Kunzig (Sort of Books, 2000)

Ocean's End: Travels Through Endangered Seas by Colin Woodard (Basic Books, 2001)

Ocean: An Illustrated Atlas by Sylvia A. Earle and Linda K. Glover (National Geographic, 2008)

Ocean: The World's Last Wilderness Revealed introduced by Fabien Cousteau (Dorling Kindersley, 2006)

Song for the Blue Ocean by Carl Safina (Henry Holt, 1998)

The Blue Planet by Andrew Byatt, Alastair Fothergill, Martha Holmes, and Sir David Attenborough (BBC Books, 2001)

The End of the Line by Charles Clover (Ebury Press, 2005)

The *New York Times* Magazine, June 27, 2010 [cover story: "Tuna's End"] by Paul Greenberg (The *New York Times*, 2010)

The World is Blue by Sylvia A. Earle (National Geographic, 2009)

World Ocean Census: A Global Survey of Marine Life by Darlene Trew Crist, Gail Scowcroft, and James M. Harding, Jr, foreword by Sylvia Earle (Firefly 2009)

ORGANIZATIONS

Antarctic and Southern Ocean Coalition (ASOC)
1630 Connecticut Ave.,
NW Third Floor
Washington, D.C. 20009, USA
http://www.asoc.org/

Promotes conservation and ensures adherence to environmental standards in the face of pressures from commercial fishing, mining, and tourism companies.

Arctic Ocean Diversity
School of Fisheries and Ocean Sciences
University of Alaska Fairbanks
PO Box 757220
Fairbanks AK 99775-7220, USA
http://www.arcodiv.org/

A Census of Marine Life project aimed at coordinating efforts to examine the diversity in sea ice, the water column, and the sea floor.

Australian Marine Conservation Society (AMCS)
Level 2/75 Cambridge Pde
Manly,
Brisbane QLD 4179
Australia
http://www.amcs.org.au/

A society that aims to save the oceans from the crisis that they face, it is the only Australian national charity dedicated exclusively to protecting ocean wildlife and habitats.

Blue Ocean Institute
250 Lawrence Hill Road
Cold Spring Harbor,
NY 11724, USA
http://www.blueocean.org/home

The Institute works through science, art, and literature to find solutions to the threats to marine life, and help restore life in the oceans.

Center for Biological Diversity
P.O. Box 710
Tucson,
AZ 85702-0710, USA
http://www.biologicaldiversity.org/

The centre works through science, law, and creative media to secure a future for all species hovering on the brink of extinction.

Cetacean Alliance
OceanCare
Postfach 30
CH-8820 Wädenswil,
Switzerland
http://www.cetacenalliance.org/

A not-for-profit network of non-governmental organizations committed to preserving marine biodiversity and reducing human impact on the oceans.

Conservation International
2011 Crystal Drive,
Suite 500
Arlington, VA 22202, USA
http://www.conservation.org/

Through science, policy, and field work, Conservation International seeks smart solutions to protect ecosystems.

Earthwatch Institute
Earthwatch Institute – United States
114 Western Ave,
Boston,
MA 02134, USA
http://www.earthwatch.org/

An international non-profit organization that brings science to life for people concerned about the Earth's future by supporting scientific field research.

Great Barrier Reef Marine Park Authority
2–68 Flinders Street
PO Box 1379
Townsville QLD 4810
Australia
http://www.gbrmpa.gov.au/

Provides for the protection, understanding, and enjoyment of the Great Barrier Reef.

Greenpeace
Greenpeace International
Ottho Heldringstraat 5
1066 AZ Amsterdam
The Netherlands
http://www.greenpeace.org/international/

The international environmentalist
network that aims to champion
environmentally responsible and
socially just solutions, including
scientific and technical innovation.

The International Ecotourism Society
733 15th Street, NW, Suite 1000,
Washington, DC 20005, USA
http://www.ecotourism.org

TIES works to promote tourism
as a tool for conservation of the
environment, alleviation of poverty,
protection of culture, as well as fun.

**International Union for Conservation
of Nature (IUCN)**
IUCN Conservation Centre
Rue Mauverney 28,
Gland 1196 , Switzerland
http://www.iucn.org/

A union of more than 1,000 government
and other organizations with more
than 11,000 volunteer scientists in
more than 160 countries, the IUCN
is the largest professional global
conservation network and a leading
authority on the environment and
sustainable development.

Institute for Ocean Conservation Science
School of Marine and Atmospheric
  Sciences
Stony Brook University
Stony Brook,
NY 11794-5000 USA
http://oceanconservationscience.org/

Seeks to advance ocean conservation
through science, with research focusing
on sharks, sturgeon, coral reefs, and
fisheries management.

**International Council for the
Exploration of the Sea (ICES)**
H. C. Andersens Boulevard 44–46
DK-1553, Copenhagen V, Denmark
http://www.ices.dk/indexfla.asp

Coordinates and promotes marine
research on oceanography, the marine
environment, the marine ecosystem,
and on living marine resources in
the North Atlantic.

MarineBio.org, Inc.
PO Box 235273
Encinitas,
CA 92023, USA
http://marinebio.org/

A conservation society that aims
to unite volunteer marine biologists,
students, professors, and conservation
advocates, and inspire science education,
marine conservation, and research.

Marine Conservation Society (MCS) UK
Unit 3, Wolf Business Park,
Alton Road,
Ross-on-Wye,
HR9 5NB, England
http://www.mcsuk.org

The MCS is the UK organization
working for the conservation of
marine wildlife around the British
Isles and globally.

Marine Stewardship Council (MSC)
2110 North Pacific Street, Suite 102
Seattle,
WA 98103, USA
http://www.msc.org

The MSC rewards sustainable and
environmentally friendly fishing
practices with a blue label of approval.

National Marine Sanctuary Foundation
8601 Georgia Avenue, Suite 501
Silver Spring,
MD 20910, USA
http://www.nmsfocean.org

The NMSF is working to establish a
workforce of volunteers to work in
marine sanctuaries and gain recognition
for the thousands already doing so.

**Natural Resources Defense Council
(NRDC)**
40 West 20th Street
New York,
NY 10011, USA
http://www.nrdc.org/

An environmental action group which
has as one of its main aims the revival
of the world's oceans. It is also fighting
for the defence of endangered wildlife
and wild places.

Nature Conservancy
Worldwide:
The Nature Conservancy
4245 North Fairfax Drive, Suite 100
Arlington,
VA 22203-1606, USA
Australia:
Suite 3.04, The 60 L Green Building
60 Leicester Street,
Carlton, Victoria 3053
Australia
http://www.nature.org/

The Nature Conservancy is a worldwide
organization working for the conservation
of the natural environment.

Ocean Conservancy
1300 19th Street, NW
8th Floor
Washington, DC 20036, USA
http://www.oceanconservancy.org/

Founded originally as the Center for
Environmental Education in 1972 this
grassroots organization helps to promote
healthy and diverse ocean ecosystems.

Oceana
1350 Connecticut Avenue, NW
5th Floor, Washington, DC 20036, USA
http://na.oceana.org/

The largest international organization
focused solely on ocean conservation,
based in North America, Central America,
South America, and Europe.

PEW Environmental Group
One Commerce Square
2005 Market Street, Suite 1700
Philadelphia,
PA 19103-7077, USA
http://www.pewtrusts.org/

This major charitable trust works towards
the conservation of the environment.

Sea Shepherd Conservation Society
P.O. Box 2616,
Friday Harbor,
WA 98250, USA
http://www.seashepherd.org/

Aims to prevent the destruction of habitat
and the slaughter of wildlife in the oceans
by documenting and direct action.

Seafood Watch, Monterey Bay Aquarium
886 Cannery Row
Monterey,
CA 93940, USA
http://www.mbayaq.org/cr/seafoodwatch.asp

This organization supports sustainable fishing and aquaculture and provides "Seafood Watch" pocket guides on what and what not to eat.

Whale and Dolphin Conservation Society (WDCS) North America
7 Nelson Street
Plymouth
MA 02360-4044, USA
http://www.wdcs.org/

The leading global charity dedicated solely to the conservation and welfare of all cetaceans.

Wild Australia
http://wildaustralia.org/

The Wild Australia programme is an ambitious, multi-year effort to identify and protect large landscapes and seascapes in remote parts of Australia.

Wildfowl and Wetlands Trust
Slimbridge, Gloucestershire
GL2 7BT England
http://www.wwt.org.uk/

A conservation organization working towards saving wetlands for wildlife and people across the world.

Wildlife Conservation Society (WCS)
2300 Southern Boulevard
Bronx, NY 10460, USA
http://www.wcs.org/

WCS builds on local on-the-ground experience on four global challenges: emerging wildlife diseases, climate change, the increasing harvest of natural resources by local communities, and the expansion of extractive industries. With a commitment to protect 25 percent of the world's biodiversity, WCS aims to save wildlife and wild places across the globe.

Wildlife Trust
The Kiln, Waterside
Mather Road
Newark
Nottinghamshire NG24 1WT
http://www.wildlifetrusts.org/

The largest UK organization working for the conservation of wildlife.

World Wildlife Fund
1250 24th Street, NW
P.O. Box 97180
Washington, DC 20090 USA
http://www.worldwildlife.org/

The leading organization in wildlife conservation and endangered species, it also tackles climate change and promotes sustainable use of resources.

NEWS AND INFORMATION WEBSITES

www.amnh.org/exhibitions/permanent/ocean/

www.californiaunderwater.com/

deepseanews.com/tag/abyssal-plain/

www.dfg.ca.gov/marine/

http://endoftheline.com/blog/archives/author/charles-clover

www.fisheries.is/main-species/pelagic-fishes/

www.fishonline.org/information/MCSPocket_Good_Fish_Guide.pdf

www.globaloceanlegacy.org/

www.grida.no/

www.invasivespeciesinfo.gov/

http://iwcoffice.org/

http://marine-litter.gpa.unep.org/facts/facts.htm

www.mcbi.org/news/mcbi_news.htm

www.mongabay.com/

www.nationalgeographic.com/features/00/earthpulse/reef/reef1_flash.html

www.nationalgeographic.com/wildworld/reef/reef.html

www.newscientist.com/topic/climate-change

www.nmfs.noaa.gov/pr/

www.oceanleadership.org/http://nsidc.org/arcticseaicenews/

http://oceanworld.tamu.edu/resources/oceanography-book/contents.htm

http://research.myfwc.com/

www.seaaroundus.org/

www.seasky.org/about.html

www.si.edu/http://seawifs.gsfc.nasa.gov/ocean_planet.html

http://species-identification.org/

www.whalesanctuary.co.uk/

www.whoi.edu/http://wwf.panda.org/

GLOSSARY

abyssal plain The plain that forms the greater part of the ocean floor, at an average of 4,000 m (13,100 ft) below the surface. It begins where the continental margin ends.

acidification The rising in the acidity of the oceans caused by the absorption of the extra carbon dioxide put into the atmosphere by recent human activity.

algal bloom A dramatic increase in the amount of algae in the water, usually as a result of the influx of nutrients, such as farm fertilizers.

bathymetry The measurement of the depth of the ocean floor, and the study of the data derived from such measurement.

benthic zone The lowest level in the water, just above the seabed.

bioluminescence The natural production and emission of light by living organisms, very common in deep sea creatures.

bryozoan Tiny creatures that grow over the seabed in colonies, like moss or minute shrubs. They reproduce by budding and filter their **plankton** food from the water.

by-catch The organisms accidentally caught up in the nets of fishing boats along with the targeted fish.

cold seep An area where energy-rich chemicals leak from the sea floor giving rise to a community of organisms independent of **photosynthesis**, such as the communities living on hot **hydrothermal vents**.

continental shelf The shallow region of sea extending up to 500 km (300 miles) around the edges of continents that was probably once dry land. Under the UN Convention of the Law of the Sea, it is also the legal limit of a country's rights over the seabed beyond its coast.

copepod Tiny, numerous, shrimp-like crustaceans just a few millimetres long that, like krill, form a vital part of the ocean food chain.

coral bleaching The loss of coral's symbiotic **zooxanthellae** algae, due to raised water temperatures, that turns coral colonies white, giving them a bleached look.

crustacean Large group of small sea creatures, including crabs, lobsters, shrimps, krill, and barnacles.

cyanobacteria (also known as blue-green algae) Tiny single-celled organisms related to bacteria that can **photosynthesize** like plants.

Dead Zone A large region of the ocean that has very low oxygen levels, usually as a result of an algal bloom and **eutrophication**, and so cannot support life.

ecosystem A community of living things and their environment that interacts and functions as an ecological whole.

El Niño event (also known as the Southern Oscillation) The periodic change in the climate of the southern hemisphere that is caused by a shift in the sea surface temperatures across the southern Pacific. It brings storms to places such as Chile and drought to other places.

eulittoral The zone between the tides or foreshore.

eutrophication The over-enrichment of the water with nutrients that results in an algal bloom and a growth of bacteria that in turn starve the water of oxygen.

finning The lopping off of shark's fins for use in shark fin soup.

fjord A deep, narrow inlet created by the flooding of a glacier-carved valley because of a rise in sea level after the end of an ice age.

global warming The gradual increase in worldwide temperatures that is occurring, probably as a result of the increase in 'greenhouse' gases such as carbon dioxide and methane in the atmosphere caused by human activity.

guyot An extinct, underwater volcano with a top carved flat by the waves that is now at least 200 m (650 ft) below the surface of the water.

hydrothermal vent A natural chimney on the seafloor created by volcanic activity and spewing out billows of hot, mineral-rich water that provide food for unique seabed communities that can live in total darkness.

hypoxic Reduced levels in the amounts of dissolved oxygen that deprives a creature of the oxygen that it needs to live.

krill Tiny, numerous, shrimp-like crustaceans just a few millimetres long that float in the ocean and form a vital part of the ocean food chain.

La Niña The counterpart of **El Niño**, this is a cooling of the surface water of the eastern and central Pacific Ocean. The Pacific trade winds push warm surface water westwards, causing an upwelling of cold water in the east, and bringing drought to western South America and heavy rains to eastern Australia and Indonesia.

lithosphere The Earth's rigid outer layer – the crust and solid part of the mantle – that forms the **tectonic plates**.

littoral The region of the oceans next to the shore, typically extending from the highest water mark to the lowest.

mangrove Trees and shrubs in the tropics that grow with their roots submerged in seawater and form large, coastal swamp forests.

Mid-Ocean Ridge (MOR) One of the long range of undersea mountains along the boundary between the two halves of the ocean floor. Volcanic activity along the ridge causes the sea floor to gradually spread either side. The Mid-Ocean Ridge is the longest of these ridges, winding down through the Atlantic and into the Indian Ocean, and forming the world's longest mountain range.

mollusc The largest of all groups of sea creatures, making up almost a quarter of all known marine organisms. Molluscs have soft bodies and no skeleton, but often a shell. They include clams, bivalves, octopus, cuttlefish, and squid.

neritic zone The part of the ocean extending from the low tide mark to the outer edge of the continental shelf.

nudibranch A sea slug that is often brightly coloured to warn predators that it is poisonous to eat.

ocean trench A deep valley in the ocean floor created by the **subduction** of the ocean floor and forming the deepest parts of an ocean.

pelagic zone Any part of an ocean that is not near the shore or the ocean bed.

pelagic fish Fish that normally live in the pelagic zone.

photic zone The upper layers of the ocean where sunlight penetrates, typically down to about 200 m (650 ft) below the surface of the water.

photosynthesis The process by which plants make their own sugar food from carbon dioxide and water by using energy from sunlight.

phytoplankton Mostly microscopic, floating marine organisms that make their own food using **photosynthesis**.

plankton The huge mass of largely microscopic, floating organisms in the sea or fresh water. The name comes from the Greek word for 'drifting' or 'wandering'.

polynya A patch of open water surrounded by sea ice, especially near the mouths of large rivers in Arctic seas.

polyp A sedentary type of animal such as a coral which has a more or less fixed base, a columnar body, and a free end with a mouth and tentacle.

ria A winding coastal inlet created by the flooding of a river valley because of a rise in sea level.

seagrass Flowering plants that grow in meadows on the seafloor in shallow, subtropical waters, and form a vital nursery for the young of many fish species as well as providing the key food for manatees and dugongs.

sea surface altimetry The precise measurement of the height of the sea surface using microwaves beamed from satellites.

sea fan (also known as Gorgonians) Sedentary sea creatures related to corals that anchor themselves in sea floor mud or sand and look like leafless bushes.

seamount A – usually volcanic – mountain rising from the sea floor that does not break the surface to become an island.

sonar Mapping and detection that depends on picking up the echoes of a sound pulse from objects and surfaces.

splash zone (also known as the supralittoral) The uppermost level of a rocky coast, reached only by the spray from breaking waves.

siphonophores A group of jellyfish-like marine creatures, such as the Portuguese man of war, with long, stinging tentacles.

subduction zone A region where **tectonic plates** converge and one is pushed down beneath the other, typically creating an ocean trench and a line of volcanoes or volcanic islands along the edge of the overriding plate.

symbiosis Describes the relationship between two organisms that live together for mutual benefit.

tectonic plate One of the 50 or so vast, slowly shifting slabs of rock that make up the Earth's surface.

thermocline A thin layer in the water in which the temperature changes more sharply than that in layers above or below.

twilight zone (also known as the disphotic zone) The zone in the open ocean below the photic zone where some light penetrates but not enough for **photosynthesis**.

zooplankton Mostly microscopic floating marine organisms that live by eating other microorganisms.

zooxanthellae Algae that live **symbiotically** in the tissues of some animals, especially corals.

INDEX

Page numbers in *italic* refer to illustrations; those in **bold** type to boxed features. Page numbers underlined relate to tables.

ACKNOWLEDGEMENTS

Marshall Editions would like to thank the following for their kind permission to reproduce their images.

Key: t = **top** b = **bottom** c = **centre** l = **left** r = **right**

1 Corbis/JAI/Peter Adams; 2-3 Corbis/Maria Stenzel; 4 NOAA; 6 Corbis/George Steinmetz; 7 Carl Safina; 8 Press Association Images/AP; 10 FLPA/Minden Pictures/Norbert Wu; 11t Ben Halpern/National Center for Ecological Analysis & Synthesis/University of California; 11b Nature/David Shale; 11t Photolibrary/Peter Arnold Images/Jeffrey L. Rotman;12 Corbis/Science Faction/Natalie Fobes; 13t Nature/David Noton; 13b Alamy/Focus China; 14-15 Corbis/Wolfgang Kaehler; 15tr Shutterstock/Debra James; 15br Nature/Peter Scoones; 16 NASA/Earth Observatory; 17t courtesy of Dr. Robert Diaz, Professor of Marine Science/Virginia Institute of Marine Science; 17b FLPA/Minden Pictures/Suzi Eszterhas; 18t Nature/Wild Wonders of Europe; 18b Shutterstock/Tonobalaguerf; 19tr Shutterstock/Anobis;19b Shutterstock/Brett Atkins; 20-21 NOAA; 22 Shuterstock/Bonita R. Cheshier; 24t Nature/Wild Wonders of Europe/Lundgren; 24b NASA/STS-109 Shuttle Mission; 25tl Photolibrary/Michael Peuckert; 25tr Corbis/DK images/Colin Keates; 26 Ardea/Stefan Myers; 27tl Jonathan O'Neil/Earth & Planetary Sciences/McGill University/Montreal; 28 Alamy/John Cancalosi; 29 Corbis/Theo Allofs; 30 NOAA/National Geophysical Data Center; 31 FLPA/S Jonasson; 32t Science Photo Library/US Geological Survey; 32b Census of Marine Life/Censeam; 33t Corbis/Norbert Wu; 33b Shutterstock/Cigdem Cooper; 34t Nature/David Shale; 34b NOAA/Charleston Bump Expedition 2003/Dr. George Sedberry, South Carolina DNR; 35t FLPA/Minden Pictures/Norbert Wu; 36 NOAA/courtesy of Submarine Ring of Fire 2004 Exploration; 37 Science Photo Library; 38-39 Science Photo Library/US Geological Survey; 38tl NOAA; 39tr FLPA/Minden Pictures/Norbert Wu; 40 Ardea/Jean Paul Ferrero; 41 Corbis/Visuals Unlimited; 42 Corbis/Momatiuk-Eastcott; 43tl Corbis/Reuters/Amit Dave; 43r Corbis/Earl Kowall; 44l Photolibrary/WaterFrame/Wolfgang Poelzer; 44r Photolibrary/WaterFrame/Ethan Daniels; 45 Shutterstock/Opachevsky Irina; 46-47 Shutterstock/Pete Niesen; 47t FLPA/Minden Pictures/Flip Nicklin; 48 Digital Vision; 50 NASA/Earth Observatory Images/courtesy of Jeff Schmaltz, MODIS Rapid Response Team, Goddard Space Flight Center; 51 Photolibrary/Waterframe/Wolfgang Poelzer; 52 Corbis/Epa/Martin Alipaz; 53t NOAA; 53b NASA Jet Propulsion Laboratory Collection NASA/Caltech/TOPEX/El Niño; 54-55 Shutterstock/Mack7777; 55b Public domain; 56 Photolibrary/OSF/Ariadne Van Zandbergen; 57 FLPA/Erica Olsen; 58 Alamy/WaterFrame; 60 Alamy/David Seawell; 61t Science Photolibrary/Planetary Visions Ltd; 61b Science Photolibrary/Alexis Rosenfeld; 62 Neil Bruce/Census of Marine Life; 63t Census of Marine Life; 63b Nature/David Shale; 64 Shutterstock/Attem; 66-67 Nature/Oriol Alamany; 67t FLPA/D P Wilson; 68 FLPA/Imagebroker/Michael Krabs; 69t FLPA/ImageBroker; 69b Press Association/AP/Eugene Tanner; 70-71 Shutterstock/Fanny Reno; 71t Nature/Doug Perrine; 72l Ardea/David & Katie Urry; 72r FLPA/David Hosking; 73 Photolibrary/OSF/Peter Lewis; 74 Shutterstock/Jose Gil; 75 FLPA/Colin Marshall; 76 Photolibrary/Jon Arnold Travel/Doug Pearson; 77 Alamy/Mark Conlin; 78 Alamy/WaterFrame; 79t Corbis/Frans Lanting; 79b Public domain; 80 FLPA/Minden Pictures/Flip Nicklin; 81 FLPA/Minden Pictures/Kevin Schafer; 82 Shutterstock/Gail Johnson; 84 Photolibrary/OSF/Paul Kay; 85 Shutterstock/Ariel Bravy; 86 Tim Laman Photography; 87 Photolibrary/AlaskaStock; 88 Photolibrary/Imagebroker/Stefan Wackerhagen; 89t Photolibrary/OSF/Splashdown Direct; 89b Nature/David Fleetham; 90 Corbis/Ecoscene/Chinch Gryniewicz; 91 Corbis/Science Faction/Natalie Fobes; 92-93 Photolibrary/OSF/Fitor Angel M; 93t Nature/Florian Graner; 94 Nature/Floriam Granger; 95b courtesy of Kyle Van Housten/Landsat 7 satellite/USGS; 96 Nature/Jurgen Freund; 98 Photolibrary/Superstock; 99 Photolibrary/Pacific Stock/Fleetham Dave; 100 Photolibrary/Robert Harding Travel/Louise Murray; 101 Alamy/WaterFrame; 102-103 Photolibrary/Imagebroker/J W Alker; 105 Photolibrary/Waterframe/Borut Furlan; 106-107 Corbis/ Stuart Westmorland; 107tr Alamy/Martin Strmiska; 106t FLPA/Imagebroker/Norbert Probst; 108tr & c NASA/Jesse Allen/Earth Observatory/USGS; 108b Corbis/Yann Arthus-Bertrand; 109 Nature/Tim Laman; 110 Getty Images/Stone/Kim Westerskov; 111t Nature/David Tiplin; 111b NOAA; 112 Photolibrary/Corbis; 114-115 Photolibrary/Alaskastock/Steven Kazlowski; 115tr Photolibrary/Peter Arnold Images/Fred Bruemmer; 116 Corbis/Science Faction/Norbert Wu; 117 FLPA/Minden Pictures/Konrad Wothe; 118l Photolibrary/OSF/Richard Herrmann; 118r Nature/David Tiplin; 119 Ardea/Francois Gohier; 120b Science Photo Library/Peter Chadwick; 121t Nature/David Kjaer; 122 Ardea/Francois Gohier; 123 Nature/Doc White; 124 Alamy/Johner Image/ Stefan Lundgren; 126 FLPA/Reinhard Dirscherl; 127t Nature/Solvin Zankl; 127l FLPA/Minden Pictures/Hiroya Minakuchi; 128 FLPA/Minden Pictures/Norbert Wu; 129 Ardea/Chris Brunskill; 130 FLPA/Minden

Pictures/Richard Herrmann; 131l FLPA/D P Wilson; 131r NASA/courtesy Jacques Descloitres, MODIS Land Rapid Response Team @ Goddard Space Flight Centre; 132 Nature/Brandon Cole; 133 Photolibrary/The Irish Image Collection; 134 FLPA/Minden Pictures/Ingo Arndt; 135t Photolibrary/Karen Gowlett-Holmes; 135b Photoshot/Franco Banfi; 136 FLPA/Minden Pictures/Norbert Wu; 137 Shutterstock/Tonobalaguerf; 138 Nature/Constantinos Petrinos; 140 Image Quest Marine; 141 Nature/David Shale; 142 Photolibrary/OSF; 143t FLPA/Minden Pictures/Norbert Wu; 143b Photolibrary/OSF; 144 Shutterstock/Isabella Pfenninger; 146 Shutterstock/Rui Vale de Sousa; 147b FLPA/Hugh Clark; 148 Photoshot/Reinhard Dirscherl; 149l FLPA/Minden Pictures/Fred Bavendam; 149r SPL/Peter Scoones; 150 U.S. Coastguard photo by Petty Officer First Class John Masson; 151 Getty Images/Win McNamee; 152 Nature/David Shale; 153t Alamy/F1online/Thomas Becker; 153b Dr. Arthur Anker, Florida Museum of Natural History, University of Florida/artour@Flickr; 154 Science Photo Library/Goddard Space Flight Centre/Scientific Visual Studio; 155tl Nature/Wild Wonders of Europe/Zankl; 155tr Alamy/WoodyStock/Wendefeuer Wolfgang; 155b Reuters/Luke MacGregor; 156 Photolibrary/MIXA Ltd; 157 Corbis/Niall Benvie; 158 Corbis/Latitude/Keren Su; 161tl Nature/David Fleetham; 161tr Science Photo Library/Nasa; 161b Science Photo Library/NASA; 162 Science Photo Library/B Murton/Southampton Oceanography Centre; 163t&b Image Quest Marine; 164 Alamy/Mark Conlin; 165 FLPA/ImageBroker; 166 FLPA/Minden Pictures/Norbert Wu; 167t Alamy/Louise Murray; 167bl Nature/Peter Scoones; 167br Shutterstock/Stephen B. Goodwin; 168bl Public domain; 168br Steve Trewhella; 169 FLPA/Minden Pictures/Flip Nicklin; 170 Getty Images/National Geographic/Paul Nicklen; 171b NASA/Earth Observatory image by Robert Simmon based on Landsat-7 data; 172 Alamy/Pictures Colour Library; 174-175 Shutterstock/Rich Carey; 176 Ardea/Valerie Taylor; 177tl FLPA/R Dirscherl; 177tr Shutterstock/Ian Scott; 178t Nature/Georgette Douwma; 178b Alamy/WaterFrame; 179 Shutterstock/Cigdem Cooper; 180t Photolibrary/Marc Dozier; 180b Aurora/Andre Seale; 181 FLPA/Minden Pictures/Chris Newbert; 182 Corbis/Momatiuk-Eastcott; 184-185 FLPA/Tui De Roy/Minden Pictures; 186b NASA/Earth Observatory images by Jesse Allen & Robert Simmon based on MODIS data; 187 Alamy/Robert Harding Picture Library/Marco Simoni; 188&189 Alfred Wegener Insitute for Polar & Marine Research/Cédric d'Udekem d'Acoz; 190 Rex Features/Sutton-Hibbert/Rex Features; 191 Photoshot/Woodfall/Tony Martin; 192 Nature/Mark Carwardine; 193 FLPA/Minden Pictures/Rinie Van Meurs; 194 FLPA/Minden Pictures/Colin Monteath; 196 FLPA/Minden Pictures/Tui De Roy; 197 Nature/Martha Holmes; 198 Chris Linder/Woods Hole Oceanographic Institution; 199l Nature/Wild Wonders of Europe/de la Lez; 199r Science Photo Library/Michael Clutson; 200 FLPA/Minden Pictures/Flip Nicklin; 201tl Photolibrary/OSF/Rick Price; 201tr FLPA/Minden Pictures/Flip Nicklin; 202-203 Nature/Steven Kazlowski; 204 Photolibrary/Alaskastock; 205t Alamy/Peter Arnold Images/Fred Bruemmer; 205b US Fish & Wildlife Service/E Winkel; 206 Shutterstock/Vladimir Sklyarov; 208 Science Photo Library/Aleixis Rosenfeld; 209t Ardea/M Watson; 209b Photolibrary/Imagebroker; 210 Science Photo Library/Peter Scoones; 211t Image Quest Marine; 211b Professor Bella S Galil/National Institute of Oceanography/Israel Oceanographic & Limnological Research/Haifa; 212 Photolibrary/Robert Harding Travel/Neil Emmerson; 213t Nature/Wonders of Europe; 213b Image Quest Marine; 214 Nature/Philip Stephen; 215t Corbis/George Steinmetz; 215b Getty Images/National Geographic/Farrell Grehan; 216 Alamy/Tao Winter Landscape; 217 Corbis/epa/Stefan Sauer; 218 Getty Images/National Geographic/David Doubilet; 219 Corbis/epa/Andy Rain; 220 Corbis/epa/Sergei Ilnitsky; 222 Photoshot/UPPA/Zhuravlev Ivan; 223tl FLPA/Mammal Fund Earthviews; 223tr Mosaic Travel/Flickr; 224 Reuters/Awashimaura Fisheries Association; 225 Ecoscene; 226 Photoshot/World Pictures; 227l Photoshot/Itar-Tass/UPPA; 227r Photoshot/Itar – Tass/UPPA; 228 Corbis/Justin Guariglia; 230-231 Corbis/Nik Wheeler; 231tr Alamy/Maximilian Weinzierl; 232 Alamy/Michael Patrick O'Neill; 233tl Jenny Huang; 233tr Alamy/dbimages/Amanda Ahn; 234 Shutterstock/Rich Carey.

Artwork credits: Marshall Editions

Global & ocean floor maps used throughout the book are courtesy of: Prof. P. Berry, De Montfort University, EAPRS Lab, UK; Dr. W. Smith, NOAA, Geosciences Lab, USA; Prof. D. Sandwell, Scripps Institution of Oceanography, USA; ESA, 2004.